The Making of a

BRITFLICK

A reality novel in diary form

The Making of a
BRITFLICK

**A reality novel
in diary form**

Robin Squire

Tagman

www.tagmanpress.com

The Making of a Britflick

First published in Great Britain in e-book form in November 2011 by
The Tagman Press, an imprint of Lovemore House Limited. Publication
in traditional book trade paperback form scheduled for November 2012.

Lovemore House Limited
Lovemore House, PO BOX 754
Norwich NR1 4GY, England UK
Tel: 0845 644 4186
Fax: 0845 644 4187

Tagman

www.tagmanpress.com
email: anthonykgrey@btinternet.com

ISBN 978-1-903571-09-5

A CIP catalogue record for this book is available from the British Library

Edited by: Lizzie Brien

Printed book preparation and cover artwork:

Brendan Rallison Ltd., Norfolk. 01692 538861

To Lynda, with love,
laughs, songs and blessings.

About the Author

Novelist and screenwriter Robin Squire began his working life as a salesman of office equipment – but found he spent more time jotting down the ideas that jumped constantly into his mind than actually selling anything. This eventually lost him the job, but led to the publication by W.H. Allen & Co. of his first novel *Square One*, which New English Library subsequently issued as a paperback. He was also invited to join BBC TV on attachment as a trainee script editor. There he not only became a reader at the Script Unit where he met his future partner, but also played a *Doctor Who* monster when, owing to a studio strike, the crew had suddenly to move its shooting location.

Other books followed, including *A Portrait of Barbara*, published by St. Martin's Press in New York and Sphere Books. He cut his screenwriting teeth on a script directed by Norman Cohen in South Africa, and has since written and re-written numerous screenplays, not all of which got made, but the experience of shaping and reshaping them into their final form has filled many working years. His creative feedback service to aspiring writers has led to books being published by talented authors of whom he is proud and to whom he feels privileged to have been an advisor.

He has also been an infantry soldier, house-cleaner, bingo steward, spare parts driver for a garage, hot-dog seller, magazine journalist, car-jockey for a vehicle hire company, security guard, film extra, professional proofreader, factory paint-grinder, ditch-digger, copy-editor, TV background artist, and has even – in work to which he says he was singularly ill-suited – sold encyclopaedias door to door. He currently lives his real life outside his imagination in deepest Hertfordshire.

Quotations

The chief beauty of this book lies not so much in its literary style, or in the extent and usefulness of the information it conveys, as in its simple truthfulness. Other works may excel this in depth of thought and knowledge of human nature, but for hopeless and incurable veracity nothing yet discovered can surpass it.

Jerome K. Jerome

1859-1927

Preface to *Three Men In A Boat*

* * *

My way of joking is to tell the truth. It's the funniest joke in the world.

George Bernard Shaw

1856-1950

* * *

The best thing about the future is that it comes only one day at a time.

Abraham Lincoln

1809-65

* * *

In the deepy reaches of the night when all seems lost I like to dream that I'm the Man from Laramie.

Me

Guest Appearances

(in no particular order or frequency)

VICTORIA BECKHAM *(who wanted to be in the film)*

JOHN GLEN *(James Bond director)*

LADY PENELOPE *(did Thunderbirds go?)*

SHIRLEY TEMPLE'S SCREEN DOUBLE *(ringlets R still Us)*

ROD STEWART *(Penny Lancaster on his knee)*

ANDREA CORR *(who got too busy)*

A GIRL FROM '*ALLO, 'ALLO! *(sings like an angel)*

THE LONDON PALLADIUM *(onstage live)*

JESSIE MATTHEWS'S NIECE *(memories of Auntie)*

DERREN BROWN'S MANAGER *(wanted to make more magic)*

HOXTON HALL *(of Music Hall fame)*

DAVE LEE TRAVIS *(birthday boy)*

TWO CASHPOINT MUGGERS *(who got no change)*

GEORGIE FAME *(Yeh! Yeh!)*

GEORGE FORMBY'S WARTIME PILOT *(still hitting the highspots)*

DECCA RECORDS *(a chance in a million)*

MATT MONROE'S EX-GIRLFRIEND *(driving that bus)*

GEORGE SHEARING'S EX-DRUMMER *(moving memories)*

VERA LYNN'S SCHOOLFRIEND *(remembers her as Vera Welch)*

THE HALE-BOPP COMET *(a sigh at its passing)*

GODFREY RAMPLING *(Olympic Gold)*

THE FOUNDER OF THE WELSH NATIONAL OPERA *(still singing)*

*... and a galaxy of others, twinkling with varying
degrees of brightness...*

Disclaimer

Although the events described in this book and the people involved in them are essentially true, some of the names and outcomes have been changed, and here and there embellished with dramatic licence to render them different in thought, motive, intention and deed from the actual people who were involved and the events portrayed.
These characters and happenings may therefore be viewed as fictional, and it is not intended to offend or impute anything untoward in their apparent real-life counterparts.

Introduction

"Hi Rob, Brian Proctor. Your Mantis *script had a good reading. We're taking it to Cannes."*

"Great."

"Tough one, though. Ever so slightly not Jackie Chan."

"It's a magical saga of mystery and dreams."

"Martial arts and mayhem seems more the going thing, matey."

"Oh, I'm sure if anyone likes it enough they'll have it completely rewritten – by an American, or the girl in the office."

"What?"

"It was you who told me only Americans can write film scripts. Oh, and only women can write women."

"Talking about that, wanted to ask you something. My girlfriend's written this story. Only rough, not been published or anything, based on her experience of living in a haunted house."

"Brian, I think I'm going to have to…"

"Wants to make it into a film. Been trying to get it going for about five years. Wondered if you might, you know…"

"I'm British, remember. I even think 'Technicolor' looks wrongly spelt."

"It's just an outline so far, but…"

"After five years?"

"Well, an ICM writer did a screenplay, but she got rid of him and went back to basics."

"ICM?"

"Top agency yeah, I know. The guy had track, too – but Cat's very particular."

"Cat?"

"Catherine. I've seen enough of your stuff to know you could probably put something together. If she could do it herself, she would – but Cat's not a writer."

"Will you be producing?"

"Looks like she's already got one. Name of Peter Jaques."

"Money?"

"Just knocked my coffee over."

"Well, okay*. No harm in taking a look, I suppose..."

*Okay, or *OK*: Probably an abbreviation of *orl korrect*, popularised as a slogan during President Martin Van Buren's re-election campaign of 1840 in the U.S.

But for me it was destined to mean '*Oh Kalamity!*'

1996

Thursday 9th

Brian Proctor rang again about his girlfriend's ghost story. Phoned her. Educated voice, divorced mum living in Barnes. She faxed the storyline through. Six pages. Sprawls, overwritten with inessentials, underwritten in essentials. She calls it *The Dark Side Of The Moon*. Looked it up in Halliwell's – Danish picture with the same title, 1986. The crit says 'ponderously slow and introverted' – hope it's not an omen.

Tuesday 14th

Found Catherine Frome's house in Barnes, an upmarket street which enhanced my insecurities and gnawed into my overdraft angst. Blonde and eyeball-friendly, early 40s, with vivacious air and a smile that lights lamps and chases shadows. Liked her at once, but felt a bit daunted too: it's strange to meet someone not actually struggling to survive. Kids at private school, Filipino au pair in kitchen.

In lounge met Peter Jaques, film producer currently doing something for BBC Films. Pleasant, bearded, burly, intelligent, perceptive, he launched into a discussion on the story. Gives me full scope to do new treatment. Catherine – or 'Cat' (which she prefers to be called) – made coffee.

Peter enthusiastic and helpful. Wants it to be like Polanski's *Repulsion* meets Losey's *Accident* with a ghost or two thrown in. Already my flesh is creeping. I adore the atmosphere produced by ghosts. "We mustn't *see* any," Cat insisted. Why not? Can't see anything wrong with a translucent figure lurking on the landing, with or without a head. "It's corny, all been done before," she explained. Oh, really? Right, no visible ghosties then. I asked how she felt about spooky sounds. Yes, wailing through wainscoting's okay, and the piano that plays itself at dead of night with the lid down.

3

Saturday 18th

Got on with a fresh outline for Cat Frome's story, trying to read her intentions. For a legal query she gave me the number of a barrister friend. Such a being scares me more than any ghost. Phoned him in awe and trembling – and had a surprisingly normal-bloke chat about trust funds, the core of the story. He deals with Cat's family trust. The only trust our family had was trusting dad to come home with the wages.

No one's mentioned money yet.

'An actor without a playwright is like a hole without a doughnut' quotes George Jean Nathan, U.S. writer and theatre critic, on this page of my diary today.

Wednesday 22nd

It's George Best's birthday. The nimble-legged turn-on-a-sixpence footballing genius is 50. The thought of him falling on his face pig-drunk is grievous.

Friday 31st

Peter tells me Cat's a granddaughter of the founder of a multinational company, and her family's worth a fortune. Hence the posh house in Barnes, private schools, hols abroad in 5-star accom. Hence her friends being top barristers, surgeons, finance experts, business magnates. It's why the characters in this film are mainly upper crust. Told Peter I veer more towards the lower crust, feel happier writing about conflicts in a tower block than country houses in the stockbroker belt.

JUNE

Sunday 2nd

8-ish by the time I got in and got some grub going. While it was cooking, tried to work out what still wasn't working for me with this film. Had a beer to aid the concentration, and got so stuck in I made the mistake of opening a second, during which it came to me what's wrong: we need to see the main character 'Laura' in full control at the start or there's no contrast when she falls apart. Obvious, really. Maybe I'm trying too hard to please Cat.

On straining the gravy it poured through the sieve straight down the sink and I realised a) I've been thinking too hard and b) that second can of lager was a mistake. This made me ponder at what point does the brain decide to let you do this. Up till a certain swallow all is lucid, but one gulp more transforms you into a gibbering wreck who pours freshly-made gravy down plugholes without putting a jug there to catch it, can't string a sentence together and walks into doors. What's happening to me?

Friday 7th

Hot, sunny and sweaty, 31 degrees – that's about 90 in old currency. Wrote a selling outline for *Moon*. Finished by evening and faxed it to Peter Jaques.

JULY

Wednesday 23rd

To Peter Jaques's production office at BBC filming HQ in Covent Garden. He tells me David Thompson at BBC Films 'half likes' our project. Wasn't quite sure what that meant. Cat arrived, and we crossed to a Greek restaurant. Director John Henderson got there soon after. He's making *Bring Me The Head Of Mavis Davis*, with Rik Mayall and Jane Horrocks. Crazy title that makes you a bit anxious. Said he'd like to direct *Dark Side Of The Moon* and looks forward to reading the script. Don't suppose there's much more he could have said at this stage, and I wondered whether this meeting wasn't a bit premature as there was nothing really to bite on apart from a leg of kleftiko, which was very nice. Cat paid, which was even nicer.

Monday 29th

Waited up till past midnight to watch Kelly Holmes run the women's 800 metres Olympic final in Atlanta. She came 4th. Really felt for her – that girl has worked so hard for this, dogged with bad luck fitnesswise. Is she fighting demons too? – her pantherish body of stamina and grace, her dauntless mind and spirit that refuse to give up despite failure after failure but *will* find a way to the top somehow? Think I'm in love.

AUGUST

Tuesday 20th

Cat took me to the Hurlingham Club for lunch with eyesparkling jewellery and hair coiffed (she, not me!). Says it's to give me background as this is the sort of place the *Moon* characters would frequent. In my old Burton's suit with the split crotch felt like Tom Courtenay mixing with the higher-ups in *The Loneliness of the Long Distance Runner*, yet felt unexpectedly at home there, too. Can this mean, as my name might suggest, that my forbears were once nobs? – or was it (as dear old Grandma Squire always insisted) just a cockney joke? Cordon bleu nosh, with red wine. Again Cat paid, generously flapping off my gesture of bringing my age-cracked leather wallet apprehensively into the open, but there's still no money on offer to start me writing. Am I expected to do it for nothing as a gesture of goodwill? (gosh, never thought of that.)

'I was very lucky. The people were looking for something different and I came along just in time.' Says Elvis Presley on today's diary page.

SEPTEMBER

Sunday 1st

A banking friend of Cat's by the name of Christopher has told her I should tart up my CV, which must look about as enticing to a film financier as a buff envelope in the post from HM Revenue & Customs. My current one shows plenty of apparent activity, with indie producers attached, but nothing actually *made* since before the dawn of time. There's *DareDemon, Dark Ground, The Dance Of The Mantis, String Horses, The Incarnate, Clairvoyant, Blood On The Dew, Darling Heart,* and more, all of which I cherish fondly, nursing them like puppies with vitamin deficiencies. Why did I spend so much time, energy and passion over the years writing these masterpieces for philistines to say no to with such determination and frequency?

So dressed up my CV in that overclaimful way we who need rockets up our career jacksies tend to do – then faxed this fabrication to Cat saying that if anyone's unhappy about me, let them bring in another writer NOW and I'll push off.

Monday 2nd

Wondered why no one's said push off yet (retires muttering to walk the streets like a lost soul in search of the ultimate filmic moment with which to illuminate the coming script).

Tuesday 10th

Cat put me on to her barrister pal Graham Lawson again, who has an idea he feels will enhance the story. Managed to argue a Queen's Counsellor out of his own idea! Am sure Graham's a brilliant lawyer, but why is he putting up story ideas that don't work? Rang Cat and asked her – she says Graham helped her develop the *Moon* outline thus far. So is the story hers or his? I'm puzzled.

Thursday 19th

Decided not to start writing the script till some payment's been offered. Rang Howard*, who hasn't been well. SO glad to hear his voice again. He says he'll give Cat a call, and that James Atherton of Charisma Films wants to renew their rights to my *Darling Heart* script – with some of that stuff which happiness can't buy, called 'm-o-n-e-y'. Whoopeeee.

Howard Pays at CCA Management on Sloane Square, my literary agent at the time.

Saturday 21st

My only post today was a letter from the bank, quivering with menace. Feel very down, think am heading for a crack-up. Dad wants me to go to Australia for 6 weeks as his 'minder', to visit my sis Davina and other rellies there. It'll be his final trip darnunder. It's lung cancer. He and Mum smoked all their lives, bless 'em. Emphysema took her, I still can't quite get it that she's no longer here and Dad's alone. He'll pay my fare if I go Economy while he flies Club. Fair enough, don't really mind sitting knees in teeth for twenty-four hours on end risking terminal boredom and deep vein thrombosis. Maybe I *should* get away for a while, no one wants to pay me to write this script and nothing else is kicking in.

OCTOBER

October 10ᵗʰ to November 23ʳᵈ, away in Oz with my father Walter who has terminal lung cancer, two new hips, failing eyesight, increasingly dodgy hearing and robust views about what he sees as his seriously misguided son. Will I succeed in anything meritorious while he's still alive? Returned with i) hat dangling corks, ii) suntan, iii) inferiority complex reinvigorated by further father-fortified views of my directionlessness as a human being, iv) loads of photos and v) a renewed resolve to get all these films I've written actually happening.

NOVEMBER

Monday 25ᵗʰ

Producer Barrie Saint Clair phoned from Johannesburg, said how about coming out there in January to work on a story about the death of the last Bonaparte during the Zulu War in 1879? Says he's acquired a copy of the Victorian handwritten records of the court martial that followed the death. Sounds fun (though I don't suppose the exiled Napoléon Eugène Louis Jean Joseph, aged 23, Prince Imperial and last of the dynastic line in France, saw it that way as he got skewered on an assegai). Barrie says he can do the ticket and let me have a bit of money. When I'd finished dribbling at the prospect of that rare element 'cash', croaked "yes".

Later, rang Peter Jaques. He's been so involved with the *Mavis Davis* film, nothing's been done about getting any payment for me to write *Dark Side Of The Moon*. Can you *believe* that? (yes) Cat Frome rang later, said she's 'full of ideas'. Oh dear.

'It is all very well to be able to write books, but can you waggle your ears?' J.M. Barrie asked this of H.G. Wells on today's page of this diary.

DECEMBER

Wednesday 18ᵗʰ

Cat has raised £2000 to get me writing *Dark Side Of The Moon*! Peter Jaques phoned, has just finished reading the *Darling Heart* script he'd asked to see and says I'm (I merely quote) "a most impressive writer." Cor. One thing I've already learned about Peter, apart from him appearing to be as rocklike as the Biblical one, is he's not lavish with his praise. So that was a surprise bonus, and producer James Atherton, whose renewed option on *Darling Heart* will see me through Christmas, tells me actor David Hayman likes the script so much he wants to direct it. I like David Hayman – in fact, for saying that, I think he's one of the finest people walking God's earth at present. Indeed, he should be given a sainthood and be transported through the streets on the shoulders of the throng. Nice one, David. Does this mean that something significantly brilliant could happen in the coming year*?

No.

Friday 27th

In this bleak back-end of the year all seems chill, empty, monochrome. It snowed thick and buried everything under calming whiteness. But my first sight of the day was a robin on the path beneath my kitchen dipping its beak into bread I'd thrown. My mascot. Hoped this was a message from the benign spirits.

Tuesday 31st

Another year gone. Bitter cold out. Valentine Palmer, actor/director contact of Howard Pays, phoned. He tells me Howard is likely to retire soon. He also said I should get a film on the screen, then go for an agency like William Morris. He calls me 'a writer about to happen'. Seems to me I've been 'about to happen' for quite some time.

Howard Pays soon to go? What then? Waited up in the glittering multi-hued glow of my festive larch and opened the Glenfiddich my lovely daughter Kerry gave me for Christmas. When the clock went 0.00 I raised a glass and croaked "Hurrah" at my reflection. It said nothing back. Indeed it looked a bit – how can I say this? – sadsville. Wished said reflection looked more like Jack Kerouac or Dino Crocetti. Tried an uneasy grin at it, but it only reminded me of W.C. Fields saying: "Start the day with a smile and get it over with." My solo world seemed silent, though beyond the windows rockets zoomed and banged, spraying the sky with coloured lights and generally being jolly and shrieky.

Kerry Melanie rang while I was sipping her Scotch, we had a merry new year chat, she a woman now and happy with her man this night as well as all the other nights in life, while a poem of yesteryonks sighed through my bleared mind and, after she'd rung off, got me mumbling it out loud, prompting dampy blinks like it never fails to do:

> *Stanmore Common,*
> *Trees in a drought,*
> *A shout of a boy with a kite on a hill,*
> *And I'm with Kerry:*
> *Her hair is very*
> *Bright against the soft steel sky.*
>
> *Today a wind is brisking,*
> *Frisking through Kerry-curls blondly,*
> *And her face is golden now, not flushed,*
> *While wild flowers, unwatered in weeks,*
> *Have brushed her running driving feet*
> *In scorched red sandals that leap*
> *Ahead of me uphill.*
>
> *A sky of milk and silk now*
> *Steeped in the colour of her eyes when she looks at me,*
> *Offering yellow petal-clusters I know not the name of –*
> *But "can we carry them home with the acorns?"*
>
> *Hawthorns have red berries,*
> *Kerry's with me! – her Pan-like shadow*
> *Shows mad, glows dusky*
> *Over musky summer scents of drought-baked grass,*
> *Chasing like bats'-wings flittering*
> *Then pausing to point, panting:*
> *And "will you carry me froo the nettles,*
> Plee-ee-eee-ee-eee-ee-yeese?"

That summer of hosepipe-ban heat had parched the grass and wilted flowers, but on that hot August afternoon when we'd got to the Common where we would walk, just she and me now her mum had left us, through cool green woods and over log-bound streams across eye-aching plains on our latest adventure, keen-gazed for bandits or pirates, stopping to feed the big horse in the field with sugar-lumps, its huge yellow teeth bared above her brave and tiny upheld palm before the great horse-lips delicately snatched the offerings from it, a breeze had started up for the first time in weeks and some boys on the hill were flying a kite.

Or trying to.

Kerry was four then, in white knicks and red shoes, her little body bronzed as if we'd been on holiday, which I couldn't afford. I never did seem able to afford anything much then. So what's new? That night I hadn't been able to sleep, so had got out of bed and written that poem.

Don't know why I did that. I'd read Kerry to sleep long since and should have been tired. But that memory of our walk together lingered, I wanted to record it. My magical Babkin and her hopeless dad. Summer. Youngness. Beautiful trustingness. Even the horse had played its part.

Don't do that sort of thing any more.

A couple of days later the long drought broke.

Must stop rambling…

Hey, it's 1997 and absolutely anything can happen!

Can't it?

1997

January 25th to February 9th in South Africa with producer Barrie Saint Clair at his house in wide open spaces outside Johannesburg, working up a screen treatment for a film about the untimely death of the young Prince Imperial – the last of the Bonaparte line, great-nephew of the mighty Napoleon – in the Zulu War of 1879. A producer on Zulu Dawn, *Barrie is hooked on the period.*

Most evenings we ended up out of our heads in his pool in the garden at midnight, heedless of creeping assassins breaking through the fencing, his pretty wife Dominique calling him with increasing exasperation from the terrace. Barrie was shouting as we splashed "You're the best fucking writer without credits I've ever known! How do you fucking manage it?"

"I wear dark glasses," I said, "in case I'm recognised."

On another evening I went on the lawn in shorts and flip-flops to watch the sun set over the doornrandjes. One of their six dogs, a dachshund called Uschi, came and sat by my feet. I thought this was most companionable and remarked on it when I went in. "She wasn't just being chummy," Barrie said, handing me a beer. "She saw you weren't wearing shoes, so she came out to guard you from snakes. This time of evening they come through the grass – and those mambas are killers*."

Barrie advised me never to go in their bedroom at night. He used to be a Para and doesn't mess about. "You'd be dead," he said. He sleeps with a loaded revolver under his pillow, and will shoot first and chat about it afterwards.

He's also a firearms instructor, and his wife Dominique was in the South African police. They took me on the firing range and we shot at man-size cardboard targets. It was the first time I'd fired a revolver, holding it in both hands with legs braced like in the cops movies. The secret of shooting is a moment of absolute stillness and focus when you line up the sights and target, and delicately squeeze the trigger. It must have helped that I'd been a marksman on the rifle in my misapplied youth, because the target's chest and head were riddled. "You're a natural," Barrie beamed – I'd even out-shot his wife. At the end he handed me my target. "*Hang this outside the glass door of the room where you sleep,*" *he said.* "*If anyone comes creeping up, it'll make them think again about breaking in.*"

   ⋆ *A few months later Barrie rang with the bitter news that Uschi had been killed by a snakebite. The mamba died, but so did that heroic little mutt.*

FEBRUARY

Monday 17th

Drove to Cat Frome's for 8 p.m. and the long-awaited cheque (for £2000) changed hands. Over wine she told me she'd once lived in a house with spooky noises and the ghost of a man in the garden. So the film is about a beautiful (of course) gifted woman/mother who falls apart when the man she thought loved her turns out to be a lesser-spotted gurg-gurg (or, as was once the expression, a rotter). Peter Jaques has stressed he doesn't want it to be a ghost story as such – more a psychological thriller with supernatural overtones. Well, I don't mind subtle, I've even learned how to spell it: the 'b' is silent – as in 'debt'.

So, nearly nine months in, I at last get to write the script!

   'I would venture to guess that Anon, who wrote so many poems without signing them, was often a woman.' Quote from Virginia Woolf on today's diary page.

MARCH

Thursday 6th

At the computer by 5.30 this morning and at 7 a.m. typed *THE END* on *Dark Side Of The Moon*. Begun 18th Feb, completed 6th March – 16 days for a First Draft. The trick has been to make a compelling drama from some pretty vague stuff – Cat is a dynamic presence, her enthusiasm wondrous infectious and she is passionate about this story, yet now we're into script the focus falls on such stuff as what are the actual nuts and bolts of 'Laura's' mental and physical decline, and how are these manifested? Exactly *why* does her doting new husband become such an out-and-out skunk? And so on. Like always (and I've heard this from other creative souls) it had felt as if the words were coming *through* rather than directly *from* me, so does this make the writer some kind of spirit medium?

Evening watched John Boorman's *Hope & Glory*. The sergeant father was played by David Hayman – and I said to his image on the screen "You're going to change my life, mate" – because he wants to direct my script of *Darling Heart**.

* *Never did hear from David Hayman again, ever, despite trying to get in touch via his agent. I wish him well.*

Monday 10th

Drove down to Kew with my First Draft of *Dark Side of the Moon* to meet Cat at the pub. Weather sunny mild. I was early, so killed time by the river. Paused in the arched tunnel under the Victorian rail-bridge (*C. Kelly, Die Hards 1940* still *just* discernible in the brickwork). That was the Middlesex Regiment, then stationed in Nissen huts where M&S on Mortlake Road now stands. Wondered whether Private Kelly survived the conflict and, if not, whether his shade still hovers here unseen with penknife poised. Soon after we first met I kissed Kerry's mum, then aged twenty, where that uniformed squaddie once stood in an idle wartime moment to carve his name. Time has eroded Private Kelly's details, but that soul-to-soul snog will always be there, some psychic will one day see our ghosts deliriously clinging, for those feelings are etched on the air forever, whatever may have happened since.

Still daydreaming in this fanciful way, wandered back under the road-bridge, past the tennis courts behind Ask's restaurant where a permanent funfair used to stand with swingboats and dodgems and a steam-driven roundabout. And on to Kew Green. Scents of Spring. Daffs out.

Cat arrived in her 4x4 and a short skirt, legs long and limber. Outside the Rose & Crown I gave her the First Draft and said I'm getting a copy to Peter Jaques. She asked me not to show it to him…

… as she's dropping him from the project.

What?

"Who's going to read the script, then?" I was in shock.

"Me, of course."

"But, forgive me Cat, you're not a professional."

"I can read English, so what's the problem?"

"Well, it's something of an art really, reading a script," I waffled. "You sort of need, er, *experience* – and, well, sort of, um, *flair*. I used to read scripts for the BBC, also ITV – and only then because I'd had a book published and had read and reported on a few scripts to see if I could hack it…"

Oh dear. Wrong thinking. Anyone can read a script, can't they? Of course they can, it's just words on paper, isn't it? Such a fret-guts, me.

"Don't worry," Cat said earnestly, "I won't just go by *my* opinion, I'll ask my friends to read it too and tell me what *they* think." Oh. Okay. Well that's all right, then. Friends. Yes.

Feel bad about Peter Jaques being gone, we'd been starting to connect with this.

Sunday 16th

Cat tells me Graham Lawson likes the script, apart from the first 15 pages *which he is rewriting*! So those crucial opening scenes are being revisited by a senior lawyer who, so far as I'm aware, has never written dialogue. It's more than a week now since finishing my first draft, yet still no industry professional has read it.

Which is why I took myself down to Cat's house at Barnes for an intensive script discussion with the lady herself, her new romantic partner Lance (nice fellow, works in a bank) and Queen's Counsellor Graham. Heady stuff, but what did it actually *mean*? Brian Proctor would appear to have either been given the heave-ho by Cat as her boyfriend or moved on to pastures new, so my last link with the film industry on this project has been severed.

This evening unzipped a can and thought nervously of getting back into *The Dying of the Light* – a response equivalent, I suppose, to an ostrich spotting a patch of nice soft sand. All about the last of the Bonaparte line killed in the Zulu War of 1879. It's Crown Prince Louis Napoleon's birthday today. He'd have been 141 if he hadn't tangled with the Zulus. His little dog, called John Bull, was with him. If I shut my eyes I see it all happening, hear the noises, the frantic barks, the screams, feel the heat and sweat and freezing fear, smell the grass and trees and tang of sinewy bodies. The shock and pain as the *iklwa* struck. The Zulus called their assegai that – it's the sound it makes when stabbed into a human body and withdrawn. *Iklwa*!

But the dog, that daft tyke. On seeing its master trapped it could have streaked off and saved its life. But it stayed with him, snarling and snapping at the oncoming Zulus till its final yelp as a spear went through it. John Bull indeed.

Wednesday 19th
Got home to find that the estimable Graham Lawson has faxed 9 pages of his rewrites and exhausted my fax roll. Put a new one on and 34 more pages came churning through. But amidst the erudite ramblings were some gems of legal jargon, how lawyers talk to each other and to judges, court procedure and so on. So I was grateful to Graham and appreciate the work he's put in on this.

Saturday 22nd
Kerry phoned, so good to hear her dear sane voice. She says there's a comet low in the sky to the north-west. "It hasn't been seen for two thousand five hundred years, Dad," she added, "and won't be visible again for another two thousand four hundred, so make sure you catch it."
Stepped outside, but it was too cloudy to see a thing. Ain't that just like life?

'She had a penetrating sort of laugh. Rather like a train going into a tunnel.' P.G. Wodehouse on today's diary page.

Monday 24th
Dark Side of the Moon revisions are done. Although the script works and construction is firm, would like a week fallow to see what faults glare out (they always do). But in her great enthusiasm Cat phones a fair bit to see how it's going, so it's not always easy to keep the thought-train on the rails. Long to show it to Peter Jaques for proper feedback, but how can I ask him now he's no longer on the case and has no doubt other fish to fry? Have been as faithful as I can to incorporate Cat's ideas re characters and plotline, yet something about the story still niggles. It needs a professional view.

Friday 28th
Good Friday. Clear sky today for the first time in a week. Around 7.30 p.m. I looked out and THERE IT WAS. In the sky in the north-west, easily

visible to the naked eye, a comet bigger and brighter than the largest star, silver white with a smoky tail streaming out behind it as it continues on its stupefyingly monumental journey towards the sun.

Was so amazed to see this celestial vision that makes mockery of our fleeting existences, ploughing on through the universe as aeons pass, I just stared and stared at it, feeling my head start to float from my shoulders. All hail, Hale-Bopp! – that silvery trail I'm gaping at is six million miles long.

Sunday 30th

Clocks went forward an hour last night. Easter Sunday. Cat says her friend Mags Stoke is now our 'script editor'. I wondered what her qualifications are. Mags's only comments on the current script so far, apparently, are: "it's too short, only about seventy-five minutes" and "the characters don't say enough to get developed." I told Cat that at an average of a minute per page, 117 pages makes 2 hours of film and is probably too long. Is Mags saying there's not enough dialogue? – the pages are crammed with the stuff. Cat said she'll ask. What am I getting into?

APRIL

Tuesday 1st

Sunny and warm all day. On breakfast TV sports reporter Rob Bonnett announced that Aintree racecourse is to be rebuilt so the jumps are the other way round. When I was growing up in Cheshire the April Fool stunts stopped at noon and 'trip-up' took over – so everyone was tripping each other up for the rest of the day. Do they still do this?

To Cat's house for one. My agent Howard Pays was there looking handsome and hale with Californian suntan – really good to see him again, he's been staying with his actress daughter Amanda and her husband Corbin Bernsen. Howard wants to package the film and get the right people together, so he'll be looking for a director too. Graham Lawson the QC was there, with Lance the banker, and I wondered if they'd taken time off work for this. I suppose it's nice that they rally round Cat in this way. Good, too, to be introduced to a line producer Howard had mentioned called Kevin Nelson, who is 'good on script'. YES! It's what's been needed and hasn't happened yet. A useful meeting – the first professional one since I handed Cat my rough opening draft three weeks ago.

Howard, with his charm and gravitas, arranged with Cat to put up £1200 for Kevin to do a full budget and time-sheet. Nice one, Kev.

'Seize the day: trust the morrow as little as possible.' Quotes Horace the Roman poet on today's page of this diary.

Wednesday 2nd

Kevin Nelson phoned me, says he likes the script – up to the last ten pages. Our conversation went something like this:

Kevin: Whose idea was it to send Laura to a sanatorium at the end of the movie, having gone insane?

Me: Well, those were Cat's thoughts. I've tried to satisfy her wishes on the story.

Kevin: A bit downbeat isn't it, the boy running up to his mother on visitors' day in a nuthouse just before the closing credits?

Me: Yeah. And I'll tell you something…

Kevin: Stuff like that needs airing. It's really edgy.

Me: … I did kind of sort of know that…

Kevin: 'Hi Mummy dear, why are you staring at me like that?'

Me: 'Why are you stuffing fish fingers in your bodice and humming the Lord's prayer backwards?'

Kevin: Exactly! The audience will either be rolling on the floor or reaching for the anti-depressants. Laura should go back to that house fully recovered at the end, the hero's journey completed, the circle closed.

Me: You're right. No funny farm. I did know that really.

Kevin: Thought you did, it'll sell a lot better…

We talked for over an hour. Afterwards I phoned Cat about this suggested revision to the ending she'd thought up. She seemed quite thrown that Kevin had wanted to talk to *me* rather than *her* about this vitally important matter – after all, it's *her* story, isn't it? Oh dear. Cat's clever and shrewd, and good with story, but maybe she needs a stronger influence than me to challenge her if she goes a bit off course in her enthusiasm. As we all do, no doubt.

Sunday 6th

Woke and knew it's Kerry's mum's birthday today. How old is that dazzle-girl of yesterlongagone? Lay there a-ponder like I sometimes do, trying to snatch her smile back fresh and young from out of the mist. So loyal, staunch, supportive and caring she'd been for so long; such immense fun, clip-clopping sweet-and-twenty on high heels along the corridors of East Tower at Television Centre where Script Unit used to be, me a reader on attachment after my first novel had been published, she secretary to HSU (the BBC love their initials), eyes wide blue, blanched hair like spun gold to my bedazzled senses, pretty as purity, a laugh that penetrated walls and caused sudden surprised smiles in distant offices, scattering perfume wherever she went. She typed my early screenplays into summer dawns in the rented room we came to share in Ealing after arriving on my doorstep with a little red suitcase one transcendentally memorable evening and simply saying "I've come to stay," showed me how the ouija board works with mystic skills and astounding outcomes; made love so intensely the skies exploded; read books to me gentle-voiced on quiet Sundays; exhorted, encouraged, enfolded, screamed with righteous rage at injustices done to me, believed in me believed in me believed believed *believed* in me... then one day stopped believing.

Happy birthday, Frances.

Wednesday 9th

Cat rang on her way back from their Cornish holiday. She's thought of another title for the film, and what do I think? *Dark Moon*. I like it. Rang Howard Pays, who agrees, and will change the front covers.

Friday 11th

Drive down to Kew in sunshine. Cat arrives to pick up the latest scripts, her 4x4 full of kids. She tells them "Rob was once a monster in *Doctor Who*" (weird but true) – so I did my 'Auton' walk with expressionless expression and they cackled like hyenas.

Monday 28th

The Hale-Bopp comet is no longer there trailing its silvery spray of cloudy light. Feel sad it's gone, pity I can't wait another twenty-four centuries till it appears again. What jest it makes of our lifetimes and the 4 p.m. closing of the garden centre café just when you're starting to fancy a cup of tea.

MAY

Thursday 2nd
Woke to a new era: the Labour Party, under Tony Blair, has won the General Election by a tremendous landslide. Hope they agree to clear up the mess, and will put money into film. Why is there always a 'mess' an incoming government has to 'clear up', whichever party is being displaced and however long they've been in power? (Discuss...)

'Some people can stay longer in an hour that others can in a week.' Says William Dean Howells on today's diary page.

JUNE

Wednesday 12th
Things are getting seriously strange. Cat phones in a taxi on her way back from Pinewood Studios. Says she's just had lunch there with Sylvia Anderson (of *Thunderbirds*, now at Home Box Office) and my agent Howard Pays, who introduced them. "We had a really good script meeting on *Dark Moon*," Cat enthuses. "Sylvia wants just one or two *changes* before showing it to *Timothy Dalton*. I'll send you the new notes so you can put them in..."
Er, um, actually, I thought I was the, um, writer on this project... er, shouldn't I have been at the meeting? (pauses to scratch head as unable to act and speak at the same time.) No, 'course not... er, right, then...

Thursday 20th
A new Tory leader. Out goes John Major and in comes a young Yorkshire chap with cheery grin and bonce like an egg called William Haig.

Thursday 27th

It's already the wettest June since records began. They're at least 130 games behind at Wimbledon, which has been washed out yet again. Cat keeps me in the loop regarding the film, but I don't know what happened with Sylvia Anderson, about whom nothing further appears to have been heard. Are *Thunderbirds* go, or have they gone?

Monday 31st

Hong Kong handed back to China today. Big celebrations – with a 4000-strong army waiting to march in. Chris Patten's daughters were in tears as they boarded the Royal Yacht to sail away, fireworks dazzling the harbour. Rain bucketed down throughout.

JULY

Thursday 3rd

Howard Pays is pushing to get a director for *Dark Moon*. Several have said no, including John Hough, because it's "not different enough." Hearing this troubled me. He sent me the latest script and I saw it has changed from when I last saw it, with – as Howard put it rather worriedly – "flatter characters and patches of dead and dying dialogue." It was hard not to wonder how that had got in and other stuff had got out. Asked Howard not to show it to any more directors till I've had a fresh look at it. Got out my earlier drafts and set to work.

Tuesday 8th

Delivered latest script to Howard's office by the Royal Court Theatre on Sloane Square. Have worked intensively on this new draft over a long solid weekend, it feels good again now, the characters have returned to life and the scary bits are spine-shuddery with a real sense of creeping mystery.

Monday 21st

Robert Young has read my latest *Dark Moon* and told Howard he wants to direct! Excellent news. Robert sez he wants to meet the writer, so a date's been set for Thursday. Howard's also got a new producer on board, Alan

Latham, who'll be there too. Alan produced *The Brylcreem Boys* not long ago. Things are starting to thrum.

Thursday 24th

Hot and humid. Arrived prompt at 2.30 p.m. in Howard Pays's office. Cat surprised me by being there already, don't know why I hadn't expected to see her at this meeting. Then director Robert Young arrived. Tall, lean, courteous, old-school sophisticated, you can't imagine anyone calling him 'Bob'. A personal assistant was with him. Howard introduced us and Robert gave me the searchlight look a director turns on a writer at first hand-shake, as if asking with his penetrating gaze what manner of strange beast is this that writes scripts? He's charming, intense, said my script is 'elegantly written', that it put him in mind of Patrick Hamilton's *Gaslight*. He also said some positive things about my dialogue – which was fantastic from such an experienced man of drama. He recently directed *Jane Eyre* for ITV. My swelling head was starting to spin. All this Cat watched quietly with an unreadable expression.

Producer Alan Latham now arrived. Young, sharp-minded, strong ideas. We're going to *make* this film! Today I feel good, and my head has nearly shrunk back to normal as I write this.

AUGUST

Saturday 2nd

World Championships athletics from Athens – watched on TV as UK record holder Kelly Holmes limped off towards the end of her 1500 metres heat with a ruptured Achilles tendon. She was crying. She works so hard and has such dedication and guts. In the army she runs in the men's races because no other female can touch her for stamina and pace. Oh my God. Guess I'm still in love…

'What is the use of running when you're on the wrong road?' Proverb on *today's diary page.*

Tuesday 12th

Hot, sweaty, steamy, sultry, muggy – but that's enough about me. Sometimes one yearns for something female that doesn't belong to a computer socket. This is summertime, though the livin' ain't easy. Worked all day on *Dark Moon*, by 7.30 was ready to print. Cat tells me she doesn't intend to be 'elbowed aside' when production gets under way. I reckon this is very much her agenda, and why she was in Howard's office when we met the director – to stay in absolute control of what she sees as *her* story.

Sunday 31st

Switched on TV first thing while exercising on my Nordic Track skiing machine (as one does) and was surprised to see newsreader Martyn Lewis looking solemn. Sensing something bad has happened, was horrified to realise it's about Princess Diana – that she died in Paris early this morning. The car she was in crashed in a road tunnel alongside the Seine at Alma, chased by paparazzi on motor bikes. Dodi Fayed was killed with her. It's unbelievable.

Walked out, sort of stunned, and bought a Sunday paper. The Indian newsvendor said, tragic-eyed, "Princess Di gone, hey?" Every face looked grim, the shock of this news has hit everyone in a universal sort of way I've never known before.

SEPTEMBER

Thursday 4th

Drove to Robert Young's house on Kew Green – the first time he and I have met as director and writer together. He wasn't home yet, so his glamorous wife Hermione sat me out the back with a glass of wine while I looked through the script again – a bit surprised (don't know why) to find it still reads well. A cat purred against me as I chatted with his charming daughter. Found myself yearning for a house such as this, plangent with peacefulness and prosperity, a smiling wife at the helm. Robert arrived and we had a lively chat to intensify the characters even more.

We said our goodbyes after a constructive evening. Good to be in touch fully with my director at last, don't know why it took so long★.

It was never to happen again on this one-to-one basis.

Wednesday 10th

Tubed it to High Street Ken this clear-skied morning and found a slow-moving crush of people so numerous the ticket-barriers were permanently open. In the street, police were herding the hordes round to the left and over the zebra crossing, so I nipped off to the right and crossed to Diana's old home at Kensington Palace a lot more quickly. Flowers and handwritten messages were everywhere – "to Di, Queen of our Hearts", "We will never forget you"; people approaching from every direction carrying more, like an army advancing with wreaths instead of guns.

The wall flanking the private road is lined with flowers – which surround individual trees like multi-bloomed shrines, candles flickering. The palace railings are clogged with floral offerings. A woman was standing weeping openly, a small child staring up at her.

No mere camera could effectively record the breathstopping sensation of first seeing it – in front of the gates of Kensington Palace is a vast lake of flowers the size of a Cornish cove, floral offerings placed there a trillion times, perfumed like a gargantuan florist's, flaming in the sunshine. I could have drowned in this immense bouquet to Diana from her people.

Walked off through the park along to Hyde Park Corner. Rows of floral offerings on the grass here too. At Buckingham Palace a large hand-painted sign is hung on the railings: "DIANA OF LOVE". On so many tributes are written: "The People's Princess" and (again) "Queen of our Hearts". Kids have left teddy bears with their messages. Flowers are piled high in front of the great gates here too, and coach-loads, train-loads, street-loads of people gaping and gawping, gasping, weeping. A police notice warns: "pickpockets are active", and thieves are stealing the teddy bears.

Was glad I'd seen Di's flowers.

OCTOBER

Thursday 2nd

Warm day with loads of sunshine. Faxed the latest *Dark Moon* amendments to Cat – "I want to see them first" she always says – though

I'd much rather be sending them straight to my director for his feedback. It's only natural, I suppose, for a writer to feel like this. It's what I DO.

Then Cat gets to work…

Friday 3rd

Woke from a nightmare in the small hours. In it, Cat was my Script Editor from Hell, laser-eyed and all-powerful, demolishing my carefully-wrought work with slashes of a pen shaped like a knife dripping blood, and black was blue and green was really orange and a nasty explosion was a brass band playing pleasingly in this crazy scary dream. It's *me*, not *her* – am starting to lose it – it's like I shout inside a vacuum so no one hears, yet no one sees my distorted features either, am drifting helplessly away into space like the inert ejected astronaut in *2001: A Space Odyssey*, ever further in infinite vastness till I'm just a speck that vanishes…

It's only a dream. Don't mind me, Cat. You're none of these things and I admire your determination and doggedness. It's me who's confused, me who can never, *ever*, get it 'quite right' for you. My fault, mine. Blame me. It's right that you talk to Robert. To Howard. To Kevin. To anyone and everyone involved with this film of which you have such hopes and dreams. I've let you down. Can't get it right. Or so, at least, it seems…

Numerous empty pages follow this ramble, indicating some kind of breakdown or depression, until:

Sunday 26th

Clocks go back an hour today. As usual I forgot, so the surprise was balm-like, like someone stroking your forehead instead of, as when clocks go forward, a bucket of freezing water in the chops. Frances would have read to me on a morning like this. With an extra hour to laze in, was drowsing when the images came, of the rain and early dark, stopped in my old car by the kerb in Regent's Park. We must have driven into London for some reason, maybe to deliver another hope-laden script somewhere, and left Kerry with a friend or her grandparents after school. Returning through the park, she suddenly said to stop. My cars back then were of a kind even the breakers' yards refused, so most of them wouldn't have had a radio, but maybe this one did because 'You Don't Bring Me Flowers' by Barbra Streisand and Neil Diamond is so strong in my memory of that moment. The Edwardian street lamp shining in on her face through the rain made ghost patterns on her cheeks so when I turned at what she'd said I wasn't at first aware that she was crying real tears.

"I'm leaving you."

A bad line from a bad play. She was my soul. Blonde hair swept back from Garboesque brow, flawless face of dreams-come-true, grief-twisted. *Learned how to laugh, learned how to cry; learned how to love, even learned how to lie; you'd think I could learn how to say you goodbye…*

In earlier times, parked like this, we'd have made magic with our body-minds blending. Not now. Not ever again. You don't bring me flowers any more.

How to say you goodbye.

Couldn't cry like her, hadn't learned how to do that yet.

Leaving you.

"And I'm taking Kerry with me."

Tuesday 28th

Shock! Around 8 this morning Cat rang – and gave me *script notes* from a meeting she and her boyfriend Lance had had with Robert Young yesterday evening! Robert had raised several story points, she said – but it soon became clear that instead of having debated these with him she'd simply jotted them down and was now passing them on to me for unquestioning implementation. It seemed a strange way of going about raising a director's draft, to leave the writer out of their creative deliberations.

Was still reeling from this call when Robert himself rang, his voice terse. "Why weren't you at last night's script meeting?" he asked curtly. When I explained I'd known nothing about it till a moment ago when Cat phoned with a list of amendments, he said "Those points were for discussion and illumination – I was cross with you for not being there."

Cross?

So then and there Robert and I had our own script meeting. No doubt Cat, in her eagerness, had wanted to move things along and felt that my presence would have been superfluous. Fair enough. But given this latest development it's tempting to quietly withdraw and leave the field clear to her.

'I always say, keep a diary and someday it will keep you.' So says Mae West on today's page.

Friday 31st

At the end of each day's writing towards 8 p.m. I light a couple of candles, put on quiet music, unzip a can of beer and let my mind go. This evening I drifted back into the past, with Frances just gone and Kerry still little, seeing me suddenly as the epicentre of her life. Her mother didn't take her from me after all, nor challenge for custody when I applied – this gift she gave me was beyond price and I thank her eternally for that, the gift of our daughter who would otherwise have become the possibly troubled live-in stepchild of some other man. Kerry became my reason to exist, her wellbeing and security my life's purpose. I cooked for her, washed and ironed her clothes, made packed lunches and took her to and from school, waiting with the other mums till the children emerged rumpled and tumbling – first at half past three; then, when she moved to High School, at four:

"Hi Dad."

"Hi Kez."

"Anything good happening?"

"Still in there sluggin', kid."

"Can we go to the swings/the woods/find an ice cream/play Pooh sticks at the stream/visit my friend Beverley/whatever?"

"Yeah – come on…"

To keep my daughter cheery and untroubled while I struggled with rent and bills was a fair trick. Her maternal grandparents, especially, were fantastic in their support. Kerry and I became a genuinely happy, funsome duo as the years went by. To make her Christmases and birthdays and New Year's Eves special, as they always managed to be, was life-enriching; it was as if, in these times of unending financial stress and rejection, some unseen helper always lent a hand. When I hear Harry Belafonte's 'Scarlet Ribbons' it really did seem like that, be it to find a dress for a party, a video recorder like her friends at school had, a tree at Christmas when my wallet was empty…

If I live to be a hundred I will never know from where
Came those lovely scarlet ribbons, scarlet ribbons for her hair.

Some three years after our walk on the common when I'd got up at midnight and written that poem, I left Kerry with her mum's parents so I could see a re-run of *Kramer versus Kramer* at the local cinema, starring Dustin Hoffman, about a man left alone with a young kid to care for. As I watched, something strange happened. Suddenly I couldn't see the screen any more. This had never happened to me before as an adult – this overwhelming liquid engulfing of the senses. I'd learned at last how to do like it said in the song – and she, *in absentia*, had taught me.

A candle goes out, I light another. Nothing of real interest on TV tonight. There rarely is, or so it seems. Hey, maybe I could write something for them! Ha-ha-ha-ha-ha-ha. The exercise would be as futile as putting my so-clearly-ideal-for-television script in an A4 envelope and posting it directly back to myself. Missed my way somewhere. Who'd be a writer? Once it had seemed so certain and right. Words flowed, images formed. Which fresh lot of jaded minds, newly spawned and nurtured in cold-eyed cynicism, are saying no, no, no, always and forever, amen and goodbye to absolutely everything I write, seemingly with no regard for any of its qualities? Whatever the answer is, I'd still rather build than knock down.

What was only yesterday becomes ages since. Faces change, laughs fade, youth transforms. Kerry grew up, met an excellent boy with the same birthday as hers but a year older, and moved in with him. They're still together today, and...

The CD has finished, the can is empty, the chops under the grill are starting to burn. It's back to the present and all that follows, mint sauce and redcurrant jelly *et al*.

NOVEMBER

Sunday 9th

"Had a wonderful chat with Robert about the script last night," Cat tells me on the phone this morning. "Lance and I dropped in to see him at his house again." Once more my insecurities kick in with steel-capped boots, my mental radar jams and emits distress signals. Am I not so much a has-been as a never-was? Or a never-will-be, or – worst of all – a never-*can*-be?

"Good," I say, biting the inside of my mouth and drawing blood. "What did you talk about?"

I jot down her response on my pad in case it might be needed, or Robert neglects to tell me himself. Put down the phone, make black coffee, sit thinking. Maybe I really am out of it, then – but what kind of script are they likely to develop between them? Cat has a way with her. She is charming, convivial and convincing. Her friends are many, she is lively and gregarious, throws parties, has lunches, dazzles dullards, blazes with bonhomie, while I tend to avoid human contact and have been known to fall silent for weeks like a monk in solitary. Sometimes I lose the use of language altogether and utter grunts if addressed, shambling away into my den hung with dead scripts and the remains of once-delightful characters shrivelled by neglect and indifference from the world beyond.

Am I getting morbid?

Thursday 20th

Cat tells me in her now-routine morning call that she's dropped Alan Latham as producer. Seems our Alan hasn't been too hot on returning her phone calls, and she sees this as a lack of respect for her authority. Ever more I learn that there's no messing with this brave lady.

But why haven't *I* been 'officially' kicked off too (yet), if I'm seemingly so constantly in need of amendment and correction? And what happened to the ICM writer who worked on this project before I came along? Will I one day stumble across his skeletal remains, his grimacing skull unable to communicate the atrocities inflicted on him?

Later, an annoyed Howard Pays rang me (never have I heard my affable agent so rattled) to ask why does Cat want to dispense with the services of the only person on this project who knows how to raise funding? Could only suggest that he ask the lady himself.

Sunday 30th

Cat rings me early. Today she sounds uncharacteristically down as I drool through my stubble and wonder not only quite where I am but on what planet? Just as well I live alone, no wife would stand for the phone jangling around 6.35 on a Sunday morning with another woman on the other end. Yet even in my bleariness I feel for Cat. Last night she hardly slept. Her boyfriend Lance has given her an ultimatum – "it's me or the film."

Doesn't the man realise that Cat breathes, eats and sleeps this film? It's sad, because Lance and she go well together and the kids like him too. What if she were to say to him, "It's me or the bank – one more bounced cheque and obscenely inflated bank charge levied against the poor offender, and I'm leaving you?" Wouldn't happen, would it? Lance would plead, "But it's my job, darling, my very life!" Hey though, it's sad.

'The more you read about politics, you got to admit that each party is worse than the other.' Will Rogers on this diary page.

DECEMBER

Monday 1st

It honestly hadn't occurred to me fully till now that Cat might be seeing herself as *the writer* on *her* project, as well as its *producer* and *script editor*. So who am I? Well, if she can do it, why not? She's that kind of buccaneering woman, and I admire her for it. I'm all for stepping into unfamiliar zones in life and conquering them, and it takes belief and guts to do this. It's like they say any dumb ox can be a producer, you just stick on a hat that says 'Producer'. Or a director? – well… some knowledge and experience might be required, but with a good lighting cameraman you'd only have to make an oblong of the forefinger and thumb of both hands, peer through and shout "Action!". Piece-a cake really, ain't it? Writer? It's only putting words on paper, after all. Hey, how about being an agent? Even if they're not always the sharpest tools in the box, if they can fluke it and get enough real talent to represent, it's a job for life. And if you can't recognise talent (as many can't), hire in enough people and you're bound to strike gold nuggets somewhere down the river-bed. So maybe Cat's right – or is it her barrister friend Graham Lawson who is managing to persuade her that this script-writing lark is all a bit of a doddle really? Like I say, can't help admiring her for transitioning through like this, with a spirit like hers empires can be built.

Wednesday 17th

Cat rang from her holiday villa in Mauritius to ask how I'm getting on with the latest amendments to the amendments concerning the additions made by referring to her and Robert Young's latest notes from a meeting to which I was (again) not invited. It's nice of her to care like this. She asked in a kindly-meant way if I'm going away for Christmas.

Going away? What am I going to fasten my shirts with if I do?

Going away?????

Wednesday 31st

This last evening of hoary old 1997, slurping seasonal sherry on my Jack Jones, I pondered whether *Dark Moon* or any of my other projects have built sufficient momentum to happen during this coming year. Have been on my own throughout the festivities, brooding on an uncertain future. The one highlight was Christmas dinner with Kerry Melanie and her partner Christopher by their sparkly multicoloured tree. She seems so serene, confident and secure in her life, which is better than a thousand gifts wrapped in fancy paper.

Will 1998 see me out of the career doldrums and attract some money into my life? Feel like a runner who hits a ploughed field that sucks at the feet, trips him on clods and slows him almost to falling. My problem, as they say. Deal with it (as they also say).

Didn't wait up to see New Year in. What's to celebrate? Noise and jollity elsewhere can be worse than dark silence. As for fireworks, the only celestial display I truly enjoyed this year was the Hale-Bopp comet.

1998

Monday 5th

Howard Pays rang for a chat. Says he's going into semi-retirement soon, will be working from home and will only be keeping a handful of clients on his books. Was pleased to hear that I'm to be one of them.

Tuesday 13th

To Cat's house for 10 a.m. Robert Young greeted me affably. Alan Latham arrived (Howard has persuaded Cat to retain him), and off we went on the final leg of *Dark Moon*, talking through the closing scenes and denouement. Over the holiday while others were away I've collated all the notes and put together a draft that seems to satisfy everyone's requirements, including the director's. One more draft after today's input and we should be there. Cat is letting me do it, but she seems distracted and preoccupied, as if some of her fire has gone out. I think Lance has gone; it's truly sad, and all because she wants this film to be absolutely right for her and can't let it go, even if it means losing her man.

Friday 23rd

To Cat's for ten. She kissed me on both cheeks – a rare honour – looking tasty. Our director arrived, then producer Alan Latham. A final trawl through my latest draft – not a great deal to do on it. Then Robert Young, revered director of film, TV and theatre, admired for his refinement, discerning eye, vast experience and dramatic erudition, looked me in the face, smiled warmly, shook my hand and said for all to hear:

"Well done Rob, this script of yours is ready to film."

FEBRUARY

Monday 9th

This afternoon to Harbottle & Lewis the film lawyers on Hanover Square where met solicitor called Abigail who is looking after the legals for Cat. Just her and me. Couldn't decide at first smile whether this attractive young female was friend or foe. We went through the draft contract she's drawn up, which looks incredibly aggressive to the writer, and presumably Cat is paying for. It reads as if they can't wait to wipe me out, would like me in a deep dungeon strung up by the thumbs out of harm's way to quietly rot where their eyes and ears will not be sullied by my poisonous presence. I'm asked to give up all possible rights (in satellite, cable, video, TV, etc. – and *systems yet to be invented*). However, am down for 2.5% of the budget for my screenplay fee, plus 2% of Producer's net profits – so I would have a share in these things if the film goes into profit.

Knew I had to talk to Howard Pays. Phoned him from Abigail's desk while she watched with the faint smile of a master card player who knows that, whatever I or anyone else might do or say, she has an unbeatable hand. Howard was convalescing at home after a serious operation. Abigail faxed him the 15 pages while I gazed with the hunted look of a man well out of his comfort zone. She pointed out that, with the current budget at £1.8 million, 2.5% of that is £45,000 – less the £2000 already paid, which means I'd get a total of £43,000. When I asked her what the chances are of the budget going up, she said "Absolutely none. In fact it will probably go down – and with deductions and other incidentals your fee could be a fair bit less even than that." Howard rang back with a couple of points on the contract, then a fixed screenplay fee of £50,000 was agreed on, plus the £2000 advance to make the overall figure £52,000.

Came away feeling I'd got a pretty good deal. Unless, of course, the budget increases significantly, in which case I'll end up with less than if I'd stayed with 2.5% of it. On phoning Cat to tell her, she seemed surprised that Howard had been okay about it. At which point I felt another chill: had Abigail been expecting a tougher negotiation? Already I was feeling the manacles closing around my wrists, the dungeon door swinging hideously open...

Thursday 19th

Robert Young rang this morning, friendlier than I've ever known him. Just back from South Africa where he toured the Zulu battlefields. He said my *The Dying of the Light* script was "very accurate", that he might be interested in directing it. He said Gordon Welland (*Yanks*, *Chariots of Fire* etc.) told him that once his scripts began to be accepted they took all his stuff previously rejected. So is there hope for me yet? Went to bed by candlelight on account of an extended power cut and read my library book by the flickery flame, feeling the present day melt away to somewhere in the deep gone past.

'That's the fastest time ever run – but it's not as fast as the world record.' Says sports commentator David Coleman on today's diary page.

Tuesday 24th

Howard rang me. "Just thought I'd give my potentially award-winning screenwriter a call," he said. Great to hear his cheery, positive tones again. He's just back from Val d'Isère where he's been skiing with his delightful wife Lynn. I used to ski, long-distance 'Langlauf' was my thing rather than the downhill or swoopy slalom stuff, in the snows of Germany, blisters an added extra. Funny to think I'm now doing the equivalent of Langlauf in my life, along long cold distances, great hills to slither up and flash down, panting, with frequent blizzards en route and the bar closed when you finally reach the hotel. Howard asked if I'd like to try writing for *Byker Grove*, the TV series for kids. If so, he'll fix up a meet with their script editor for Friday. Okay, worth a go I suppose, but I've never felt I was really television, which seems to require a different set of thinking/writing muscles to the ones I've acquired over the years.

Friday 27th

Still can't quite believe it, so will set this down as it happened (creaks into writing mode):

She looked twenty-something, tall and elegant, long squirrel-grey coat hugging model-trim waist, matching faux fur collar snugging her neck, yet there was nothing *faux* about the urgency with which she was darting forward to thrust leaflets for Snappy Snaps at passers-by and passengers emerging, like me, from Baker Street tube, most of whom avoided her as if she was handing out plague-pills that would strike you dead if you touched them.

The February wind was chill, so the high-heeled shoes which showed off trim ankles and perfect legs should more sensibly have been high boots with sensible socks. Although her clothes were modern she looked as if she'd just shimmered through a time-warp from the 1920s and was wondering quite what she was doing here, daintily impeccable, slender as memories of long-ago 'gels'. Her porcelain-pretty face, too, was from another age, creamily flawless, narrowing from a broad forehead massed with russet curls to a trim chin beneath pouty rosebud 'It' girl lips of glossy carmine red.

As this vision from an era of squonking cabs and horse-buses pushed out a leaflet-bearing hand, I was about to mutter 'no thanks' in the way we Brits have when thus accosted, when she stumbled and grabbed my arm to avoid falling, crumpling the exhortation to bring my films to Snappy Snaps, win a holiday on a Greek Island and live contentedly for the rest of my days.

"Sorry." It was almost a sob. In a moment the contact was gone as she righted herself and looked me in the face, elevated from her five-feet-eight or so by the tottery heels. Her eyes on mine were wide jade pools hemmed with black lashes, expressive in a half-scared puzzled way as if imploring me to answer the question of how she had arrived here and what was she doing in this particular dimension of space and time? Her vivid Titian hair was topped by a floppy cap of dark green velvet, and hung to her shoulders in coils and curls.

She was gorgeous.

"Are you okay?" Silly question, she was perished.

"Yes. Thanks." Silly answer. Her legs were trembling, a blueish tinge around her mouth. She looked about to collapse and the wind would send her Snappy Snaps leaflets blizzarding into the traffic.

"Would you like a coffee or something?" It wasn't a pick-up, I was never much good at that. She was too young anyway, and I'd long since stopped fooling myself about age differentials. The vision smiled warily, honey and peaches with perfume. "It's okay…" I touched her ice-cold hand. "You look a bit shaky, that's all."

Which is how we came to be sitting knee-to-knee in a clanky hissy noise-polluted engine-room of modern-day refreshment at the top of Baker Street, she with hot tea and toast with Marmite. After a while her shivers subsided, a bout of giddiness passed and warmth crept under the rouge on her cheeks. Her name was Lynda. An actress trained at the Guildhall School in London, she'd done theatre, commercials and television, and had been a fashion model. "I was with Michael Whittaker's Modelling Agency," she sighed "Catwalk, showroom and 'house' modelling. I was a favourite of his, modelled for Harrods, Laura Ashley, all sorts – and for Lee Cooper jeans," she added wistfully. But now, while Lynda's theatrical agent was getting her ever less castings, she was working with a temping agency that gave her jobs such as selling tights at London stores; on other days they got her typing, switchboard work or handing out leaflets in the street.

Like today.

"And I sing, too." Quietly she began 'Look for the Silver Lining' in a soft, thrilling soprano with a touch of vibrato. People glanced from other tab'⌐s. She was indeed from times gone by – enunciation, everything. ·That's Jessie Matthews," I said, shocked at how good she was.

"You've heard of her?" She looked astonished.

"'Course I have! It could've been Jessie dancing with Fred Astaire instead of Ginger Rogers. She had a better voice than Ginger, too – like yours. You're amazing."

"I'm not!"

"Trust me, I'm a writer."

"Are you?" There was something childlike about her. Her forehead was Bambi-ish, her eyes on mine huge as a fawn's. "What sort of…?"

"Oh, a couple of novels…" I boasted truthfully but feebly, adding "Some time ago now," in case she got the idea that I was in some way hot, or even lukewarm. "Freelance journalism – for magazines and things. And scripts. One of mine's threatening to get made into a film right now."

"Honestly?" Eager saucer eyes, parted lips, glint of teeth and tongue-tip.

"If there's any chance I can get you a part…" I found myself saying, sounding like the biggest cheapskate phoney ever to crawl out of woodwork.

"Oh, you mustn't even *think* about it…" But she was excited. My heart ached for her.

"Just a crazy long shot," I muttered. "But if you've anything I can get to the casting people…"

"I'll send you some publicity…" she said a little breathlessly. "If that's okay?"

"Sure." I was on my feet. "Got to get moving, I'm afraid. *Byker Grove* beckons." She looked enquiry. "Production office just down the road – my agent's put me up to write for the programme."

"*Byker Grove?*"

"Yes."

"Well… good luck." I was glad she didn't say 'break a leg'.

Yet she seemed like Truth sitting there, saying without saying that 'yes you need the money and credits but this isn't the way. Play to your strengths, don't push your weaknesses. Kids programmes? Live issues with reference to youth culture? The very idea makes you yawn, doesn't it?' Or maybe it was simply me being honest with me, that Geordie tai chi and biscuits just wasn't going to be my thing.

I gave her one of my calling cards made cheaply at the machine in the post office because I couldn't afford to go to a printer. She took it delicately with well-groomed fingers. "You never know," I said, trying to sound positive.

"It's so kind of you to suggest it. Thank you." She stared at my card with a tiny smile. Even her manners were from times gone by. Then she looked tragic for a moment and the lights in her eyes died, as if she was well used by now to things not happening for her and that this would be just another example.

"Will you be okay now?"

She nodded, glancing up. Then said, in a rush, "That Snappy Snaps man will probably fire me, but I don't care. I usually do get fired from these jobs. I can type, but can't use computers. Or switchboards, it usually ends up with the wrong people talking to each other. Thanks for the tea. Oh…" She fumbled for her purse. I didn't suppose there was much in it. "Can I…?"

"On the house. Take it easy, right?"

"Thank you. You've been very kind."

She looked so dainty, desirable and lost. "Here's looking at you, kid," I growled with a corny flash of Bogart in modern setting taking leave of his dewy-eyed Ingrid Bergman, or so I foolishly imagined.

When I walked out into the chill air my feet seemed to float down Baker Street towards my ultimately pointless destination with a script editor called

Helen. They didn't usually do the floating bit, not any more, so I wondered what on earth could have been the matter with them.

MARCH

Friday 6th

Was surprised to get an A4 envelope addressed in flowing handwriting. In it, the CV and photos of the leaflet girl, Lynda Styan, with a letter thanking me for offering to show her details to the casting director. A tang of perfume came off the note. She lives in Golders Green, north London. The handwritten presentation looks weirdly Edwardian, or even Victorian, from before typewriters or computers were invented, and I wondered again whether I hadn't met a lovely ghost that day.

She asks in the letter how I got on with *Byker Grove*. Well, I'll be pushing it to come up with anything, would more likely want to throttle the little creeps over their spotty relationship angsts, heightism preoccupations and oatmeal breakfasts than write about their self-centred lives. Not at all the attitude a chap needs when approaching such a task, but I did thank Howard for giving me another chance I've probably blown.

My fragrant correspondent added that maybe we could have another 'cup of tea' some time. Well, tea is safe. I know girls often like to keep a man as a friend only. Especially an older one. Fancying him is another country, and there's no chance of that here. She must have a boyfriend anyway – unless she prefers the feminine touch. Can't tell these days. Her photos, taken a year or more back, show her hair in a Louise Brooks bob, eyes even wider and more radiantly innocent. I wrote back suggesting next Wednesday or Friday.

Tuesday 10th

Message from Cat – there's a casting meeting on *Dark Moon* today with Robert Young, Alan Latham and Kate Plantin the casting director. I wondered what part Lynda Styan might play.

This evening the lady herself phoned! – voice honey in my ear. She can't make tomorrow, but would I like to 'call on' her on Friday? Even the phraseology was quaint. Walked on clouds a bit, had a drink and dream, then came back down. Just friends, okay? – this one's young enough to see me into my dotage and still not have to go for electrolysis or a neck-lift.

'The natural state of the football fan is bitter disappointment, no matter what the score.' Quotes writer Nick Hornby on today's page.

Friday 13th

Friday the thirteenth. Cat rang, excited because Rufus Sewell's agent, Tor Belfrage, has told Kate Plantin the script of *Dark Moon* is 'excellent' and is recommending her client to play 'Bryce'. I saw Rufus in *Cold Comfort Farm* – brilliant. Now we await his decision, as well as Greta Scaachi's word on playing 'Laura'. Don't ask me where the money will come from – Alan Latham's territory – but does this mean we're almost there then?

This evening drove to Lynda Styan's at Golders Green. (Feel like cranking into writing mode, tear a couple of sheets from pad to insert in diary). It's a big old house on the Finchley Road, divided into flats. The same shimmering girl of yestermoon aspect oped the front door and, with slightly guarded Clara Bow smile, bade me step into a gloom-shrouded hallway hardly changed from a decade before the *Titanic*'s maiden voyage: walls wood-panelled, derelict fireplace with original tiling, cobwebs in high corners that hadn't seen a brush since the garden outside trembled to bombs in 1940. Now, with Alice-band-held-back flame-hued hair, slender body in sleeveless pink top and tight white jeans plushly segmented, testing my jaundiced gaze as surprised fresh lights flashed into it, she wiggled ahead of me up creaky stairs past a stained-glass window the Zeppelins had failed to destroy, paused on the first landing at a heavy oaken door that creaked back at her push like an accessory in a haunted house, and led me into the flat she shares with her sister.

The flat, like what I could see of the rest of the well-worn dwelling, appeared to be sinking into terminal disrepair by courtesy of a neglectful landlady now (I was told) too ancient to care. Musty. Curling lino, threadbare carpets. Lost in time. Like Lynda, except musty she ain't, but perfumed and gleamy, healthy-young, with all plaster intact.

Her sister, who occupies the adjoining room, was out, but Lynda made a cuppa and took me into hers because there's no lounge – Brunel or his architectural equivalent had neglected to design one – and the kitchen was too tiny to sit in: the plastic swingbin fought for space with two chairs cramped under a table that might have graced a dolls' house, while the 1950s-style fridge, whining loudly and no doubt carrying ice in a box at the back in case the electrics blew, was crushed against a cast iron cooker straight from the set of *Ten Rillington Place*.

Feeling like a wanderer in someone else's skewed fantasy I gaped around her bed-cum-living room, at the lofty ceiling with its original mouldings, the crumpled double snoozer with sad single pillow, pallid sheepskin rugs like leftovers from a shearing accident, ancient dressing-table swamped with cosmetics, rusted fixtures (like the shoe-scraper on the front doorstep) that modern folks back in 1914 would have mocked as being out-dated. Gaslight jets still protruded from ceiling and walls as if waiting to be lit by a maidservant in long skirts who'd got press-ganged by mistake into Nelson's navy on her way to light them.

Lynda was talking. A bird flew down the chimney, she said, last summer; it emerged from the open fireplace and slammed and flapped around the walls, and she was so scared she had to get the man downstairs to come in and throw open a window because she hadn't the strength to wrench the sash up. Spiders don't bother her though, they get in the bath and she lifts them out with her hands.

There seemed no question in her mind that there was anything less than perfectly normal in my being there only feet away from where she dribbled and dreamed her seemingly solo nights to oblivion. I was older and seasoned enough to sit back with my tea, an honorary female for the evening. I needed to remind myself that she was a trained actress. Such massive innocence. Wasn't it? The room smelled of Chanel and talc; in a dark old wardrobe hung stylish dresses and flouncy outfits most girls wouldn't wear these days but I knew would look ideal on this one as she kicked up the dust to an impromptu Charleston.

On the wall dangled framed photos of Lynda in various theatrical productions. Statuettes from the '20s and '30s adorned the mantelpiece, idealised versions of herself in cloche hats and svelte clothes. A wooden ukulele and ukulele banjo lay on the settee. She moved them aside so I could be more comfortable. This was her sanctum sanctorum into which I continued to feel both privileged and astonished to have been invited. The dressing-table drawers bulged with clothing, underwear spilling out.

Her sister would be in soon, she explained, so I expect she felt safe. Or perhaps she cherished the illusion that older men don't jump on one's limbs and start gasping imbecilities. Yet I'd be lying not to admit that Lynda's great green eyes spun spells around me, her body weaved a saucy gavotte, wiggled wondrously, sat down, stood up; while she chatted, at times tossing in something outrageous like a grenade with only a small charge so it didn't blow your head off but made you sit up a bit straighter.

"Most men can't handle me," she said.

"I don't suppose they can."

"Sometimes I sing out loud in public, or make a scene so everyone turns to stare."

Her eyes on me were challenging. I wondered how Cary Grant might have responded in one of those crackling-dialogued romcoms. 'I'd either slap your wrist, young lady, or run pell-mell for the nearest horizon," I said in what I hoped was his voice, trying to capture the steel beneath the surface flippancy but managing only to sound like a drunken Australian.

Eyes widey-big, a little startled, fist on hip as she warily assessed me. "You're not *violent*, are you?"

I couldn't help smiling at the concern on her lovely face. She had made it up specially for my visit. The deep-red kissy lips, eye-liner and stuff that blackened long lashes, teeth like pearls in a frozen grin that left the merry eyes to lose their laughter on their own.

"Don't worry about me, I'm a pussy cat."

"I don't like violence. But I like pussy cats."

"You're referring to the animal, I take it, rather than a seemingly easy-to-tread-on man?"

She was silent, as if secretly translating my words into some unknown tongue, then back into English again.

"I've got a musical group," she announced. "Or had."

"Pardon?"

"It's called 'Red Hot and Blonde'. Or was."

"Why 'had' and 'was'?"

"My boyfriend was in it, but we've broken up. I was 'Red'," she jabbed a finger into the Titian hair exploding pyrotechnically from the Alice band. "Ukulele and vocals. 'Blonde' was Janet, on accordion."

"She's, er, blonde?"

Lynda nodded. "Trained at the Royal Academy of Music. And Simon was on banjo. He was 'Hot' because he could play his instrument fast. Joke though, really. My sister thought of the name."

"Why did you break up with 'Hot' Simon?"

She peered down at me. Her glossed lips twitched. "I beat him up."

I couldn't help blinking. "I thought you didn't like violence."

"He was ignoring me. He never showed any emotion, I was trying to get a response from him. I'd had two pints of Guinness and wasn't used to drinking…"

"Ah."

"So I punched him and tore his shirt when he tried to get away. He thought I'd gone mad. I felt so ashamed afterwards, still do. He'd brought his bike with him."

"What?"

"His pushbike. Do you know what he said?"

"After you'd beaten him up?"

"Yes." I glanced at her frail fists and doubted they'd have done much damage. "He said in that toffee-nosed voice – he was a chartered surveyor you see, not really what you could really totally call, a, um… though he *was* very good, had his own band at one point. He… what was I saying?"

"You were about to tell me what he said pursuant to your duffing him up."

"Oh yes. Sorry. He said 'I'm going to put on my bicycle clips and go'. And he did. I can see him now, wobbling away along the pavement under the street-lights. I wanted to call after him, but…" The girl called Lynda blinked sadly at me, and I realised that her eyes were damp. "That was weeks ago, I haven't heard a word since and he doesn't return my calls. Do you think he's really gone?"

And there again was that imploring, puzzled expression she'd had when I first met her. I looked at Lynda for several moments and laughed, falling back on the settee. "Sounds like it," I said. "Gone with the wind that blew through. Plus bicycle clips. Forever, I'd say. Unless he likes being bopped by beautiful girls and having his shirts ripped." I watched her carefully, afraid I may have touched a tender spot. "Did you love him?" I asked, leaning anxiously forward.

"Yes and no."

"Which of those comes out stronger?"

She paused, weighing up the question. "'No'," she decided after several moments.

"Ah."

"But 'yes' too – I don't want to be unkind." Again she paused. "So now I'm looking for another 'Hot'."

"Aren't we all?"

"D'you want to see it? The group? And my showreel?"

I felt like someone she'd invited in to look at her collection. My role in this was already established: we were kids together, me the quiet boy from up the street who intrigued her faintly, she the one with the personality and energy who needed an audience.

Her video showed her as 'young housewife' and 'flapper girl' in commercials, plus a scene with Gorden Kaye in the TV sitcom *'Allo 'Allo!*, Lynda extremely young in beret and belted raincoat being funny in a French accent. There was footage of her trio 'Red Hot & Blonde' as they appeared on a TV show. Great vivacity, she with exuberant singing voice playing ukulele George Formby style. 'Blonde' Janet, on accordion, was also strikingly eye-engaging – they made a fantastic pair – but 'Hot', on banjo, didn't look so hot. Poor guy. I felt for him, thinking of his cycle-flight from the light of his life with bruised ego, bruised whatever else and torn shirt.

Lynda's sister Nicola came in, lovely too and engaged to be wed, more here-and-now than Lynda with similar amazing hair a shade darker (mum's brunette, it's dad who has the barnet that makes pre-Raphaelite-preferred poppets of his daughters with hair like burnished sunglow).

Then I was out in the roaring realities of Golders Green streets again. Till next time. Would there be one? I was in uncharted waters, having long since lost the language to make the next move. But anyhow, we could only ever have been just pals.

Tuesday 24th

It's all gone horribly quiet on *Dark Moon*. Rang Cat, who was subdued, seems to think I'm pushing her for information (I am). Meanwhile out there like a peaceful balm and smiling flame is the girl called Lynda who I visited nearly two weeks ago and never heard from again. Or was that a dream too?

Wednesday 31st

Still no word from Cat. It starts to feel weird, all momentum gone from *Dark Moon*. Why? We have a good script, good director, good producer, good casting director, access to funding – what's going on? And I've sent Kate Plantin Lynda Styan's CV and pics. No word back. Nothing. Not from anyone. Do I actually exist or am I a figment of my own internal ponderings?

APRIL

Friday 10th

Was at the computer with the TV on when a message came about the Northern Ireland peace deal. Switched over to get the closing speeches – there is PEACE in Ireland! – all parties including Sinn Fein have agreed. Good Friday, 1998, Peace in Ireland! I wondered what my Irish forbears like great-grandma Sarah Larkin from County Clare would have thought of it – reached for the poteen or hidden the guns?

'Men are those creatures with two legs and eight hands.' Says actress Jayne Mansfield on this page of the diary.

Friday 17th

The girl called Lynda phoned! Not sure how I feel about being 'just a friend', intermittently at that, but it's what happens when the years start kicking in, women see you differently. The rules changed when I wasn't looking, odd not to feel you're in with at least some kind of a chance. But I should be pleased that such a beauty at least courts my company. Arranged to call round there tomorrow at four. Admit am looking forward to it, she chases out the greyness that has sunk into my bones.

Saturday 18th

(Adds a couple more sheets) Glad to get out to Golders Green where met Lynda Styan again. She un-merged from her time-warp into the modern day, smiley and perky in brown leather boots to below the knee, long fawn swirly skirt and sheepskin jacket as it's not that wildly warm. She likes silk scarfs, this one shaded with the colours of autumn sunset, tied at her throat, hair spilling in russet coils from the same green velvet cap she wore on Snappy Snaps day. Even as she stepped across the pavement to my car, drivers and male pedestrians looked, looked, looked. A passing lorry blared its horn and a loud whistle pierced the air as it thundered on.

What to do with such an eye-swiveller? How to entertain her? What if we run out of words? Remembering the special place I used to take Kerry when she was a kiddy, walked this vision to the old duelling ground where the little lass and I would fool around sword-fencing with twigs, hidden among trees up a secret shady slope at Kenwood on Hampstead Heath – and had it all to ourselves. Scents, sounds and sighs of Spring, grasses wildflower-splashed. My companion surprised me by suddenly singing out loud with perfect professional pitch a song called 'Telling It To The Daisies', her voice mellow-thrilly and bell-pure through the trees and no one but me, the birds, and a few rabbits and squirrels to listen. I'd never heard the song before, nor of Annette Hanshaw who Lynda tells me sang it back in the 1920s and early '30s. Youngly pretty and cute as custard, Hanshaw worked with the likes of Red Nichols, Benny Goodman, Jimmy and Tommy Dorsey, Jack Teagarden – names long forgotten by modern bumpers, stompers and rappers. But clearly, with Lynda around, the melody lingers on, and I was glad of it.

On seeing a magpie she says "Hello Mister Magpie, how are you; how's your lady wife and the children too?" – and there have to be two magpies together or it's bad luck. Back at the car I drove us around and down to Victorian choo-choo-train memories of Hampstead Heath Station area where bank holiday flockers once crowded from carriages and rumple-tumbled up the road to the summer funfair, huge-hatted happy families merrily picnicking on sunny grass. I told Lynda about them, and she saw them too, through narrowed dream-filled eyes, with a rapt parting of cherry-ripe lips.

Outside the Magdala Tavern opposite the station I showed her where Ruth Ellis shot her lover David Blakely in 1955 for not paying her enough attention. Lynda stood fingering the bullet-marks still in the wall.

"Beats the pips out of ripping shirts," I said.

"If I'd had a gun that day," she said worriedly, "it scares me that I might have done something like this to Simon." Lynda paused, looked horrified at what she'd just said. Her hand flew to her mouth. "Oh! Of course I wouldn't *dream* of doing anything even *remotely* like that! I couldn't *imagine* even *imagining* actually... *killing...* anyone." She shivered.

I couldn't help smiling at her appalled expression. "Well," I said, "at least you wouldn't have been hanged for it. You'd have probably got three months suspended sentence with a trip to Bermuda thrown in."

"Did she really shoot him dead right here?" Lynda remained fascinated, eyes big and frightened.

"Right there where you're standing," I told her. "Ruth Ellis was the last woman to hang for murder in this country. It's reported that she gave her hangman, Albert Pierrepoint, a little smile as he slipped the noose over her head."

Lynda shivered. "I wouldn't have thought it was anything to smile about."

"No, I don't suppose it damn well was."

After a drinky-snack inside the pub – she a jacket spud with tuna and sweetcorn and a lime with soda – it was getting dark. We walked up Parliament Hill and stood looking high across the lights of London to the night-shrouded hills beyond, then strolled down past the lake, coming on figures sitting on the dark grass or padding silently by in the gloom. Lynda said she would never dare to walk the Heath at night alone, or even with her sister, so this was a new experience for her. Her arm slipped into mine. It gave her a sense of being protected, she said.

MAY

Sunday 10th

Yes, chumming chummily as friends only, and glad of it. Think of all that emotional and sexual energy one isn't required to expend any more. Bask in the sunshine, don't run around in it like a sweating heartlorn loon – time has moved on and so have you.

A blazing Sunday morn. Lynda agreed to come to Chelsea with me for the screening of director-to-be of *Dark Moon*, Robert Young's, *Captain Jack*, written by Jack Rosenthal. Felt proud to have her on my arm, dazzly and flamey – a glimpse of the big time that usually takes place in a different dimension to the one I inhabit. Robert, holding court in the crowded foyer, introduced me to his young female agent with Duncan Heath, and I introduced Lynda to him. She glowed. Actor Bob Hoskins, who stars, was there, and Lynda and I sat a couple of seats from Maureen Lipman, who is also in the movie and Rosenthal's wife. A life-affirming film, powerful at the end. It was so invigorating to tap into the energy that flows around people for whom things are actively *happening* in the privileged world of acceptance and acclaim.

Sunday 17th
Greta Scaachi has finally said no to *Dark Moon*. Thank you, Miss Scaachi. Can't think of anyone more stunning to be turned down by, even though it took longer than the gestation period of the African elephant to do so. So who will be our 'Laura' now? And what part can Lynda play in our film-to-be?

'In politics if you want anything said, ask a man. If you want anything done, ask a woman.' Says Margaret Thatcher on today's page.

Friday 29th
Met Lynda at noon to take her out for the day. Found her in such distress – Primi Townsend of Roget Carey's theatrical agency has just told her they can't keep her on their books. She wept heartrendingly, wrenching at my hand as I drove. "I try so very, *very* hard, all the time, but nothing ever happens for me," she sobbed. "It always falls away into nothing, whatever I try to do. Now I've got no agent…" Despite her terrific looks, personality and talent all she gets is set-backs and ends up selling tights in department stores to snooty females who treat her like a skivvy, or handing out leaflets in the street to people who don't want one. This girl is so gutsy and brilliant, yet every inch of her route seems uphill. Like mine is. Is that our connection? I know that struggle so well, and have never understood why it should be, when lesser talents seem to flourish like weeds.

Drove a distraught Lynda down to Hastings on the south coast through torrential rain and hailstones that matched her desperate mood. On the way I played a cassette with Fred Astaire jauntily singing 'Things Are Looking Up', and told her we'll beat the bitches and bastards yet. I also said, as Spencer Tracey did to Katharine Hepburn in George Cukor's *Pat and Mike*:

"I may not be able to lick you, and you may not be able to lick me, but together we can lick 'em all." Or something like that. And gradually Lynda's sobs subsided.

Later, parked on the night-black beach at Rockanore in the cocoon of the car, fish and chips, a sliver of new moon ("It's bad luck to look at it for the first time through glass," she insists; "unless you wear specs, in which case it doesn't count."). She was calm and smiling again, like the passing of the storm, phosphorescent wave-crests running lullingly in, the muted sea-roar softed into our senses, a star-silvered sky shimmered – and all the bitter unfairness, ill-judgement by twats-in-office and general madness ebbed away and, for a while at least, we were at peace.

JUNE

Tuesday 2nd
Barrie Saint Clair asked me to get my script of *La Miss* to director John Glen. As a reality-based action/love story turning on the Free French Brigade's incredible stand at the desert outpost of Bir Hakeim in 1942 against Rommel's Afrika Korps, with an Englishwoman involved as the general's driver, this will make a compelling movie (he sez).

Posted the script to John Glen at an address in Earl's Court. This man directed *For Your Eyes Only*, *Octopussy*, *A View To A Kill*, *The Living Daylights*, *Licence To Kill* – the first three with Roger Moore as James Bond, the others with Timothy Dalton. He was Assistant Director on *Moonraker*, *Superman*, *The Wild Geese*, *The Spy Who Loved Me*, *Shout At The Devil*. He's also a film editor and sound editor of considerable experience. Can such a being possibly like my *La Miss* script enough to want to direct it?

Wednesday 3rd
Cat is definitely dumping Alan Latham again and has biked *Dark Moon* to an alternative producer called Clive Potson. I didn't enquire why, maybe it's best not to.

Friday 5th
Cat in turmoil because Clive Potson says he'll need 'rewrites' if he comes

on as producer for *Dark Moon*. I couldn't help but smile. *Here* we go again. You could show some producers *War and Peace* or the shooting script of *Casablanca*, and copious 'rewrites' would be called for. Until these people have overseen the re-painting of the Sistine Chapel by someone they feel more comfortable with (who *is* this Michelangelo guy? – bring Bill in) – they don't feel they've contributed significantly to a project.

Monday 8th

Robert Young is being icy with Cat for dropping Alan, and Clive P is very keen. It's interesting how Cat has taken control of this, as if to say 'It's my story so I therefore claim the right to make all the decisions, hire and fire, etc.' Yet now it's only *based on* her original story, because already it's changed quite a lot with the input of others – especially including my own. A lesson here: if you make like you're in charge, people will fall in behind you – already this extraordinary woman has taught me a piece of life-craft I wish I'd learned years ago.

Wednesday 10th

Barrie Saint Clair rang. John Glen has read my *La Miss* script and wants to direct it!! Fantastic news! Barrie is coming over from South Africa next week and has set up a meeting with him in London.

Meanwhile Cat's replacement producer to Alan Latham, Clive Potson, is calling for extensive rewrites on *Dark Moon* which will only delay things and reduce the quality of what is already a nifty script again with a director and (previous?) producer raring to run with it exactly as it is. Crazy or what?

Monday 15th

More great news today. My civil engineer nephew Tim Lucas – son of my sister Rosalind – has won an international competition to design a bridge over the River Liffey in Dublin, being built to celebrate the new millennium. He can't be more than 23. How proud Rosalind, who died when Tim was little, would have been – she a professional artist and designer. With Tim it looks like a case of artistic flair meeting technical know-how. Fantastic!

Tuesday 16th
Seeing John Glen with Barrie Saint Clair today. A tube strike, so drove the car in. At Earl's Court parked free (because of the strike) and walked to Glen's place, a spacious basement flat on Barkston Gardens. A tall, sturdy-looking man. "You've written a nice script," he said to me, gave positive suggestions for amendments, we got on well. I had to suspend disbelief that I was talking to the man who directed *Octopussy, For Your Eyes Only, A View To A Kill* and so on. Two hours later John Glen was officially on board as director and keen to get started. He saw us to the door, shook hands, and agreed that he and I would get together soon.

"A good meeting," Barrie enthused as I drove him back to where he's staying on the Cromwell Road, and he gave me the address in Paris of Susan Schlegelmilch, née Travers, whose character and actions are reflected in the film. We agreed I should visit this lady in Paris. What a day!

However, my euphoric moment vanished this evening when Cat phoned from Robert Young's house at Kew. Clive Potson was there too, talking about *Dark Moon*. "Robert is still on board," she said, "*and agrees to the script changes Clive wants.*"

Sunday 21st
"When you dream tonight," I said to Lynda as we lay out under the sun in the Totteridge fields with no souls about but our own and green spaces all around, "what kind of dream will it be?"

"A midsummer night's one," she said. Then added drowsily: "'Feed him with apricocks and dewberries, With purple grapes, green figs, and mulberries; The honey-bags steal from the humble-bees, And for night-tapers crop their waxen thighs, And light them at the fiery glow-worm's eyes…'"

I suppose this sort of thing happens if you go around with an actress.

'The holes in your Swiss cheese are somebody else's Swiss cheese.' Melvin Fishman on today's diary page.

Monday 22nd
Could've done without Cat phoning about the 'script meeting' she's just had with Clive Potson on *Dark Moon*. So I'm out in the cold again while

that poor script waits apprehensively for God-knows what further indignities to be heaped upon it as this new producer gets into his stride.

Friday 26th

To Robert Young's house on Kew Green. Clive Potson there with Cat. Well, at least I was invited to their deliberations this time, yet sat there like a spare part as no one sought my counsel on anything. They now seem to collectively think that the lawyer 'Grimstone' and 'Laura's' sister can both be ditched to get to the guts of the story. *What?* – it's ALL ABOUT Grimstone, can't they see that? Grimstone is secretly obsessed by the heroine and the entire story turns on this hidden fact. At last I got talking and tried to explain why he *must* stay in. Somehow cinematographer Jack Cardiff's name came up in the exchanges, and Robert blinked when I told him that this great man, who worked with Bogart and Hepburn on *The African Queen*, has recently (via Howard Pays) expressed a wish to direct two of my other scripts. I even have Jack Cardiff's voice on my answerphone to this effect. This seemed to make a difference, and Cat looked a bit frozen.

In the end they left it to me to come up with a new First Draft acceptable to all, but it's an uncomfortable feeling and I'm tempted to hand the whole thing over to Cat and let her get on with it.

Steffi Graf knocked out of Wimbledon on a sunless day – this once great player gaunt and out of form.

Saturday 27th

Cat phoned early, saying "I know I'm not supposed to call you, but…" and went on to propose more changes she's just thought up, bless her cotton socks and all hail to the gods of creativity. Her inventiveness is akin to genius, her vitality and incisiveness seem to sap the marrow from my bones. I feel ever more like the bemused writer played by Alexei Sayle in *The Strike* – the Comic Strip take on the Hollywoodisation of the British miners' protest against pit closures, with 'Arthur Scargill' played by Peter Richardson as Al Pacino, and "Yuh cain't have the miners *losin'* – they hafta goddamn WIN!" – of which this *Dark Moon* set-up increasingly reminds me.

Monday 29th

Lunch with Peter Jaques by the river at Mortlake. It's good to have a sane head to consult with. His advice is to cut my losses and walk away from the increasingly confused *Dark Moon* situation. Yet I'm fond of Cat, and although her developing skills as a screenwriter may be starting to bite, I've a strange feeling it might bother her if I vanished from the scene.

Tuesday 30th
Watched the World Cup match between England and Argentina. Fast and explosive, 2-2 a lot of the time. David Beckham⋆ was sent off for, when down, tapping an opponent with his foot. No 'golden goal' in extra time, the game settled by penalties – which Argentina won.

At Wimbledon, Tim Henman got through to the quarter finals (again) – usually as far as he gets. Maybe this is as far as I get on *Dark Moon* – still haven't got/can't get started on the latest revised version of the revised revised version of the latest revised revision.

⋆For months after this incident Beckham was pilloried by press and public for having 'let down his country' by that gratuitous foul and lost England their chance in the World Cup. How could I have known that this famous player – or, rather, his wife – was to become involved with the ongoing fortunes of Dark Moon? *Read on.*

JULY

Tuesday 14th
Disaster! A writer/producer called Richard Filon phoned me from Paris, has just had lunch with Susan Travers and got my phone number from the letter I sent her asking if we can meet to discuss *La Miss*. So this was my revered heroine's reply – on Bastille Day, too. Filon said Susan has agreed to have her life story written, and Sony Pictures are interested. In other words 'Keep off, she's mine.' So my lovely exciting film can't now be made? All those notes and research, all that *work* gone for nothing – even though I found every piece of information in war-history books in the public library. So although my script is entirely legal, Filon talked gleefully of 'two-million dollar writers' in Hollywood working on 'their' script. What? Yanks writing about an upper-crust Englishwoman of the 1940s fighting for the Free

French under British control in the Libyan desert? Why not throw John Wayne in as well? It beggars belief. Gutted is hardly the word.

Wednesday 15th
Barrie Saint Clair rang – says Filon is bluffing: Barrie's contact at Sony Pictures says no such film is on the stocks. Their lawyers can't possibly stop our film* – all the information I used is in public domain – we proceed as planned, with John Glen directing.

*But really it was the end of it. The lawyers saw to that. Thus are the vagaries of the film business. My script of La Miss was perfectly legal then, and remains so today (especially as I had semi-fictionalised the lady for better filmic effect – and have since re-titled it Grain of Sand so as to entirely eliminate any imagined legal problem), but at the time it was considered to 'conflict' with the book this incredible Englishwoman had had ghost-written following the recent demise of her husband. Had Mr Schlegelmilch stayed alive for only another year more, my script would have been filmed – with sales agents Burlage Edell in Hollywood behind it and John Glen directing – and my future would have been very different. A bitter loss indeed.

Monday 27th
Cat phoned, back from Portugal. It's the first time anyone's come back to me since my latest *Dark Moon* draft. She began with "I'm afraid it's not right yet."

I smiled into the phone. It didn't smile back. "Who says?"

"Clive Potson and I have been talking. The script can't go out as it is. Some of the dialogue… characterisation… crass… (it was a word he used, she said) – he said he can maybe fix it in the office, though…"

It was as if someone had suddenly turned green and sprouted horns. I told Cat rather huffily that if her newly-generated producer was going to mess with a perfectly good script I wanted my name off it, but I also want my full legally-agreed fee if and when this film ever gets made.

To me the issue was clear, felt no regrets. I can walk away knowing I've done the job to the best of my abilities – even if they remained unrecognised. Put the phone down expecting to feel awful, but instead felt cleansed and free despite the fact that instead of two films in contention for imminent production I now have none.

AUGUST

Monday 3rd

Lynda Styan rang. Her offbeatness is a tonic, I can forget my crumbling film career and look through her into an alternative world. She has now attracted the attentions of a randy vicar and a roofer she met somewhere is plying her with flowers and long impassioned letters. She says it's like taking part in a *Carry On* film. As our relationship is platonic, I can smile indulgently and enjoy the crazy dramas she inspires.

Tuesday 4th

Still can't believe what's happened. Abigail of Harbottle & Lewis phoned me, trying to negotiate that I be paid only 50% of my £52,000 fee to fund some other writer *to rewrite the script* of *Dark Moon*! When I recovered I said: "I don't understand. Why should I pay £26,000 of my hard-earned fee to someone else to rewrite the perfectly good screenplay that already exists?"

Abigail's argument was that surely I should be grateful for *anything* rather than *nothing*. "Wouldn't £30,000 be nice?" she said, upping it slightly. "Do you want to lose that, and not have the film made at all?" She sounded like someone who isn't very good at talking to children talking to a child.

Afterwards I wondered what kind of mug they thought I was. More disconcertingly, *why* they thought it. By a fluke of nature I happen to have 20-20 vision, but it's as if they were trying to persuade me that I need heavy duty specs and a white stick.

'I like pigs. Dogs look up to us. Cats look down on us. Pigs treat us as equal.' Says Sir Winston Churchill on today's page.

Wednesday 5th

Went to bed last night but couldn't sleep because that weird conversation kept coming back to me. None of it made sense, because earlier this year we were ready to go with everything, including the script, in place.

Finally drifted off and woke to a sunny day – ideal weather for escaping. However, assuming that Clive Potson is behind this latest madness I first rang Harbottle & Lewis and urged Abigail to ask her client to stand by me on *Dark Moon* or this film could suffer terminal damage. I think Abigail thought I'd phoned to climb down and accept her surreal offer. She coldly suggested I talk to her client myself, and rang abruptly off.

Out then went I into the merry day. Lynda answered her door looking fantastic in long dark silky dress patterned with flowers. A dreamy drive to the coast, weather fabulous. Who cares about these people? Freelance journalism keeps me just about solvent, maybe I'll pack in films and develop that side of things more. Truth is, though, and whichever way I look at it, it appears to be the films that have packed *me* in.

Friday 7th

Still can't quite believe what I learned today! None of this confusion is Cat's fault. Met the lady at her request at the Rose & Crown at Kew, we sat out back in sweltering sunshine and at last, over pints of beer, the awful truth of what's been happening came out. Her barrister friend Graham Lawson is at the core of all this misunderstanding and pointless conflict, having written *his own version* of the entire script of *Dark Moon* and jettisoned mine. However, according to Cat, it rambles on and "nothing happens till page 75" (I quote). Incredibly, this version was sent to Robert Young to supersede mine. I said is this why Abigail asked me to surrender half my fee – to pay Graham for having put together this alternative draft? Cat made no clear response, but didn't say no.

Then another terrible thought struck like a thump in the gut – was Clive Potson given Graham Lawson's version, AND HE THOUGHT I'D WRITTEN IT? Small wonder our new producer wants me completely rewritten if this is so. Quite where I go from here is debatable, but that horizon is looking enticing.

Monday 10th

Rang Robert Young's number and left a message saying am back on the case, or prepared to be, despite the delivery to him of an alternative script that doesn't work and which I had nothing to do with. Indeed, I asked, is he still interested in directing this picture if we can re-create the script he would have been happy to shoot *seven months ago*, which is still on my computer?

Wednesday 19th

Still no response from Robert Young to the message I left him 9 days ago. When Cat phoned me from holiday somewhere expensive I pressed the point till she admitted that our director, once so praiseful of this project, had been bewildered by Graham Lawson's draft, said he couldn't use it and has gone abroad.

SEPTEMBER

Wednesday 2nd

Edged my way back into *Dark Moon*, the awful draft they'd been messing with, but it's like trudging through sludge with holes in your boots. Whoever it collectively was have drained 'Laura's' speech of all personality – and made 'Bryce' a witless woodentop. All the chemistry and sparkle between them has gone, along with any glints of humour, wit or irony that had helped define the characters. Scanned in Cat's latest batch of 'notes' and incorporated them into this new, disastrously compromised script. I know it will never be as good again as it's already been, but am no long agonising over that. If this is what it takes to get a film made, so be it. I really feel for Cat, having to see her cherished project mauled around like this. I *can* see a clear way back, but will I ever be allowed to take it there?

Friday 4th

Following my further attempts to reach him for a creative discussion, was surprised to get an email from Robert Young to say he is (quote) 'waiting for the new producers, who have got themselves into a muddle.'

Muddle indeed.

'Television is an invention that permits you to be entertained in your living room by people you wouldn't have in your home.' Says David Frost on today's diary page.

Wednesday 9th

On a bit of a high again re *Dark Moon* and the way it's newly developing. Now the director and writer appear to be communicating again, I feel free for the first time in ages to do what I can to bring some style and quality back into the script, though a lot of restoration work is needed.

Thursday 10th
Cooler and rainy, yet at its centre is a tropical feel that has you in a slight sweat: the aftermath of one of one of the hurricanes that ripped through America. Looks, too, like Bill Clinton's in big trouble as the truth comes out of naughty goings-on at the White House.

Monday 14th
Nose to grindstone to reach the end of the 'new 2' *Dark Moon*. Spent rest of day reading through and revising. During this, Cat rang. "You're a star," she said when I told her it was done. Have never felt so exhausted over a script before.

It's cooler now, heading for autumn.

Friday 18th
On the Isle of Man with producer Debi Nethersole to see the Film Commission in Douglas about funding for future scripts. We met Hilary Dugdale, the Commission's attractive co-head. Saw a poster on the wall there of Alan Latham's latest production *When Darkness Falls*. I mentioned Alan in connection with *Dark Moon*. "Oh, I love that script," said Hilary (speaking of an earlier version). "It keeps coming back to me – we'll certainly be happy to get behind that." When Debi told Hilary I wrote the draft she was talking about we thought it best not to mention that it's since been changed a fair bit by others, so I wonder if this chance for funding has already gone.

Steve Christian came in, bright and sincere, and the two gave us the lowdown on getting funding from their Film Commission. Essentially it was: Give us the right guarantees and we'll provide facilities and up to 65% of the money to make it. From banks and their own government sources. So this was what Alan was working towards when he was eased from the project? I can't bear to think about it...

Tuesday 22nd
Peter Jaques rang, said he sat next to John Glen at a movie function last week and they talked about me, and John said he likes my work. I need that

kind of reassurance after all this debilitatingly negative stuff from the *Dark Moon* encampment.

OCTOBER

Thursday 15th

The silence on *Dark Moon* deepens, nearly three weeks since handing in the latest draft I'd felt so pleased with. I wonder what on earth, and awfully, they are doing to that poor script that had got colour back into its cheeks and a gleam into its eye, like an invalid risen from bed to breathe pure air that promises to revive it fully unless someone, or a consortium of same, decide to kick the legs from under it again and smother it with a pillow in the name of 'further improvement'.

Saturday 31st

Still no word on *Dark Moon*. It's positively spooky. Total funk, and fear for my own sanity, prevent me from phoning Cat or Robert Young or Clive Potson, or the Samaritans, to ask. Perhaps I imagined it all, and am only now waking from a ghastly dream to find that the whole thing never happened.

Went out with Lynda later. We walked the dark towpath at Kew through muddy puddles. They're welding track on the old Victorian rail bridge across the Thames – eerie lights and sparks. A dog with a flashing red collar floated by in the gloom. We watched kids 'trick or treat' dressed in white sheets, candlelit pumpkins at a doorway, a Halloween party in excited progress. Time melted.

NOVEMBER

Friday 6th

To Cat's house for 12.30. Mags Stoke there. Blonde, sturdy, well articulated, sincere manner. So this is the lady helping Cat to bring *Dark Moon* into the world. Liked her at once, very sensible and solid, works as a script supervisor in TV and film. We went through the script, which emerged surprisingly unscathed. By 4.15 we'd finished, then off the women raced to collect their kids from school.

This evening to an arts centre in a church hall in north London and watched Lynda in a show, set in wartime, written *for her* and directed by the vicar she mentioned. The play was good. She came on in a 1940s frock, acted strongly and sang sensationally. There was a moment when she sat in a spotlight and sang 'The Very Thought Of You'. And when she stood up, half-facing away as if into the dawn, she looked utterly beautiful.

Monday 9th

Cat rang, pretty high. Mags says we have a 'fabulous' script now. 'Could be a classic' 'Americans will love it' were other comments she'd apparently made. "Once the amendments are finished, of course," added Cat. "Amendments?" I echoed nervously.

'If you become a star, you don't change – everyone else does.' Kirk Douglas on today's page.

Wednesday 18th

Bombshell! Cat has learned from Robert Young's wife Hermione that he's booked up for most of next year making films in Spain, which seemingly scuppers any chance of him directing *Dark Moon* till after that date (she sez), so Cat has told Robert he's off the project as this film must be made in the coming year. In dismay I tried phoning Robert, but he's not there. Left him a message asking is it true that he's off the film? No response. Did he get fed up waiting while 'the new producers' in their 'muddle' messed about?

Knowing that John Glen and I have worked together, Cat now suggests he reads *Dark Moon* with a view to directing it. I said it's not his kind of movie, but she urged me to ask anyway. Certainly the prospect of putting *Dark Moon* on ice for the whole of next year is unthinkable.

Thursday 19th

Phoned John Glen and pitched *Dark Moon* to him and would he be interested in directing it? He said he's off to his other home in Australia tomorrow for Christmas, but if I can get the script to him by this evening he'll read it on the plane.

Unable to raise a courier in time, drove the script to Earl's Court myself through the worst rush hour traffic I've ever known and pushed it through his door. The deed is done.

Monday 23rd
John Glen rang me from his other home in Perth. Says he's read *Dark Moon* and *would like to direct it*! I reached Cat on her mobile and told her this. She went ballistic with excitement. How weird, that although it was made impossible for John to direct *La Miss*, here we are working on a film together anyway.

DECEMBER

Tuesday 1st
To Cat's house. Kate Plantin opened the door. Kate was married to Marcus Plantin, whose sister Monique married my cousin John Keutenius. Does this mean we're related? We smile at the idea. Cat poured wine – a civilised custom, especially in the morning.

Rang John Glen's number in Australia from Cat's phone, got his lovely wife Janine who called him in from the garden. Put him on to Cat, and the two seemed to get on. John told her he really likes the script and has already directed the film in his head. Brilliant!

Tuesday 22nd
To Lynda's for half ten this morning. I'd arranged to take her to a carol service at Guildford Cathedral later. We stopped in Richmond Park and walked quite a way – talking, talking. On then down to Guildford, chimes and hymns, rhymes and prezzy purchases, choir-voices a-soar, her own amazing soprano higher and stronger than theirs, lips glistening in candle-glimmer, eyes happy green suns. Christmas breathes its piney perfume, flickers and sparkles and flashes, myriad-coloured, promising perfection and child-like joy.

Sweet astonished nectar sips, the day dimming to night-brightness, then dazey-dark lanes and the most incredible sighs.

Lynda and I are no longer just friends.

1999

Saturday 16th
Back from South Africa where stayed in Johannesburg with Debi and Vincent. Are we fully funded on *Dark Moon*? Rang Cat, she was very up and positive – we'll meet Tuesday. John Glen is our ace card. Clive Potson wants a hundred thousand pounds to co-produce with Cat. Nice work if you can get it.

Wednesday 27th
Cat begins by saying Mags Stoke says I have a 'rare gift' of writing movement cinematically. Keep talking, Mags, I like it. But Mags also remarked that there's 'padding' in the script and one or two scenes are in the wrong place. Uh? Mags also (sez Cat) wants to put in little nitty-bitty detail of movement that I know will end up on the cutting room floor and be inappropriately expensive to shoot. I began to wonder, given that the script editor never talks directly to the writer, that maybe it isn't Mags saying these things at all.

I had to get out or go nuts. Drove down to Hastings with Lynda and had a wondrous time roaming over wind-scoured pebbles past beached fishing boats at dusk, snuggling in snugs with beer, fish 'n' chips on the dark shore and all that followed…

'Human beings are perhaps never more frightening than when they are convinced beyond doubt that they are right.' Says Laurens van der Post on my diary page today.

FEBRUARY

Tuesday 16th
Shrove Tuesday. Am invited to Lynda's place for a pancake party. She left

one of her black gloves in the car on Sunday. It sat beside me on the front seat – and as I drove I found myself holding it, as if it was her hand. And the most exquisite feeling came over me when I did so – a melty, drifty sensation that relaxed every fibre of me, softly thrilly – and I realised it was a feeling of utmost peace.

When I arrived for pancakes I gave her the glove back. It must have been a magic one.

Thursday 18th

John Glen rings me from Oz. He likes the latest *Dark Moon* script, with certain amendments. He gives verbal notes and I realise that storywise this man is brilliant. Cat later gave Michelle Guish as possible casting director, so would I send her a script?

Hello, I thought Kate Plantin was casting this…

MARCH

Tuesday 2nd

Got back to my place towards 10 p.m. to a message on the machine from Lynda: "Our washing machine's exploded. Can you come round?"

Drove to Golders Green with my Hoover Aquamaster. Myra, the edgy woman who believes the world is trying to get at her, and who rents the downstairs flat, had just settled in bed to read when there was an explosion from above and water gushed through her ceiling. When I arrived she was hysterical and had to be sedated. Don't suppose it did her persecution complex much good. (I know I shouldn't laugh, but…)

Thursday 11th

Big news: Ros Hubbard of Hubbard Casting has read *Dark Moon* and is willing to cast it. So what happened to Kate Plantin? Or, indeed, Michelle Guish? Angela Shapiro has rung Cat, offering funding. It all seems so vibrant – but also confused.

APRIL

Wednesday 14ᵗʰ

Rang John Glen, a cordial and informal chat. He saw the actor Greg Wise yesterday and was impressed. He played the darkly handsome rotter in *Sense and Sensibility*. So it looks as if already we have our 'Bryce' for *Dark Moon*.

'With charm, you've got to get up close to see it; style slaps you in the face.' So says British poet John Cooper on today's diary page.

MAY

Friday 21ˢᵗ

John Glen rang me: *Shallow Grave* actress Kerry Fox says that 'Laura' is a terrific part and she wants to do it. So she and Greg Wise are meeting on June 7ᵗʰ. At last we have our two leads for *Dark Moon* – though there's the Machiavellian lawyer 'Grimstone' to find. This is getting so exciting!

Monday 31ˢᵗ

UK sales agent Denise Cotton has contacted Cat to say *Dark Moon* is 'incredibly improved' from when she last saw it. She hadn't want to be involved then, but does now. I wondered what she means by 'incredibly improved'? Which/whose version of the script did she read last time, against which this rescued one stands out so starkly? Perhaps it's best not to ask.

JUNE

Sunday 6ᵗʰ

How much longer will this drag on? John Glen rang to say he's no longer seeing Greg Wise and Kerry Fox tomorrow because he doesn't want to lead them up the garden path with the producers dragging their heels like this. What producers? Where did Clive Potson go, and why?

Monday 21st

Sank a couple of meditative beers in the strange midsummer twilight. It's the shortest night, as the French girls say (old joke). Tennis at Wimbledon started today (for us Brits, another old joke).

Wednesday 23rd

Around half past ten this evening walked with Lynda to the top of Parliament Hill and roamed Hampstead Heath in the balmy air, the sky strangely luminescent. Guys were playing football there – even though it was technically dark you could see that well. A dog with three legs hobbled past, some way behind its striding master. "That poor dog," gasped Lynda, "I can't bear to look. Shall I run after that man and tell him to slow down?"

Which reminded me of Marilyn Monroe's sympathy for animals – at home with Arthur Miller one rainy night she saw a cow in a neighbouring field and begged him to let her bring it indoors. Miller's response wasn't recorded, but the thought of sharing his lounge with a wet cow may not have appealed. Lynda's a bit like that, a sweet vulnerability though tough at centre. When we watched *The Misfits* she was screaming and crying right there along with Marilyn at the men for rounding up those wild free horses to be sold for dogs' meat.

Friday 25th

Cat rang to say our new sales agent Denise Cotton wants an extra scene to show 'Laura' being snappish when pregnant. Wrote this scene and realised that not only did it have dramatic validity when extended a bit, there's a perfect acting part in it for Lynda. Faxed the scene to John Glen for his approval.

Saturday 26th

Now Mags wants more in the script about how awful it feels to be pregnant. I, being a mere male, felt unable to comment, except to say I've lived with a pregnant woman who was cheerful and stoic all the way to the birth, and even during it. I know, because I was there. I said to Cat that this film isn't about Mags, it's about 'Laura', and to have the character whingeing on about stomach cramps and varicose veins could alienate the audience. Does anybody listen? I mean, does anybody lis--- (*ssshhh*, you're only the writer...)

'You can't tell who's swimming nude till the tide goes out.' Quote by businessman Victor Kiam on today's diary page.

JULY

Thursday 29th

The day sweltery. To John Glen's at Earl's Court for 10 a.m. to go through the *Dark Moon* script. A Citroën 2cv was parked outside, with '007' and a gun painted on the side. John said it belongs to a Frenchwoman a couple of doors away. He caught her stepping out of it the other day and told her "I directed the film in which that car appeared." Can't believe madame wasn't impressed.

With John's beautiful wife Janine we walked through hot streets to a restaurant on the Brompton Road for lunch, with Chardonnay. Yesterday they'd looked at a flat built from/in the old Harrods Depository by the river near Hammersmith Bridge – and bought it outright. I tried to imagine being able to do that. Asked about Marlon Brando, who John directed in *Christopher Columbus* – seems he was really nice, not difficult at all but liked to be in on production decisions.

Then the famous James Bond director, his film-star-looking wife and yours truly sauntered chattingly back to Barkston Gardens. Ahead of us a woman was struggling along the pavement with a heavy suitcase. Without a word John strode up, took the case from her and carried it to her door. I wondered if she thought she was being mugged – but John's grin and gallantry got her smiling grateful thanks.

Back in his flat we worked on the script. He said re the production set-up at *Dark Moon*: "They're running around like chickens with their heads cut off." At last we finished – very happy with what we'd done. John showed me photos of his daughter and sons, and of his garden in his house in the country (where they're going tomorrow). A lovely man. We shook hands at his door, and up the steps I floated to the square again. It was 5.45.

And so the usually-sidelined, garret-exiled penman drifted home, oblivious of the rushy crush, dreaming of respect and perhaps even a touch of fame, with riches previously only imagined flashing and glittering just beyond.

AUGUST

Wednesday 11th

Eclipse of the sun today. Just after eleven this morning went in the park. Although the sun was casting shadows it was an eerie faint twilight. Lay on my back and looked through the sun-viewer bought for the purpose at a petrol station yesterday. The moon had taken a huge bite out of the sun, just a dazzling sliver left. Here it's 95% total. Crows hopped about looking puzzled. I hoped Kerry was getting the full experience in Cornwall where she's gone with Chris for this, where the land will go completely dark. Amazing. Not till 2090 will there be another such eclipse. Don't suppose I'll be around for it. Will *Dark Moon* have been made by then?

Tuesday 17th

What is this compulsion of people to change the script all the time and get rid of key personnel on a whim? Has *Dark Moon*, which once sang and danced, been reduced to a limping croak yet again?

John Glen rang me later. "We're dealing with rank amateurs here," he said in the closest I've heard this imperturbable man come to exasperation. Are he and I the only ones aware that at every new draft called for the film is weakening again?

SEPTEMBER

Friday 3rd

Restaurant fronts wide open, tables out on pavements, people still sitting or strolling around at eleven p.m. or midnight: how quickly we Brits would adapt to hot weather like this if it was a permanent feature of our lives.

'Too bad all the people who know how to run the country are busy driving taxi cabs and cutting hair.' Says comedian George Burns on today's page.

Thursday 9th

This being 9/9/99 (and many a computer system liable to crash because of it, apparently), such a run won't happen till October 10th 2010. Funny what you think about while trying to keep from thinking about *Dark Moon* and what savagery may be being inflicted on it elsewhere, even now, by God knows who, whom or why?

Thursday 16th
John Glen called me this afternoon and the shock of what he said was like a face-slap. He asked why hadn't I been at the script meeting at his flat this morning? Cat had arranged it. I could only say that the lady – no doubt for her own excellent reasons – had neglected to tell me about it. "She doesn't get what I'm saying to her," he said. "You do." So – as with Robert Young before him – we had our own script meeting on the phone and he went through his final revisions for the second time today.

OCTOBER

Sunday 10th
Today met 'Blonde', in Lynda's group. Drove to the house Janet Beale shares with her partner. Long fair hair, smiling, appealingly pretty, trim figure, Janet plays amazing accordion, trained at the Royal College of Music. She also plays piano, flute and saxophone with accomplishment. 'Red' and 'Blonde' together are incredible enough, but both have been looking for their 'Hot' since the previous one fled on his bike.

Well, today they found him. His name is Andy Eastwood, and Lynda persuaded him to do a session with them. She's known Andy since he was a lad at the Ukulele Society of Great Britain. Now he's studying for a music degree at Oxford University, already a phenomenal exponent of the ukulele, better and faster than the great George Formby – and still only twenty years old.

In came Andy, easy and unassuming, tousled hair and friendly grin. He took his expensive ukulele banjo delicately out of its case like a baby from its cradle. Lynda took hers too, Janet put the accordion round her neck, and, with a "One, two, three, four" from Andy's northern voice they launched into Al Jolson's 'Baby Face'.

Never in all my born days have I heard anything so astonishing – an explosion of rocking, rollicking sound, Andy's instrument like a musical machine gun, yet subtle and sensitively balanced, every note and nuance perfectly played at such bewildering speed you wonder what happened to your breath. Janet matched him with her niftily melodious squeezebox, and Lynda did too, and, although her uke deferred to his, her voice soared with that exultant soprano in perfect time and rhythm.

Together they built the song into a great number to audition next week for a charity gig at the London Palladium. Finding that they could do an extra number in the allotted time, they decided on 'Leaning on a Lamp Post'. Before they die, everyone should hear Andy Eastwood play the solo ukulele break on that song. It was totally phenomenal, and he a phenomenon the like of which I've never heard or seen. Formby himself would have been flabbergasted.

Yet somehow he didn't overshadow Lynda or Janet, on either side of him, who enhance his presence with their own beauty and vividness. What a unique trio they make. Together they could shake the world.

Sunday 17th

Audition at Bojangles Club in Guildford. The girls got into flapper dresses, Andy into tuxedo. Loads of other acts, the place packed. Six judges at a table. 'Red Hot & Blonde's two test numbers came across terrifically, the place erupted at the end, huge applause from the other acts. They sailed through the audition and the upshot was they'll be appearing onstage at the London Palladium in January in a show to celebrate the new millennium.

DECEMBER

Tuesday 20th

The millennium footbridge over the Liffey in Dublin, designed by my nephew Tim, was opened today. He says it vibrates slightly and is known as 'the quiver on the river'.

The smarties are calling the coming year YIIK.

'Sex is only the liquid centre of the great Newberry Fruit of friendship.' Quote from writer Jilly Cooper on today's page.

Friday 31ˢᵗ

Listening to *Top Songs of the Century* by Paul Gambuccini on the radio I was intrigued to hear that no.3 was 'Bridge Over Troubled Water' by Simon & Garfunkel – which I always thought rather saccharine; no.2 was Hoagy Carmichael's 'Stardust'; no.1 was Paul McCartney's 'Yesterday'. Of the *century*? Now *wait* a minute. Okay, Simon's supremely superb, Hoagy's humungously hyper and Paul is prodigiously peerless, but what about Cole Porter, Irving Berlin, George and Ira Gershwin, Johnny Mercer, Jerome Kern and all that lot in the 1920s and '30s, the timelessly haunting ballads of the 1940s, Lead Belly's seminal song 'The Titanic' in 1912 (jolly little number, always went down well), Morrissey of 'The Smiths' being miserable now, Bob Dylan blowin' in the wind, Big Bill Broonzy – and, hey, don't forget Leapin' Pete Splurge's deathless 'Garble-Arble-Arble' played on the Jew's harp in 1908 and … oh my God, what about *Woody Guthrie*? (well, I thought it was silly…)

In fact felt a bit sorry for myself, with Lynda gone to her parents, seeing in the new year and all the rest of it on my own, but it was my choice because I wanted space to savour, contemplate and consider the future. If I don't get paid properly soon, or other writing projects don't kick in, I can't make the offers I'd like to to Lynda. She says it doesn't matter, but it does.

At 10 p.m. had a drink for the South African new year, thought of Barrie Saint Clair and Debi and Vincent over there, and wished our film projects well. At 11 o'clock switched on the TV for the Continental New Year. A spectacular display on the Eiffel Tower.

At midnight popped open the champagne lovely Kerry gave me. She and her Chris have gone into London to join the throngs. Kitchen window open, a mild night. My pad with the larch-tanged Christmas tree and coloured lights, candles burning. Fireworks all over London, the Thames lit by huge displays. And, for nearly an hour afterwards, as I gargled champers, the brand new millennium (still challenging us to spell it correctly) rolled in and became here-and-now reality, a crackling banging explosive celebration of incandescent brilliance.

So a new year, new century and new millennium are here, bristling with more possibilities than ever. As veteran jazzman Mezz Mezzrow used to say, "Grab a dose of millennium, gate!" Now I shouted it from my open window, half drunk and crazed with hope: "*Grab a dose of millennium, gate!*" I never did know what it meant, but it always sounded cool. My response was the sizzling whoosh and vivid bangfest of red white and blue stars igniting the clouds. Hey guys, the Brits have hit the thunky funky double thou – and got there before the Yanks did!

"GRAB A DOSE OF MILLENNIUM, GATE!"

What will the coming year bring? Lynda is strong in my thoughts. The coming times are exciting for her too, with her group re-formed with a dynamic new 'Hot', their first gig on the stage of the London Palladium – and me with a film called *Dark Moon* that must surely, *surely* happen now.

2000

Wednesday 12th

Cat phoned during a boozy lunch with Kate Plantin. Kate knows someone who'd be perfect for the part of Bryce's sexy cockney secretary/lover in *Dark Moon*: Victoria Beckham – alias Posh Spice, who in fact, as it happens (these things are so strange) I saw on TV last night interviewing various people (including her own husband David) and found her very engaging. Apparently Posh phones Kate daily, hoping for a film part that suits her.

'In love women are professionals, men are amateurs.' Says director François *Truffaut on today's diary page.*

Sunday 30th

'Red Hot & Blonde' perform at the London Palladium today.

Awesome. Let me write that again:

'Red Hot & Blonde' perform at the LONDON PALLADIUM today.

Drove an excited Lynda there for 8.50 a.m. Loads of people outside the Stage Door on Great Marlborough Street. It boggled the mind, entering through those famous portals into the hallowed backstage area. Joined Andy and Janet in the stalls with the other acts. They're to run through the show all day. Lynda's eyes were wide with wonderment like her life was beginning. Off I went and left them to it.

Returned there this evening, theatre packed, atmosphere vibrant. Lynda's sister Nicola and their parents Joan and Peter were there, also my bril nephew Tim Lucas. The show depicted music through the decades of the previous century. When 'Red Hot & Blonde' came on, both girls looked fantastic, Andy debonair. Lynda's voice was strong and sweet, her uke-playing nifty, Janet's accordion lively and nimble, while Andy was phenomenal when he let rip on the uke-banjo solos. They did 'Baby Face'

73

and 'Red Robin' for the 1920s section; then changed costumes and did a terrific 'Leaning on a Lamp Post' for the 1940s. Tremendous applause when they took their bows. If the London Palladium is Lynda's re-formed group's first gig, who knows where they can go from here? *Hot* or *what*?

FEBRUARY

Wednesday 2nd

Cat rang to tell me she had a 4-hour meeting with sales agent Denise Cotton yesterday. They'd both gone through the *Dark Moon* script together with a 'fine toothcomb' (as Cat puts it) and a 'few changes' are required! To say I was dismayed is nowhere near the mark.

We then had a lengthy talk citing all the 'changes'. Among others, Denise has deleted the scene in which I've written a lively part for Lynda that John Glen has already approved. I fought to restore it – the scene highlights 'Laura's' growing distraction as she psychically tunes into her husband's distress as he gets deeper into trouble, and Lynda's character is a comedic counterpoint to give light to an otherwise tense sequence and thereby strengthen the drama going on elsewhere.

Sunday 6th

Cat rang early, I was still in bed. Ros Hubbard phoned her last night wanting 2 scripts as she's off to the States first thing Monday. So what did I do but drag myself from bed and print them out, including the scene with Lynda.

Drove down to Hubbard Casting off Goodge Street in the Sunday morning quiet and delivered the scripts. A smiley young Irish chap opened the door, and Ros herself called me in for a few minutes. Felt immediate rapport. We talked about Dublin, and how they take their time in pouring the Guinness in the pubs there. Told her how I once drove around the Ring of Kerry, and she said she and John have a cottage there. I mentioned Lynda Styan being in a scene, that she's just played the London Palladium, and said that she and John cast her in a commercial a while back (true). On taking the scripts I'd brought, Ros said briskly in her Irish voice, "Okay, now let's get on the engine!" We live in exciting times.

Monday 7th
Not a thing has happened since 'Red Hot & Blonde' performed at the London Palladium. Lynda phoned in some distress this evening, back from doing temp sales work. In one of those hideous tricks fate likes to work she was given Liberty's store to shift boxes about in – on Great Marlborough Street, right across from the stage door. So every time she looked out of the window she broke down in tears to see the famous theatre where only a few days before she'd sung and played with her group to a packed house to thunderous acclaim.

Eventually she had to be sedated in the medical room. My heart went out to her as we talked it all through, and in time she was smiling again*.

*I get that feeling again now as I put this diary together, and have had to stop for a while to get myself together in order to continue with it. Life can be such a bastard.

Wednesday 9th
John Glen rang and we had a long talk. He says he wishes now he'd never got involved with this production and all the 'jumping about' (as he put it). With the new sales agent now actively agitating to spoil what we have too, prospects for *Dark Moon* start to look ever bleaker. They've deleted Lynda's scene again, but John says he'll make sure it stays because "it's valid and it works." However, he's having dinner with actor Christopher Lambert this evening (Tarzan in *Greystoke: the Legend of…*) – and if the film they're discussing comes off he won't be able to direct *Dark Moon* this year. Can't say I blame him.

'The marvellous thing about a joke with a double meaning is that it can only mean one thing.' Ronnie Barker on today's page.

Friday 11th
Frosty freezing. Lynda came out, russet hair in Louise Brooks style, long grey hip-hugging skirt and purple woollen twin-set, slender, sparkly and smiling. Drove her to an audition at Hornchurch in Essex. In the car she played tapes of Binnie Hale singing 'Spread a Little Happiness' – her voice sounding uncannily like Lynda's, who reckons she's been reincarnated and knew the period well in a previous lifetime.

After the audition we drove off randomly into the night. Stopped at a pub somewhere near Rainham and she got out her ukulele in the carpark under the stars and sang/played 'Baby Face' with Formby-style split-stroke. Seeing a sign to Southend we decided to go there. Lights and life along the front, Lynda was enchanted by the place. Found a quiet spot on the prom, Orion hanging above the sea ahead, fish and chips in the dark and all that came after. Mad sweetness. Who cares about *Dark Moon* with its built-in wrecking crew? I mean, it's only my livelihood and credibility as a writer they're screwing up too. So what? Ha ha!

Monday 14th
Valentine's Day party at Cat's house. It was great to take Lynda with me. John and Janine Glen were there too. John responded positively to Lynda, who looked mind-blowingly glamorous and had a wonderful way of making him laugh, and they talked about the scene she's to be in, clearly approving of her. Then he regaled the table in a highly entertaining way with stories about making James Bond movies. A great raconteur. He said, pointing at me: "This is the mainspring, without the writer there'd be no film." It's really great to have such a champion – and Lynda being in the film is now assured.

Friday 25th
Cat asked would I send a *Dark Moon* outline to Posh Spice's agent Tara Joseph at William Morris. Posh wants to know what the rest of the story's about, but doesn't want to have to read the script all the way through. So in my outline I added in a bit more about 'Lucy' (the character she's up for) being staunchly loyal to her man while the world berates him – I felt she might empathise with how things were for her husband following that incident in the World Cup when the whole country turned against him.

MARCH

Wednesday 1st
Victoria Beckham has read the outline I sent and agrees to play 'Lucy'! Feel really chuffed she went for it. She's very much as I imagine that character – pretty, sexy, feisty, a touch of cockney. Her character has an

affair with 'Bryce' when things deteriorate between him and 'Laura'.

Saturday 4th

A meeting's been arranged for next Thursday, when John Glen will meet Victoria Beckham to discuss the part of Lucy. Later this evening, as I watched the Rock & Pop Awards, there towards the end was the lady herself singing soulfully with the Spice Girls. To me she looked an absolute delight, and tender with it, as emotional tears ran down her face.

Thursday 9th

Cat rang early to say they have no scripts for today's meeting so could I print three off and bring them to Tara Joseph's address in Soho, where Posh Spice will be? Bound the scripts and found the agency on Lexington Street. John Glen, Cat and Mags were already there. We were shown up in a lift and around creaky corridors by Tara Joseph, young and trim, who led us into a tiny room.

Because of its smallness we were jammed together, John next to me. Then in came Victoria Beckham – exquisitely pretty, daintily slender, quiet arresting eyes, seemed a bit apprehensive to be crowded in with two middle-aged women, two sturdy men *d'un âge certain* and her lissome agent squashed in beside her. It felt unseasonably warm, as if early spring had suddenly jumped into high summer.

Posh looked emptily through me during Tara's introductions, then perched delicately on a chair a foot or two from me while John outlined the part of 'Lucy'. She said she likes the part and the story, that it puts her in mind of *The Hand That Rocks The Cradle* – but said she was keen not to be exploited or give the media any chance to 'get' her. She sat very still and poised, like a dancer at rest, watchful. The possibility of sex scenes had been discussed with her agent. Mags assured her that these would be minimal, and tastefully done. "Don't worry," said John in his vigorous, no-nonsense way, "I'll hold your hand." On explaining that she'd be playing an 'Essex girl' he said, "You'll have no problems with that."

When we got up to go I took Posh's hand and said, "It was lovely meeting you," and meant it. To this she responded with a small but real smile as her eyes focused on me for the first time. There's a feeling of aloofness about her, and the way she holds her head with up-tilted chin, which may be due to shyness but is no doubt the reason for her Spice Girls nickname.

Then Cat and Mags, John and I went to a café for a coffee. "A good meeting," John said, and I thought it had gone well too. Cat rang Ros Hubbard because we *must* get the main cast in place now – and Ros said for Cat and Mags to go round and see her right away. John and I shook hands and 'speak soon'. He said he'd enjoyed meeting Lynda the other evening and would make sure she got that part. Then off we all went.

Later, Lynda rejoiced when I told her. She's read the scene I've written with the role in it for her, and when we went to the Bull and Bush for a mini-celebration she spoke the lines back to me, word-perfect, lively-yet-deep, energy-full. She'll be fantastic. Her eyes shone. Our director has resisted all the women's efforts to delete that telling scene, Posh Spice has joined the cast, all systems are go!

Friday 10th
At 7 a.m. Cat rang and said to my amazement how 'furious' she and Mags had been with John Glen for behaving so 'disgracefully' towards Victoria Beckham yesterday. I didn't know what she meant. She and Mags had gone straight to see Ros Hubbard after yesterday's meeting – who confirmed that Greg Wise, auditioned and approved by John, will be available to play 'Bryce' when the film is shot this summer.

Lynda performed at a hotel in Hastings this evening. It was with the Carl Spencer band, and she had the watching diners on the floor trying to match her movements as she demonstrated the Charleston, so exuberant did she feel. During this Cat rang my mobile to say, amazingly, that Posh is refusing to work with John for calling her an Essex girl! I couldn't believe it – he was just being gruff and jokey. I went into the corridor and yelled into the phone that John is fine, we work so well together, this film's ready to go, what's the matter with everybody? Suddenly I felt really down, sensing untold delays again just when all looked at last to be running smoothly. Hope they'll come to their senses by Monday.

'An artist should know all about love and learn to live without it.' Says ballerina Anna Pavlova on this page today.

Saturday 11th

Sunny, mild air, sky bright. Checked out of the Hastings hotel with Lynda after lingering happily over breakfast and drove along the coast to Bexhill where we sat outside a café overlooking the sea, not another soul about, seagulls soaring and squealing. Perfect tranquility. *Dark Moon*, Cat, Posh Spice *et al* seemed far away. On then to Pevensey in the Spring-like air and parked on the beach, imagining French ships landing here nearly a thousand years ago, troops swarming from them to march to the place called Battle and defeat King Harold and his British stoics exhausted from their long slog south. Now all was pebbles and peace, a shining sea under a quiet sky.

It was here Cat got me on the mobile again. She said, incredibly, that she's having to tell John Glen he's off the film. "We've all decided it's for the best," she added.

"Who's 'we'?" I said in absolute dismay. "*I've* not agreed – aren't I included in 'we'? As principal writer on this film I oppose it strongly. It's insane. Who's going to direct it if John Glen goes?"

"Mags can find someone," she said vaguely.

Lynda was looking at me, seeing my distress. When I shut off the phone she said quietly, "My part's gone now, hasn't it? They'll take it out before the next director sees it." I couldn't speak, felt so choked. "It's okay, honestly," she added, and took my hand. "But thanks so much for trying…"

Wednesday 15th

Emailed John Glen to express my dismay at the madness of what's happened, and to please stay in touch. Don't suppose he will now, but I want to show solidarity. Another of the females against him is Denise Cotton, who he robustly told to leave alone the script he'd worked on with the writer and that any suggested changes should be referred to him. Fat chance. I imagined these women all plunging knives into John, as was done to Julius Caesar on the senate steps.

Not till then did I realise what today's date is.

The Ides of March.

Thursday 16th

Met Lynda at Kingsbury tube and brought her back to my place. She looks almost surreal in her striking elegance, vividly coloured against the backdrop of grimy streets and grunge-clad folk with their plastic bags and pushchairs. Sometimes I warble in the car, and today this super songstress remarked that I sing 'in tune'. So began the following conversation:

"I hit the right notes, do I?"

"Yes."

"Reckon I hit the right notes on this *Dark Moon* script?"

"Yes. That's why Robert Young and John Glen wanted to work with you."

"But Cat's got rid of them, with the help of Denise Cotton and whoever else."

Lynda looked at me almost pityingly. "She has her reasons," she said quietly. "I'm very fond of Cat," she went on. "I think she's a kind and lovely person, so please don't get me wrong when I say this. It's not so much to do with talent as such, but with politics. And now that both the directors who wanted to work with you have gone, do you think she might want to keep the next director to herself?"

I couldn't answer, the imponderability of it was imponderable.

JUNE

Wednesday 7th

Cat phoned, sounding a bit down – director James Dearden has 'passed' on *Dark Moon*. Why do I find that expression irritating? – it's not proper English, is it, to 'pass' on something, unless it's a disease? Sounds snooty too. Will this film ever get made now? Why am I sounding ratty? Cat rang again later, perked up that the script is with Nick Roeg, who directed *Don't Look Now*. Well, you never know – wish I could generate the kind of energy driving Cat, I'd be out of the financial doldrums in no time flat less time off for good behaviour.

'The word "now" is like a bomb though the window, and it ticks.' Says playwright Arthur Miller on today's diary page.

Tuesday 20th

Woke to an overcast day, the recent intense heat cooled. It's 'Hot'

Andy Eastwood's Music Finals Performance at Oxford University. Lynda and I hired BA academic gowns at Castell on Broad Street for £10 each and parked near New College where Andy's studying.

He was performing in the Music Room – a square white building in which Handel once played – and is making history today: the first time 'popular' music has been performed for the Finals Recital in this hallowed sanctum. Andy's instrument of choice, and the music associated with it, is the ukulele; always before, in the centuries leading up to this ground-breaking moment, instruments and repertoire have all been classical.

In we solemnly filed in our black gowns and took our seats at the side, me on the end of the front row close to the little stage, which had three of Andy's wooden ukes and ukulele banjos on stands, a grand piano behind, the organ – which Handel played in the 18th Century – on the wall at back. The three deans, or is it dons?, walked in and gravely took their seats facing directly down the hall to the stage.

Andy came on, tutor Nick Salwey accompanying him on piano. Walt Eastwood, Andy's dad, looking as incongruous as Lynda and I did in academic gown, had set up recording equipment and looked as tense as any dad would. But Andy was cool and composed, and away he went. He was fantastic, didn't put a finger wrong. Eleven items, starting with 'Little Ukulele' and ending on 'Leaning on a Lamp Post', with brilliant medleys and melodic playing in between which were mesmerising in their artistry.

At the start, the examining dons, one an expert in medieval music, looked starchy-faced, disapproving and tense, but by the end they were on their feet grinning and clapping along with everyone else. It was just terrific. History has been made today, and we were part of it*. Lynda's 'Hot' has never been hotter.

*Andy Eastwood graduated with a 2:1, a BA (Hons) in Music. An excellent violinist, he was also leader of his College orchestra. Lynda and I will never forget that day, nor stop imagining how it could have gone on from there with her group to universal acclaim with this young genius.

Saturday 24th
Woke from a dream of being in a mildewy place furnished so well that only I can tell how tawdry and corrupt it is beneath the fine furniture and fresh linen. I wonder what it means.

JULY

Monday 3rd
Cat rang first thing and said we've got our new director! He's Peter MacDonald, directed *Rambo III*, *Young Indiana Jones* and several other Hollywood offerings. And was cameraman on epics like *Cabaret*, *Superman*, *A Bridge Too Far*, *Pink Panther*. Also, he camera-operated *Girl On A Motorcycle* with Marianne Faithfull, directed by the marvellous Jack Cardiff whom God preserve. Am hoping this is good news.

Wednesday 5th
Via Margit Bimler, Bruce Beresford has sent a list of 36 directors, of whom 4 might do – so Cat will try their agents to see if they can make a quick decision – i.e. by next week. How vague and hopeless it still all looks.

Thursday 6th
Cat came zapping the thought-flow by phoning me about directors yet again. Says she's sent covering letter and synopsis of *Dark Moon* to Sue Rodgers at ICM with a view to Danny Boyle directing it.
Danny *Boyle*?
The sun came out for the Wimbledon semi-final between American sisters Venus and Serena Williams which Venus (the elder) won. I wondered how much sisterly psychology was at play.

Saturday 8th
Watched Venus win Wimbledon from Lindsay Davenport. Never have I seen such sheer joy on a face as the winner jumped up and down. It made me feel quite emotional that such delight can exist in this world.

'The process of scientific discovery is, in effect, a continuous flight from wonder.'
Albert Einstein on today's page.

Monday 17th
Cat's away on holiday somewhere expensive and exotic. Meanwhile Ros Hubbard has recommend a director called Philip Goodhew, whose agent at ICM is getting a *Dark Moon* script to him today.

Monday 24th

Drove down to Hastings with Lynda and went up the East Hill in the Victorian lift. We walked along the cliff and had the whole place to ourselves with the sun and seagulls. Struck off through woodland, memorable and sylvan – I imagined my mother Mabel here as a girl on holiday, merrily haunting these glades before marriage and kids took her over. On our way back Lynda sang 'Dream A Little Dream', her voice floating out over the sea accompanied by the gulls' shrieks. Joyous.

Lynda remembers Philip Goodhew as a young actor in TV's *Crossroads*. Now she prayed out loud: "Dear God, please let Philip like *Dark Moon* so much that he wants to direct it, and let the film go on to great success. Thank you, Lord, who sees and understands all things..."

A classic moment, Lynda's slender form against the sky and sea, her exhortation floating into the clear air, answered by yewling gulls. It reminded me of the closing shot in *Gone With The Wind*, Vivien Leigh shaking her fist at fate and the elements.

Tuesday 25th

In Cat's continuing absence I rang Alex Graham at ICM to ask if Philip Goodhew has read the script yet. She called back to say Philip has responded positively and would like to meet me and talk *Dark Moon* tomorrow, giving the address of a club in London where he'll be. A treasured chance at last, then, to talk the story and characters through with our new director on a one-to-one basis.

Rang Lynda and said her prayer has been answered – Philip likes the script and wants to direct it! She was overgleed with squealy yelps. When Cat rang from Jamaica later I could hardly not mention it, adding that she can safely leave it with me and enjoy her holiday. Cat said she's returning tomorrow so "might be back in time to join you, in fact I'll do everything I can to be there." I insisted there really was no need – and then I remembered what Lynda had said.

Wednesday 26th

Arrived just before the appointed time at the private club by the Curzon Cinema to meet Philip Goodhew. No sign of Cat, so was eagerly looking forward to an illuminatingly creative talk with our new director when a black chauffeur-driven 4x4 screeched up and Cat leapt out, having engaged a driver to speed her from the airport. So up we went together. I liked Philip – his mind receptive and positive, smile warm and engaging – 40ish, good-looking, with ideas to brighten the part of 'Laura' at start of the film, which he confirms he would like to direct. With her turbocharged energy Cat seemed to do most of the talking while I sat alongside her feeling ever-so-slightly out of it. During this we consumed 4 glasses of beer each and were getting heady. The bill was £43. Cat paid, bless 'er.

AUGUST

Wednesday 2nd

Ros Hubbard is suggesting Anne Heche for 'Laura', so could I get a script to her in Los Angeles? Began printing out the good one John Glen and I had worked on, with Cat soon on the phone. "Has Philip called you?" she asked anxiously. I put her mind at rest with a 'no'.

Thursday 3rd

Our new potential 'Laura', Anne Heche, is 31, delightfully pretty and having an affair with actress Ellen de Generes. She played Marion Crane in the recent remake of *Psycho*, and starred with Harrison Ford in *Six Days, Seven Nights*. Got her script packed and summoned DHL. £42 to Los Angeles, on my credit card. Off it went with our hopes sealed in it.

'Tragedy is if I cut my finger. Comedy is when you walk into an open sewer and die.' Says Mel Brooks on today's page of this diary.

Sunday 22nd

No word from or about Anne Heche as to what she thinks of the script – but suddenly the lady herself is in the papers this morning, and the story is on breakfast TV. She was found wandering in a daze after what looks to have been a breakdown. Ms de Generes has left her. Stuff like this you can't invent.

Wednesday 30th

Fantastic news. Anne Heche has read *Dark Moon* (in hospital?), thinks

84

it's (quote) 'brilliant' and wants to play 'Laura'. This after Ros Hubbard was telling Cat to move on, that Anne has had a breakdown and is uninsurable, etc. No she's not, she wants to do it! And has said a resounding yes to the part having read the last draft of the script I did with John Glen! You'd think now, surely, there wouldn't be any need for further revisions?

SEPTEMBER

Wednesday 13th

All petrol stations are closed: about 90% in UK now have no petrol. And still the government are 'toughing it out' and 'not buckling under pressure'. Don't they realise that the people who pay their taxes are sick of the high price of fuel largely made up of taxes levied by the said government? Maybe they'll wake up soon and smell the coffee. Or the petrol – if there's any left.

Friday 15th

Olympic Games start in Sydney today. Watched the opening ceremony, very spectacular. Kathy Freeman, the great Aussie hope in the 400 metres, was a key performer. She must have nerves of steel as well as being a prime athlete. Does being tremendously fit focus and clarify the mind too?

Thursday 21st

Kees Kasander from a Luxembourg company has been brought in by Denise Cotton as the latest producer. Not sure what happened to Clive Potson, but on this production key personnel seem to come and go like the survivors in musical chairs. This new man will be flying over to meet Philip Goodhew next week. Pre-production on *Dark Moon* is now scheduled to start in November, filming in January 2001 – in France and UK now. They talk of freeing up £50,000 front money soon – so I can get some cashflow into my beleaguered life?

Saturday 23rd

Great news from Sydney – Steve Redgrave and team won Gold in the coxless fours for the fifth Olympics running (or should that be 'rowing?'). Wonderful, and he gets an Olympic pin, whatever that might be. Perhaps I'll get a *Dark Moon* pin one day.

Monday 25th

Olympics hotting up, though the weather cool in Sydney. Kathy Freemen won Gold for the host nation in the 400 metres. The pressure on her was enormous but she didn't blow it – what an astoundingly cool-headed character and role-model. Jonathan Edwards of UK hopped, stepped and jumped to Gold – 17m.71 – for Britain. Just fantastic, can't really find the words, success like this changes one's whole psychology and lifts the heart.

AND DENISE LEWIS WON GOLD IN THE HEPTATHLON!!!

Sometimes life doesn't seem so bad.

'A lot of the time, what acting is really about is meeting someone's eye.' Says Tom Cruise on today's page.

Friday 29th

Cat called, cockahoop – she says our new producer Kees Kasander has already put ALL the money together to make *Dark Moon*, and suggests that he, Philip Goodhew and Cat fly to Los Angeles to meet Anne Heche as a matter of urgency.

Evening meal with Dad, my brother Jonathan and his wife Carol at Godstone in Surrey. The old man looks frail and coughs quite a lot – deep, rattly, hacking. Afterwards, Jon (known in the family as 'the successful' son) dropped us off outside the warden-controlled flats where our father (who art in Reigate) now lives, and zoomed off with Carol in his trendy Merc. Outside, I said goodnight to Dad then watched him with my face pressed against the glass door as he wobbled up the communal hallway on his artificial hips. He didn't know I was there as he shakily unlocked his door, one shoulder permanently higher because of cancerous complications, clutching the fold-up sheepskin pillow he sits on wherever he goes, and passed on inside. I have never seen anything so sad.

Drove home, silent. Played no music, let the sadness eat in. Wished I could have done better for him, and realised I love the crotchety sod – have never felt that before, not in this visceral way, wanting to gather up his hurt and bundle it away, kill off the debilitating excess of years so the pace comes back into his step and his head goes up and his clothes are smart again instead of rumpled and stained. I'd let him call me a no-hope fool as much as he liked then, if only the lost look would go from his pouched eyes.

OCTOBER

Wednesday 11th

Anne Heche has turned down Philip Goodhew as her director on *Dark Moon*! I simply couldn't believe it. So they're now going for Peter Medak. What a story this is turning out to be – our heroine wants the script but doesn't want the director, who is a most gifted, sensitive and fine one. Nothing makes sense.

If the women hadn't got rid of John Glen I reckon we'd be filming by now, with that last script he and I worked on – with Kerry Fox as 'Laura' and Greg Wise as 'Bryce'. Lynda would be eagerly preparing to act in that special scene I wrote for her, and I would have already been paid my full writer's fee and be moving on to my next project with a strong screen credit to my name.

Friday 13th

Here we go! Cat rang to give me a summary of 'script enhancements' considered necessary. On whose authority? I suspect Denise Cotton's hand in this. I told Cat the only person I want to discuss 'script enhancements' with is the director, whoever he or she might now turn out be – certainly not with a sales agent who gives me no credence or respect as a writer. Am I being difficult? I didn't envy Cat's self-imposed task of telling Philip Goodhew that Anne Heche didn't like his last film, which I'd enjoyed. It's a lousy business – if it's fairness you're looking for, don't come here.

Saturday 14th

Drove down to Sussex with Lynda. Great to get clear of the nuthouse and have a laugh. Lunch at the Queen's Head, Winchelsea. It was very crowded, so we sat in an empty back room. Here she quietly sang the song she did at an audition yesterday: 'It's a Fine Life' – Nancy's from *Oliver!* – earthy, strong, with a cockney twang – have never heard her do this stuff before. Then she sang 'As Long As He Needs Me'. Beautiful. The young waiter brought in our lunch just as Lynda was saying in her carrying voice: "…my body simply couldn't resist it" (she was talking about a cold virus, but he didn't know that). She laughs and laughs.

Plenty of activity in Hastings – bonfire ready for lighting on the beach, folks in pirate costumes, monks and so forth. At the lifeboat station we came on a group of drummers, a Caribbean rhythm, and began rocking with everyone else. A couple of girls with blackened faces told us it's a yearly celebration, the Battle of Hastings was fought today in 1066. Strange that Agincourt was also in October. Perhaps they preferred their battles in the autumn with all that armour, bugger battling in a heatwave. "Come on, lads – it's that time of year again…"

Later, with the streets to the sea closed to traffic, Lynda and I joined the throng on foot to watch a torchlight procession with incredibly real medieval atmosphere as huge metal dishes of fire were dragged along on slats and rollers, drums beat, fireworks exploded. We danced along with them, then lingered in the whispery dark like we do and didn't get back till one in the morning. Not till then did I think, wait a minute, the French *won*, didn't they? What were we celebrating?

Wednesday 18th
Cat phoned in panic to say Anne Heche is pregnant! *Six Days, Seven Nights* – now *Nine Months*. And still no director. Better hurry, folks…

'I never hated a man enough to give him his diamonds back.' Says Zsa Zsa Gabor on this page today.

Thursday 19th
No word from America re a director for the pregnant Anne Heche. Ros Hubbard can't cast the film till we have one. It's unbelievable. Carry on at this rate we'll have Anne's baby in the movie too. No pre-production money either – so I'm going into final revisions with no director and no advance on my (unpaid) fee. It's disturbing.

By evening got into it, tuning into a more funful 'Bryce' with 'Laura's' 5-year-old son. I tapped into my experience of bringing up Kerry and the scene went like a breeze. Could have worked up a real dazzle, but what's the point with this lot? So I keep it unthreateningly flat while still retaining life and personality.

Sunday 22nd

Worked on the *Dark Moon* 'polish', despite being utterly potless. Looks like there could be something from the budget in November when Kees Kasander pays into escrow for Anne Heche. Meanwhile Ros Hubbard will phone ICM and try to get Danny Boyle on as director. Having abandoned the thought of Danny before, what a coup that would be. His hard-nosed take in *Trainspotting* of sex 'n' drugs culture in Edinburgh broke the mould.

Danny would be sure to call for rewrites. Take a scene like this:

```
INT. BANKSIDE LODGE, DINING ROOM — NIGHT

Laura and Bryce have dined by candlelight.

                    LAURA
        Bryce... sometimes I think I hear noises
        here.

                    BRYCE
        Noises? Could be anything, darling. Wind in
        the eaves, squeaky floorboards. This is a
        very old house.

                    LAURA
        And just after you left yesterday I thought
        I heard a crash on the driveway. I ran out to
        look, but everything was normal.

                    BRYCE
        It's stress. You really must learn to relax,
        Laura — for the sake of the baby.
```

He reaches out and takes her hand.

                        BRYCE (cont'd)
                    (romantically)
        Shall we go up?

Smiling, he helps her to her feet.

I imagine Danny changing it to something like:

    INT. BANKSIDE LODGE, DINING ROOM — NIGHT

    Laura and Bryce have dined by candlelight.

                        LAURA
        Bryce... sometimes I hear strange wee
        whistlin's in this hoose an' noises like a
        banshee wi' an arm shot full of methyl
        benzydrene.

                        BRYCE
        Gae fuck yersel' ye crazy jade.

                        LAURA
        An' I see things tu.

                        BRYCE
        Then tak' oot yeer eyes, rub 'em on yeer poxy
        ass an' stick th' bastids back in.

                        LAURA
        I *mean* ut, Bryce! T'other dee the walls was
        closin' in on me heid and the bath wiz full
        of blood, bubblin' like shit in a cauldron.

                              BRYCE
        Ach, ye're battier than a mashed tattie. Could
        be worm-chewed beams a-creakin', wind vomitin'
        through   the   eaves,   squeaky   floorin'
        regurgitatin' the sound of yer fuckin' feet...

                              LAURA
        Ye think sae?

                              BRYCE
                          (romantically)
        Aye. Nae quit worryin' and gie us a suck on
        this...

Only kidding, honest!

Monday 23rd
Told Cat I absolutely must have some money to complete this script
polish – even £500 till the front money's released. She said she could
manage that herself – come round Thursday with the revised script and
she'll give me the cheque. So I got on with it, didn't I!

Tuesday 24th
Picked up Lynda, she a delight in blue-grey sheeny tights from Aristoc,
the black-and-white patterned shoes I bought her, the long grey woolly skirt
that clings, a white wool top. I said, eyes popping, 'you've dressed up for
Andy Eastwood – lucky man' – she said "Oh no, I put these on for *you*."
Headed down the M3 with my perfumed glamchick, reached the
Eastwoods' house in Dorset at 12.30. 'Blonde' Janet already there, recording
saxophone for the backing on 'Mean To Me' for the group's CD that Andy
and his dad Walt are putting together. Did a photo session for the group in
their garden, the girls in catsuits – Walt taking the pics. It didn't work out
too well as the light was bad, it was cold out there, and parts of Janet's
anatomy kept popping annoyingly out (annoying for *her*, that is...).
   Andy and I talk of making an off-the-wall movie starring the group – a
sort of *Hard Day's Night* thing. What a ball we'd have putting that together.

Lynda's a trained actress, he can tread the boards a bit and Janet could play the silent Harpo (Accordiono?) type. Andy's already had a short film made about him (*The Ukulele Man*). And, as Walt pointed out, raising his camera while a bitter wind scythed through us and the girls shivered, you don't have to follow the same tired old rules any more. Walt's theory is that anyone can do anything they set their mind to. Maybe Cat thinks the same way regarding writing scripts, bless her. And who's to say they're wrong?

'There is a great man who makes every man feel small. But the real great man is the man who makes every man feel great.' So says writer G.K. Chesterton on today's diary page.

NOVEMBER

Sunday 19th

It's teeth-gritting time again. Cat rang to say she's 'doing the notes' herself from the latest 'script meeting' she's had with Denise Cotton, just the two of them with their heads together. Was ready to scrap the whole thing after this latest example of writer abuse – but into my head creep words like 'money', 'screen credit', 'renewed credibility', 'cottage in the country', 'freedom from debt'. 'Marry Lynda' is in there too, and the reason why she and I don't move more positively into that area is because neither of us can afford it yet, entirely because of situations like THIS, when everything that seemed ready to happen is whisked away on a whim.

Thursday 23rd

Arranged to take Dad to Brighton to look for a hotel for him to stay at over Christmas with his companion (it's almost five years since Mum died a few weeks before *Dark Moon* began – thank God, at least, she was spared all this). Flintily rugged as ever, Dad knows he isn't long for this world. Solely because I want to see this film made, I worked last night till 11.30 doing all I could to modify Cat's and Denise's latest inroads into the script. Then, this morning, was at the computer at a quarter to 5 a.m., still trying to bring their revisions under control.

Was in Reigate by 7.30 a.m. and drove Dad down to Brighton. After some dead ends he booked himself in for 4 days over Christmas at the Norfolk Hotel on the seafront, then took me to lunch at Wheelers fish restaurant. When I mentioned what was happening on *Dark Moon* he gave a curl of the lip, looked coldly at me and said: "Never give a sucker an even break." Yeah. Right. I'd never thought of it in that way before. Sucker? That's me, right? Hey. But all I really want to do, whatever it takes, is GET THIS BLOODY FILM MADE!

Sunday 26ᵗʰ

An item in today's *Observer* about a new medical development where the throat box can be transplanted from a cadaver into a living person. I found it eerie to think of the voice of a dead person coming from a live one, especially if you knew the former in life and the accent was the same.

"If I've told you once, I've told you a thousand times!" comes that shatteringly familiar voice through the darkness several months after its original owner died. Oh – my – God, IMAGINE!

'Don't ask the barber whether you need a haircut.' Says Daniel S. Greenberg on today's page.

Tuesday 28ᵗʰ

Still no word from possible directors. Cat is getting jittery, because if one doesn't show up soon this film could fall apart (again). God only knows which version of the script they're reading, if at all. What a mess it all is.

DECEMBER

Friday 8ᵗʰ

Up at 5 a.m. and computer on. Funny how the mind knows how much it's got to do and how long it will take. Soon after 9 had completed all the amendments and new additions and faxed the lot to Cat. She came back to say the new elements I've incorporated are 'absolutely great,' and said she hadn't understood them when I'd tried to explain on the phone. Blimey.

Ros Hubbard has suggested Kenneth Branagh as director for *Dark Moon*, sez Cat, and could I get a script to him? Okay. So I composed a letter to Branagh as if written by Cat, but on trying to print out a script to go with it had to wrestle with the printer to make it work. I've come to learn that if the equipment gives you a hard time it's usually warning you that the procedure is pointless★. Finally managed to squeeze out a complete script then drove into Shepherd's Bush and delivered to Branagh's secretary at a smart house, pretending to be a minicab. She was young, very pretty, had a large fluffy dog and the nicest smile. Even as I drove away, Cat was in my ear on the mobile asking have I delivered it yet? Her keenness is intoxicating (is that the word I'm seeking?). Or should that be 'makes you feel like getting intoxicated'? (Only joshing, Cat...)

This still happens today, and when it does I take heed. Another such warning the equipment has is to fail to send off an email for no apparent reason. There is a reason, even though you don't know it, and it's invariably right, so don't push it. The equipment always knows.

Sunday 31st
New Year's Eve alone again. My choice, again. Lynda and I can't be fully together till something useful kicks in – I have nothing to offer her, and we all need security. So she's with her parents and sister on the south coast. By half past ten I couldn't bear the idea of dragging through another hour and a half to 'celebrate'. Celebrate what? A few fireworks were fizzling and booming outside so I put earplugs in and went to bed.

Goodbye 2000, I'm not unhappy to see you go. And you began with such promise.

Next year things will be different.

Won't they?

2001

So here we are, the year Stanley Kubrick and Arthur C. Clarke felt was far enough ahead in 1968 to set their Space Odyssey. Moments I cherish from this film are when onboard computer HAL (voiced with malevolently polite murmur by Douglas Rain) takes control of the spaceship and refuses Keir Dullea's commands to open the hatch. Keir has to climb into the control centre and decommission it, and we hear the computer regressing to the earliest recorded robotic voice singing 'Dais-eee, Dais-eee, give me your answer do-o-o-o' (a great gag of Kubrick's). Then the mesmerising sequence when our intrepid spaceman travels at the speed of flickering light through a wormhole (stargate?) with an expression of stupendous awe. Magnificent.

But my own reality as 2001 began was somewhat different.

Tuesday 2nd

Cat rang – it was good to hear her voice, so quiet have things been. She was talking again about Joseph Fiennes for 'Bryce' in *Dark Moon* and I said it's all cloud-cuckoo unless he's read and likes it and the funding's in. And Nick Hamm as director? (the script goes to him today). His film *The Hole* comes out this year, and the synopsis of it looks interesting – shades of my *Gateway To Yesterday* (but that, literally, is another story…).

Friday 19th

Cat's opening words were "We've GOT him!" Nick Hamm. He's read the script, "loves it" and wants to direct the film. I yelled down the phone. Great, great, great – beautiful, beautiful. Let's not cock *this* up! It made me realise how persistently negative this world has been, draining energy, sapping vitality, penalising pointlessly – now here is a great big YES! It means we can get this film moving again and have cameras turning by June. And I can get out of debt instead of constantly deeper into it, move forward into sunlight and flowers!

'Film acting is not so much acting as reacting, doing nothing with tremendous skill.' Quote from Michael Caine on today's diary page.

Wednesday 31st

The meeting with Nick Hamm and Kees Kasander is at 7 p.m. tomorrow. Denise Cotton will be there, and Cat. Not me, though – I'm not invited. I said surely Nick will want to talk to the writer? "No," Cat insisted, "it's not a creative meeting, we'll just be talking about money."

FEBRUARY

Friday 2nd

6.30 a.m. Cat woke me with a call. Said she hadn't been 'impressed' by Nick Hamm yesterday evening, that he was demanding 'huge changes' to the script. I said let me talk to him, we'll roll up our sleeves and work to realise his vision. The more Cat went on, I got the feeling the 'changes' were a bringing out of the backstory more ('seeds which need watering,' is something Nick said, apparently). Also, the discussion had clearly been a creative one, not just about money, so I knew I should have been there, and it bugged me that I'd been kept away. Even so, Nick Hamm's agreed participation as director was like a door opening on to a sunnier landscape.

Friday 9th

Kees Kasander had a great meeting with Steve Dontanville yesterday and signed up Anne Heche for 'Laura'. He said Anne is really excited about doing it, loves the script and her part in it (she was talking about my earlier version though, the last one I did with John Glen). Whatever, Nick Hamm is to fly to L.A. to meet Ms Heche, who is keen to work with him. I look forward now to getting to grips with his ideas, and again stressed to Cat how vital it is that I meet the director as soon as possible to work up a draft that successfully incorporates his vision.

'Life is a tragedy when seen in close-up, but a comedy when seen in long shot.' Charlie Chaplin on today's page of this diary.

Wednesday 21st

Nick Hamm phoned Cat and said why wait till September to film Dark Moon, let's go in May. Brilliant news, yet still no firm deal has been struck with him, despite his keenness to get moving. What on earth is going on, and why haven't I met him yet to talk about the script?

MARCH

Tuesday 13th

Cat *really* rattled my cage by saying the reason Denise Cotton and Kees Kasander are giving for not having done a deal with Nick Hamm is "the script isn't right yet." When I'd got my breath back after this amazing piece of nonsense I said that Nick was sufficiently attracted by the current one to want to direct the film, but we must now secure him (with money Cat says she's able to raise) so I can work with him on the director's draft and then we WILL have a script which IS 'right'. How can they expect a script to be 'right' before the director has given his vision on it? I'm fascinated to know what ideas Nick has, yet *still* we don't get together.

Saturday 17th

Drove into London to meet Lynda at Dickins & Jones on Regent Street, spotted her in the Hosiery Department wearing a Wolford badge – trim in shop uniform yet empty-eyed as she sold tights. Some wealthy women customers treat her like a servant, rude and offhand – it's what money does to you if you don't have hard experience in life to leaven the possession of a never-empty purse. Lynda's face brightened when she saw me, like Kerry's used to when I collected her from school. She went off to change and we arranged to meet at the Argyll Street exit.

When Lynda stepped outside, there across the road was the front of the London Palladium where last year she played and sang with 'Red Hot & Blonde' to a packed house and thunderous applause. To stop her dwelling on it I steered her to the Westbury Hotel and bought her a drink in the Polo Lounge. She loved the upmarket ambience there, her smile came back. "I *will* get that group going again," she said, eyes shining, "I *will*!" It was like a scene from a Hollywood tearjerker.

Tuesday 27th

Cat says a meeting is arranged this afternoon with her, Denise Cotton and Nick Hamm. I asked with what patience I could muster why the sales agent needs to see the director at this stage? Shouldn't he be talking to the writer about his ideas for the script, so shall I come along? "No," said Cat firmly, "we'll be discussing policy with him, not script."

'Never argue with a fool – people might not know the difference' quotes Arthur Block on today's diary page.

Wednesday 28th

Never have I heard Cat so close to tears. Yesterday's meeting with Nick Hamm had been 'a disaster', she said, with Denise Cotton arguing fiercely with him that the script didn't need any alteration. Unbelievable. This after all they'd been saying about the script not being 'right' yet. Now Nick has just phoned Cat to say he wants off the film, that his heart is no longer in it. She let slip to me that Nick had said he'd wanted to meet the writer to discuss changes, also there were still no filming dates nor money on the table.

So that was Nick Hamm that was, and I never even saw the whites of his eyes.

APRIL

Tuesday 10th

Got home late from being with Lynda, to a message from my brother Jonathan to ring him. Did so at once, waking him. He told me Dad died at 7.30 this evening at a friend's house in Brixham, Devon – he timed the moment well, having just finished his second gin and tonic, collapsed in the kitchen while chatting – his tumour had haemorrhaged and he died quickly.

Put down the phone. Poured whisky and had three or four in the dark lounge. Wished Dad well, wherever he's gone to. Realised I'd never at any moment felt sorry for him – he'd always seemed so positive and resilient no matter what. His passing was a release from an aged body he'll be glad to be free of, with artificial hips, half blind, didn't hear too well and could only have got worse. I imagined him up there, young again with his film star looks, and saw no more the sharp-tongued dotard in a rage with the world and his disintegrating faculties. Goodnight, Dad. Goodbye.

MAY

Tuesday 1st

Cat getting active again after the long silence I scarcely noticed, so preoccupied have I been with Dad's funeral and the aftermath of his death. She asked me to fax the *Dark Moon* outline to a friend of Patrick Bergin who 'knows Hugh Grant well'. I did so – but all kinds of technical hiccups attended this simple task so I wondered (again) if this was my equipment telling me that the procedure was destined to lead nowhere. Presumably Hubbard Casting have now quit the scene. Has Ros got off the engine, then?

'I am firm. You are obstinate. He is a pig-headed fool.' Katherine Whitehorn on today's diary page.

Monday 14th

Have picked up some bug, was slumped sluggish and spluttering in bed around 7 a.m. when Cat phoned and talked again about getting the script 'right'. She and her friend Liz, whose daughter goes to the same school as Cat's, and a male friend who works in electronics, Alvin, have been talking about *Dark Moon* and have some 'great ideas'. Incredibly, and awfully, she then put this man on to me. At seven in the morning. He said a few things about the story in an Irish accent. I said "Cat, they're not professionals." "No, but they're intelligent," she countered, "and they can read, so what's the problem?"

What I now learned, and which explained the long silence, is that Denise Cotton had commissioned a Hollywood writer of her acquaintance to rewrite my entire script. "The first 20 pages of it are okay," Cat now said cautiously, "but the rest is bullshit." She's told this to Denise, and they've fallen out.

Which is why I'm back on the case without having realised I'd been off it – but only because Denise's replacement appears to have screwed up quite badly. So to Cat's for 6.30 p.m. feeling like death warmed up. The offending 'Hollywood' script was on the coffee table. No energy emanated from it and I didn't want to touch it, it had the qualities of a corpse. Met Liz, a nice lady. Also Alvin, 50ish and pedantic. We embarked on an evening of ideas for *Dark Moon*. Pointless me pointing out that we've had 2 top directors on this and other hot ones keenly interested plus an A-list Hollywood actress wanting to make it *as it was before* – this is a whole new refit with amateurs throwing in their thoughts.

Back home, steeled myself to skim through this American writer's rewrite, remembering how Brian Proctor thought none but these mystical beings were able to hack a film script. But it didn't take long to realise that his version was no threat to mine. So the fragrant Denise Cotton had advised Cat to sweep me away forever, and if this Hollywood scribe had got it right I would indeed have been curtained, because he'd removed absolutely everything of mine that would have given me a chain of title claim and replaced it with his own stuff. But this was horse manure between blue covers, and I wondered how much it had cost whoever had paid him to have it done.

Cat then asked can I do the revisions in a few days? – putting back in all my stuff this guy threw out, so it can go to Cannes? A work of restoration, in fact (again) – and a revised outline by noon tomorrow? She cautiously agreed an advance of £500, repayable from my eventual fee. Okay, okay.

I'm back on the case.

Tuesday 22nd

Early afternoon Cat called from Denise Cotton's house where she'd gone to talk about the script (yes). Next thing is Denise comes on the line and asks what my vision of this film is. It's the first time we've ever spoken. I tell her patiently, with feeling – and for the first time our interfering sales agent realises that I'm aiming for the same things that she is. Indeed, Denise seemed sort of astonished, and we got on well, sparking off each other. Afterwards I got on with some freelance magazine work, a commission for £400. I need the dosh, and it's ever so good to be doing something completely different.

AUGUST

Saturday 25th

Good to drive with Lynda down to the Eastwoods' in Dorset again, she all smiles in wraparound sarong of greeny silk, with creamy top and pretty black shoes with bows. Weather warm. Janet already there, looking tasty too. 'Red Hot & Blonde' rehearsed some storming numbers on ukes, accordion and piano, Andy and the girls perfection as ever, then recorded another track for the now-nearly-finished CD. Lynda so excited about the group again. Walt reckons they could go out for £500 a time.

On the way back she and I stopped at Bolderwood in the New Forest and walked woodland tracks in the deepening dusk. Lynda sang 'The Hills Are Alive', her voice ringing through the trees, all of which we had to ourselves, glade upon glade of them into sylvan distances. As we stood looking into the dazzling dregs of the day I pondered that in five billion years that same setting sun will swell up to blot out our sky and engulf this planet in fire, so what's all the fuss about? We savoured the air and stillness till it was night and the whine of a mosquito made us move on.

There's always a mosquito.

SEPTEMBER

Thursday 6th

Phone call from Cat asking could I do some alterations before printing out another script because her cat has crapped on the last one. I said I have no intention of changing a word of it, and that I'll be sending a bill to her cat for additional time and resources in printing out another. She didn't laugh. I asked why a director wasn't reading the script right now, and she said it isn't 'ready' to show to one. I said yes it is, who says it's not 'ready'? "We all do," was the reply. On asking who "we all" are it turned out that no one's read it except her, and she doesn't like some of my dialogue. In fact Cat hates my dialogue, considers it a grave weakness of mine and that she's much better at it than I am. In almost unbearable frustration I told her to make the changes herself if she must, I've had it.

Oh dear, have I thrown all the toys out of the pram?

Tuesday 11th

Turned on the TV around 9.30 this evening and was astounded to see pictures of chaos and devastation in New York – terrorists have hijacked passenger jets with people aboard and flown suicide missions, crashing two planes into the twin towers of the Trade Centre, another plane falling in flames en route to the White House. Both towers stood for a while with smoke and steam escaping, people on upper floors desperately waving from high windows – then, one by one, the towers collapsed in on themselves and slid to the ground in vast piles of rubble and dust. Thousands are dead. The sight was horrific, profoundly shocking, unbelievable, like watching some incredible reality action movie. Islamic fundamentalists are thought to be the perpetrators. It's the worst atrocity against USA since the Japanese hit Pearl Harbour in 1941.

Tony Blair came on and cancelled all flights over London, in case we're next. So the sky is strangely quiet here tonight. President George Bush looked very shaken, I wonder if the Americans wish it was Clinton and not him at the helm.

Friday 21st

Just spoken to Cat, who sounds like she's got the cream and maybe she has. Since my exasperated outburst a couple of weeks ago she's taken me at my word and put together sections from three past drafts and sent the result to Denise Cotton. What a woman! – she never ceases to make me grin at her gall. The reason Cat phoned me is that Denise has come back positive and reckons she could bring on Roger Spottiswoode to direct. What a mess this had become, though – all it wants is a Dutchman as script editor, but I'm told Kees Kasander has departed from the project after a dispute with Denise. Wait a minute, hadn't he already raised all the money to make the film? (best not to ask…)

Heaven knows what Cat and Denise have made between them now of a script once strong enough to have hooked or strongly interested at least 5 top-class directors and a Hollywood star – not to mention actors of the quality of Kerry Fox and Greg Wise. Cat said she'll email me the result, but that I'm "not to change a word of it" – her words and thoughts must be regarded as sacrosanct.

Saturday 22nd

Steeled myself to read Cat's new collation. In a funny sort of way my heart went out to her. She's used some of the thin stuff the now-discredited American writer put in at the start, and appears to have created whole new scenes herself. But – and no doubt this is not Cat's fault but the result of others' influences, the friend I now consult in these matters because I've got too close to it again says that the balance, timing and tension have gone from the screenplay and vital character/dialogue exchanges have been eliminated.

Over a nerve-soothing candlelit beer this evening it occurred to me that Denise could be being political here. By praising Cat's valiant assemblage of previous scripts she may have thought I would walk away from this in absolute dismay and let them get on with it. So, for what I hope will be the greater good, decided to give it another go. Suddenly I saw a clear way through it all by joining forces with Cat, if she'll let me, and making what might be described as a rescue bid for what is, after all, a cracking good screen story for which she deserves every credit.

Quote by Marcel Achard on today's diary page: 'Women like silent men. They think they're listening.'

Monday 24th

Pushed on with the *Dark Moon* 'rescue', but can't help feeling it really needs to be done over completely again from scratch. I would even do it for nothing, just so as to have a film to be proud of when it comes to the shooting. However, being realistic, I can't see this happening in the current confused set-up.

Thursday 27th

Message on my mobile from Cat, seemingly ecstatic about my latest non-paid version of *Dark Moon*. "Oh you clever man, it's just *fabulous* now…" It's nice to have such apparent enthusiasm after all the silence and stress, but I'm nervous.

OCTOBER

Wednesday 3rd

Lynda rang, I feel so happy for her – she's just phoned Michael Vine*, hot showbiz manager who she's been trying to get to manage the group. He says the now-ready 'Red Hot & Blonde' demo CD, titled *Running Wild*, is 'superb', as are the publicity photos she sent. Looks very much as if he'll offer them management if he likes them in performance. Positive connections are happening in Lynda's life at last, I pray they continue, and thank heaven she's there to keep me sane.

* *Michael Vine was at the time managing successful comedians such as Joe Pasquale (who he built from small beginnings), Adrian Walsh and Bernie Clifton; the Three British Tenors; the group Casablanca Steps (he also founded an earlier group which I remember, Stutz Bearcats); and is destined to bring magician Derren Brown to international stardom. So his interest in 'Red Hot & Blonde' – generated entirely by Lynda – was a terrific coup for her and her unstinting efforts on behalf of the group to bring it to fame and fortune.*

Wednesday 10th

Exciting times continue for Lynda. She met Michael Vine at PJ's restaurant off the Strand. They had wine and champagne. He seems really sold on her looks and vivacity as well as her voice, and is most interested in the group. Before committing, Michael wants to see how they perform together so will travel up to see them at the showcase for new acts at Stratford-on-Avon next month.

Monday 22nd

Working on a new improved version of *Dark Moon*. Denise Cotton wants to take it to the MIFED film fair in Milan later this week. But the last time I rushed a script through I heard no word for six weeks, then found it had been entirely rewritten by someone else.

'When the eagles are silent the parrots begin to jabber.' Sir Winston Churchill on today's diary page.

Thursday 15th

To Stratford-on-Avon where 'Red Hot & Blonde' are doing a Showcall Showcase in the Civic Hall, agents and bookers sitting around tables hoping to find bookable new acts. The critic from *The Stage* was there, and Michael Vine travelled from London especially to see them.

When 'Red Hot & Blonde' came on they walked side by side from the dark at the back on to the brightly-lit stage, Lynda and Janet in flimsy leopardskin-patterned dresses (in fact nighties from M&S), Andy Eastwood in black tuxedo. They looked a knock-out as they launched into their four numbers, ending with 'Yeh Yeh'. They were brilliant, dazzling, faultless, and the energy that came from them was mesmerising.

Michael was overwhelmed. He told them "That was sensational, you got the audience in the opening seconds. I expected you to be good, but that exceeded all my expectations."

He would have signed the group up at once – but something scarcely believable then happened. Andy said he had his own solo career and therefore couldn't commit to the group except for occasional outings. No pleadings by Lynda or Janet could change his decision, justifiable though it might be given Andy's personal brilliance which means he can stand alone not only adequately but supremely, so my songstress's dream of taking her group to stardom seems nipped in the bud. Because of this entirely unanticipated setback, instead of taking the three of them out for a celebratory meal as he'd planned, and to start excitingly planning their future together, Michael Vine made a subdued farewell and took the next train back to London.

Friday 16th

After yesterday's shock by Andy, this hasn't been a good week for either Lynda or myself, who seem fated to work our hearts out for nil return or recognition. Not having heard from Cat I phoned her from the guesthouse in Stratford-on-Avon – and went cold when she announced that she has 'finished' the script herself and as Denise Cotton *must have* it today is sending *her* version in its entirety. "I *so* enjoyed putting it together," she said.

"Good, excellent," I muttered distractedly into the phone, like Hugh Grant having a dithering fit in front of a beautiful woman. Part of me couldn't take it in because it made no more sense than a group-member turning down a top showbiz manager. The fact is, I felt numb. I'll wake up soon, this is all a ghastly dream. Except it isn't. I made sure that Cat will tell Denise that it's no longer my work, then instructed her to take my name as screenwriter off the *Dark Moon* title page.

Thursday 22nd

Something extraordinary happened today. Around 11 o'clock Denise Cotton rang, in confessional mood. To my surprise I found her enormously sympathetic. She said that the version of the script Cat sent her (with my name now off it) is "utterly dreadful in every way" (I merely quote what Denise said). "It's the worst script I've ever read in my entire life," she went on. "She's certainly no writer." Denise then rather strangely expressed a wish that she herself could be a writer, but knew that she wasn't one. "Did you know?" she went on, "that Cat had someone else (not the American) re-write this script not long ago? It didn't work out, but I can see she's used bits of it here and there in this script."

No, Denise, I didn't know that. But it got worse. She (Denise) said Cat had also paid a "BBC writer" (another mythically wondrous being almost – but not quite – as magically prestigious as 'Hollywoodwriter') to have a go at the script, but that hadn't been right either for her. I was amazed to hear about all this time-(and money?)-wasting activity going on elsewhere without my knowledge and to such seemingly little purpose, yet felt oddly relieved to hear about it now.

Denise told me how she saw the story, and it again became clear to us both that her thoughts are on the same lines as mine. There were story/character elements that she herself hadn't understood, so I did what I could to clarify and illuminate. It felt like healing.

Friday 30th

A special programme late on TV about George Harrison who, I was shattered to learn, died yesterday. A real shock. George was not only, with Eric Clapton, Jimmi Hendrix and their ilk, one of the great guitarists – he was also (like Joe Brown) an excellent ukulele player and George Formby fan. Lynda tells me that at one of the bi-annual sessions of the Ukulele Society of Great Britain at the village hall in Digswell in Hertfordshire, George once turned up unannounced, did a brilliant turn on ukulele-banjo, then joined the free-for-all onstage with the other players at the end of the day's performances. A lovely, interesting, sensitive, deep, hugely talented, original and fascinating man. It makes you want to scream to the skies that, if there is a God, why *him*?

DECEMBER

Saturday 1st
Went out with Lynda. She's put up decorations in her flat, a little Christmas tree with coloured lights. Can the festive season be on us already? Sainsbury's and Tesco and garden centres have all been trying to tell me for months. Now it's suddenly here.

'It's just a job. Grass grows, birds fly, waves pound. I beat people up.'
Muhammad Ali on my diary page today.

Monday 3rd
Up at 6 and read through my very latest *Dark Moon* again. I feel it hangs together pretty well, develops and maintains pace, even dances and glitters a bit. Some of the style is back. Certainly this is strong enough again, I'd have thought, to attract a decent director. Emailed the script direct to Denise Cotton with a detailed message explaining what I've done with it and why, and that I'm sending Cat a copy too.
Now it's my turn to feel jittery – what will Denise make of my script?

Thursday 6th
Email from Denise Cotton says she's only read the first 50 pages of what has now become 'Rob's version' but she was (quote) 'engrossed at last' and 'really feeling something' for the characters and 'felt part of the movie'. She urges me to hang on till she's read it all.

Sunday 9th

With Lynda, roast chicken after wine by the Christmas tree lights in my place. I like a real tree, it gives that child-remembered tang of larch. When Kerry was growing up we always had one, however broke I was. A glowy feeling.

Monday 10th

Denise Cotton emailed to say she has now fully read my version of *Dark Moon* and is happy to go with it. She said (quote) 'Everything falls into place. It's exciting and compelling and I love and emote with the characters again. I can happily take this to the film fairs, and casting can be sought.' Furthermore, she's told this to Cat. Excellent news. So can we move forward again with this with hopes refreshed? When Cat phoned she was congratulatory. "Denise says the dialogue is brilliant," she continued. "Well done, you." Life can be sweet, but why am I still suspicious?

Thursday 13th

What I heard today really shook me. Mags Stoke phoned out of the blue, wants to know how *Dark Moon* is getting on, having been doing work elsewhere. Was able to tell her that the sales agent now has the script she wants, so systems are presumably go again, but we do need a new producer this end to put things together. Mags then confided that she'd known a while back when the script was being completely re-written by this Hollywood writer because Cat had asked if she could put any money towards his fee! Mags had said no, so a wealthy friend came up with the $15,000 this writer's agent was asking!!

So, at a time when I was struggling to survive financially, some stranger in the U.S. of A. was being paid the equivalent of *ten thousand pounds* to rewrite my *Dark Moon* script in its entirety, and when he cocked it up I was brought back in to restore it – at a payment of £500.

Durrrr (dribbles lower lip and makes like a Neanderthal). What was that you said about suckers and even breaks, Dad? How right you were.

Now then, another pretty amazing thing happened: a large ornate Christmas card arrived today, covered with robins – 'to Rob from Denise' – with 2 kisses. I could really like Denise, we really do see eye to eye in so many things and I was genuinely delighted to receive this card. Sent her one in return. Feel chuffed and relieved she likes my latest version, and it's great to know that we can really 'get on the engine again' after the Christmas break.

Wednesday 19th

Kensington's Royal Garden Hotel sparkled with lights, twinkled with Christmas trees. In went Lynda and me in our finery to the Park Terrace Restaurant for the Festive Night Buffet, the larger tables crammed with companies having their annual bash, we at a table for two. The starters were superbly presented, likewise the carvery, lots of turkey and ham, hot mulberry sauce with real fruit, then excellent dessert, mince pies, crème caramel, trifle. All this plus a fine Shiraz. Sitting at our little table in this upmarket ambience, the red buses of dear old London and the edge of Kensington Gardens seen through the huge windows, it was joyful, and to be with this beautiful woman was heaven.

Yet Lynda seemed distracted...

Y'know, life's funny. Maybe we were both thinking of other partners we've known, other lively eyes reflecting candleflames long since snuffed. Can 'Red Hot & Blonde' ever happen now? Lynda didn't want to join the other revellers on the little dancefloor, distractedly left her address book in the loo, had to phone later and have them post it to her, and...

I'm on a pavement in Golders Green, alone in my only suit. It's past midnight. Lynda's gone indoors with a pouty smile that hardly reached her lips and certainly didn't reach mine. If I hadn't stopped smoking yonks ago I'd have lit a cigarette and looked glitter-eyed through its fumes. Cost me a bomb, that did. A nightingale sang in Berkeley Square but I didn't hear it. Was that a dream or was it true? Angels dining at the Ritz? Should I try writing song lyrics then sing them to no one?

Thursday 20th

To Lynda's for quarter to 2. She looked – I don't know – sort of dips her head and looks up at me and quietly says "How are you?" I put her ukuleles and costume case in the back of the car and we drive down to Surbiton, a Care Home for the Elderly with dementia throughout. She was shown into a room to get changed where two old ladies sleep. Uriney smell everywhere. It's their Christmas party and this is Lynda's first job doing this work. She got into the sheeny gold-sequinned dress she wore onstage at the London Palladium, and we went into the main room with the threadbare carpet where the residents and visiting family members were gathered, and she sang and played to them for an hour – and I fell in love with her all over again. She was so nice with her audience, many in their dotage, one an ex-sailor with one leg, another nursing a fox toy as if it was a baby, and Lynda sang beautifully the good old numbers and played terrific ukulele. Had them clapping and stomping by the end. Some looked asleep, yet their feet were tapping and twitching to the rhythm and their mouths moved into small smiles.

We took our leave. Bitter cold out, cars frosted up. We stopped for tea at Newens in Kew. I suddenly realised she was crying. When I dabbed at her face she stopped and took out her powder compact, and smiled. It was like the sun coming out.

Monday 31st
After seeing New Year in with Lynda and her family on the south coast, we drove into Worthing and walked on the pier. A huge moon in a clear sky, Orion to southward. We stood against the rail and looked at the high tide, and her mum Joan said the new tide would wash away all the bad things and bring in the fresh and new. Lynda said a little prayer for the success of 'Red Hot & Blonde', and also *Dark Moon* and all my other films.

That sea down there reflecting stars and a full moon has been mystically transformed – it now belongs to 2002, a year destined to be filled with success and opportunity.

Isn't it?

2002

Tuesday 22nd

Cat phoned with the first real news this year – Denise Cotton wants to introduce a new producer to replace Kees Kasander on *Dark Moon*. His name is Fons Verhoeven, a Belgian who operates from Ghent. Cat has already spoken with him. Then she went on to say: "He's reading both versions of our scripts."

"Both our...?" I was puzzled.

"He'll be in London next week. Why don't you and I meet him?"

"Hang on a minute," I said. "You mean that, as well as the one I've just done and Denise has approved, this man is reading that version you put together and sent to her in the middle of November?"

"Why not?" she said. "As Fons is going to produce the film I thought he should choose which one he'd like to run with."

"But..." It was as far as I got. Cat had already gone, like a whirlwind on its way. I caught myself in the mirror as I shut off the phone – the idiot looking back at me had developed lockjaw and a glazed stare. It'll be all right, of course it will. Hard to know quite what's going on, though.

Wednesday 30th

Cat rang around 9 a.m. to say she's just received Fons Verhoeven's notes on the two scripts, that I'm "not to get upset," and that whatever happens I will have a sole screen credit and she won't want to share it with me as writer. What was *that* about? I was soon to find out.

Lynda said I should look smart at today's meeting with the new producer – first impressions and all that. So I got into a suit and my Philip Marlowe raincoat and tubed it into London. Walked to the Mayfair office of Denise Cotton's lawyer. Cat was already there. She let me look at the notes from Fons. I couldn't believe what I was reading. The Belgian had written that, of the two screenplays shown to him, he 'far prefers' Cat's version. It was like a slam on the head, a shock to the system, a challenge to the senses. His English in articulating this on paper wasn't too hot. I almost laughed. Common sense would prevail, our sales agent would set things straight.

In came Denise, a kiss on both cheeks. Then Fons arrived – shortish, glasses, scruffy hair, dirty jeans and trainers, oldish coat. It now became obvious that both he *and Denise* had gone through Cat's script and *made notes* on it, and I realised that I was on the floor without covers again, with a chamber pot being emptied over my head.

Returned home feeling more than ever like Alexei Sayle's increasingly bewildered writer in the Comic Strip's *The Strike*. So when Cat rang and started on about what a good meeting it had been I could only whimper like a kicked dog. Nothing made sense any more.

So I wasn't in the best of moods this evening driving to Camden Town to meet Lynda to see Georgie Fame with his old group the Blue Flames. Needing cash, I went to the machine by the tube station. Had just inserted my card and keyed in £60 when someone tapped my left shoulder. I glanced round to see a young mid-eastern bloke holding a £20 note, saying, "You dropped this." Aware in a nanosecond that I was being done, I looked back just in time to see the hand of his accomplice reaching for my £60 just emerged. I grabbed the hand and we looked at each other for several moments – he too was young and middle-eastern – while my other hand rescued my card and cash from the machine. No police were about, so I let him go and he ran. His mate had already gone.

Joined Lynda at the Jazz Café venue and she said I looked shaken up, and I told her I'd nearly been mugged at the cash machine but that I'd grabbed the thief's hand in time and had felt a bone crack. Lynda said "Poor man, he was probably desperate, I hope he wasn't hurt." I don't suppose today was the best time to try and steal anything from me – my pride and credibility as a writer had already been stolen earlier.

Georgie Fame and the Blue Flames were terrific. Afterwards, Lynda and I made our way through the crush and found Georgie upstairs, all on his own. He was amazed that we'd bypassed security and found him, and he sort of cowered back as Lynda handed him the CD of her group, in which she sings Fame's *Yeh! Yeh!* "Can't listen to it for three weeks," he grunted, and vanished into his dressing room*.

*Never to be heard from again. He must have thought we were nuts.

112

FEBRUARY

Friday 1st

Escaped with Lynda to her parents' bungalow in Sussex. We took their cavalier spaniel Toby for a walk. The wind on the coast was gale force, flattening the dog's ears to his head, white-crested waves pounding in. This evening to Bognor Regis and saw Andy Eastwood in a music hall starring Danny La Rue, who is now 74. Andy was as terrific as ever in his playing and stage presence. Afterwards we met him and Walt backstage. We congratulated him and wished him all the warmest and wellest and finest and fullest.

Yet on the way back Lynda cried. "I miss him and the group so much," she said.

Yet all was not quite over yet for *'Red Hot & Blonde'*.

Monday 4th

From: Denise Cotton
To: Rob Squire
Date: 4 February 2002
Subject: Dark Moon

Dear Rob

I think everyone now knows that I preferred your draft of the script. Although I chanced to bring Cat's earlier one with me to the meeting, this was an oversight as it was your new draft I had been working on. Might I suggest we let Cat to do what she wants to at this time? If she wishes to re-write the changes herself then so be it - I just can't keep fighting on this one and as I am sure you noted during the meeting with Fons I kept silent about their agreed changes. I will be happy and eager to read the new draft when Cat has completed it, and will definitely air my views when that time comes – whether they be good or bad*.

Best regards
Denise Cotton

113

This response from Denise was revealing. If, instead of staying 'silent' at that meeting, she had spoken up, the outcome might have saved grievous amounts of time now destined to be lost in bringing this film before the camera.

Sunday 17th
Cat has finished the amendments to her version of the script following her consultations with Fons, and says she's had a terrible time with it. "Now I know what you have to go through," she added. 50 copies of this are being run off for handing round, with Cat's name now under the title as sole screenwriter as I insisted that mine be removed.

Cat asks that when she's incorporated the Belgian producer's notes on her work, would I put it into industry format? "I'll pay you something," she said, "and next week you and me will go and have a nice lunch together."

Monday 18th
Cat rang around 8 a.m. to say Fons has now 'approved' her work, amendments have been made, and she's just emailed the result to me. My job, for which she will pay me, is to format this new script, but I'm to "make no attempt to change any of the writing." So I'm to be a sort of clerical functionary – it feels a bit odd but am aware I mustn't get above myself.

Well, I opened it up and got to work. Gritted teeth and left it exactly as it was, then emailed the result to Verhoeven in Ghent, troubled to think that this is to be printed out 50 times and sent to potential financiers, film distributors and the like, and is also intended to grab the attentions of a quality director.

Wednesday 20th
Met Peter Jaques for lunch at Strand-on-the Green. Good to see him again, a wise head amid the turmoil. Had a couple of pints while I brought him up to date. It's always good to talk to Peter, he brings things into focus. "Let it fly," he said, "and see where it lands. It's news to me that Cat's a writer, but if that's so she's got a hell of a journey to travel and will want to have her head on this. It's one of the toughest things in the world to get a screenplay right, as you well know, and maybe she's having to find out the hard way, so you'll have to back off and let her breathe. That's all you can do, then see what happens."

Monday 25th

To lunch with Cat as she promised. She took me to the Petersham Hotel near Richmond, with views of the Thames bend from its windows. A fine meal with a bottle of Pouilly Fuisse – rack of lamb on cabbage. Cat said Denise Cotton has read the first half of what she's done 'and likes it' – but she hasn't read the second half yet and her buyers are lined up to see it. The bill was £75, which Cat kindly paid. She also wrote me a cheque for £150 for putting the script into industry format. Thanks Cat, I'm being really *calm* about this, please note. Peter was right – no point getting in a state.

Thursday 28th

Cat phoned, disturbed because when she just spoke to Denise Cotton in Los Angeles (where our sales agent has gone to sell *Dark Moon*) she was very off with her, even 'hostile'. I consoled Cat by saying Denise may just be having an off day.

Later, driving back from a gig with Lynda, it was announced on the car radio that Spike Milligan has died. Felt sad that Spike's no longer in the world. What a party they'll be having up there in Heaven, which is surely where he's gone.

MARCH

Friday 1st

Cat is still talking about Denise's continuing negative attitude to her 'new' script. I simply don't know what to say to Cat, but it's rough out there once the maulers get to work. You could write *War and Peace* and they'd still have a go, negative responses are not necessarily a reflection of your work's true worth. Fons Verhoeven is her staunch champion throughout all this and gives her constant encouragement in a foreign accent, while I'm regarded by him as some kind of hanger-on without an ounce of talent. So be it, each to his – or, indeed, her – own. I'm cool about it, why get wound up? It's even – dare I say it? – healing to see someone else on the receiving end for a change.

Friday 15th

Went with Lynda to a care home in Hemel Hempstead today. She brought colour and cheer in with her and spread it around the gloomy communal room, which needed the windows open to breathe properly. One elderly man gazed amazed as Lynda split-stroked on her ukulele and perkily sang George Formby's 'When I'm Cleaning Windows'. Afterwards, as she went around talking to people like she always does, this man told us, "I was George Formby's pilot when he came to entertain the troops in North Africa in1942. I was detailed to fly him to the front." Lynda was totally fascinated. "What was he like?" she asked. "Lovely chap – his wife Beryl was the sharp one," the man said, smiling reminiscently. "They were about to board the plane when I said 'Give us a song first, George.' Beryl said, a bit waspish, 'That's quite impossible.' We kept on about it but Beryl kept on saying, 'Absolutely not!' So then I said, on behalf of the crew, 'No song, no flight.' So George gave that goofy grin, took his banjo thing out of its case and did 'Leaning on a Lamppost' right there on the tarmac. Beryl didn't know where to put her face."

The Ideas of March are here again. Why do I feel filled with ghostly daggers?

Monday 25th

Got a call from Cat on her way to meet Ros Hubbard with Denise Cotton and 'that' script. I wonder if Ros will notice that Robin got off the engine.

APRIL

Thursday 18th

Cat phoned. We haven't spoken for more than 3 weeks, and Lynda is doing ever more gigs, with me as a sort of roadie while I try to drum up more writing work – which, with Howard Pays increasingly incapacitated – is demoralising. With so many genuinely gifted writers around with brilliant material seeking publication and production, I really do need a full-time agent who believes in my stuff and is prepared to get it into the most promising areas. *Dark Moon*, which had once seemed a break-through project, now looks such a sad lost cause, with Cat carrying gutsily on with her version of the script, determined to see her baby thrive. She told me it's currently with Simon West, director of *Lara Croft: Tomb Raider*. A friend of mine said to me, no doubt unkindly, that Simon will probably want to bury it deep and put a slab against the entrance in case it rises zombie-like and tries to walk, that this is one tomb Lara would *not* want to raid. Oh dear.

It's my birthday today. With Lynda looking delightful in lacy white Edwardian top, black bead skirt and velvet jacket, drove to Kerry's workplace in West Ealing. Out came my lovely daughter, young and fresh and smiley. Life has its compensations – wretchedly poor and sidelined as I am in many ways, supremely rich and celebrated in others. With my two favourite females, opened my cards and prezzies in the City Barge by the river with a pint, then to a Nepalese restaurant for a wacky-wild laughter-wine time. The hours melted and Kerry and Lynda got on so well they've not stopped laughing yet. I can still see their faces creased with merriment as they rock to and fro. I may have been poor this morning, this evening I was rich.

MAY

Thursday 30th

Simon West has turned down Cat's version of *Dark Moon*. She was puzzled and hurt. She now tells me there's an Italian director, Liliana Cavani – who directed (and wrote) *The Night Porter*, with Dirk Bogarde and Charlotte Rampling. I remember it well. Powerful and challenging. How fabulous to have such a mind and talent engaged with this. Now Cat is waiting for Ms Cavani's agent to okay the script for her client to read. Cat went on to say (do I hear Denise's voice here?) it may need a "slight polish." More like a comprehensive going-over in a steam laundry followed by the attentions of an alchemist, says my friend. I didn't listen, but if I'd said anything as scurrilous as that myself it would no doubt be regarded as sour grapes.

JUNE

Saturday 1st

Drove Lynda down to Ham House by the Thames in Surrey where she's performing all day at a craft fair with Janet Beale for £75. 'Red & Blonde' only. 'Hot' has gone cold, re-confirming (yesterday) his refusal to sign a contract with Michael Vine to be part of the group managed by him.

Lynda had a rotten night thinking about Andy and the group. She's even written a letter giving him one last go – but Andy has his own strong agenda which, sadly for them and maybe for lots of other people (who can possibly say?), doesn't include the girls. Lynda wonders if Michael Vine will be prepared to manage just her and Janet without him – but I suspect not, it was the tremendous energy that came off that unique line-up that made him want the three together. With such a powerful and successful manager, within 3 years they would have been playing the stages of the world, with recording contracts, TV shows, the lot. But now?

At least the weather was nice.

'People ask you for criticism, but they only want praise.' W. Somerset Maugham on today's diary page.

Friday 7th

Liliana Cavani's agent said 'no' to *Dark Moon*. Cat still couldn't understand why. She then said – surprising me – that Denise Cotton had wanted to run with my version of 16th December, but was 'outvoted' by Cat herself and Fons, the Belgian producer who continues even now to 'far prefer' hers. So, in Denise's view, I didn't have a vote – which would at least have made it evens, and they could have got a professional reader – or the Writers' Guild of Great Britain (of which I'm a Full Member) to arbitrate. Too late now. Not granting me a vote is why they went forward (and are still doing) with Cat's version of the script, which she and Fons continue staunchly to defend. Cat now she tells me that Fons is trying to get the ICM agency to package it.

Saturday 29th

Cat rang in a right old state – Denise Cotton has had Cat's script read by a professional reader, and the report says all sorts of negative things such as flat characters, dead dialogue, the story collapses three-quarters of the way through and so on. Again, I really felt for her – this is a bastard business, and horrible scathing things are said about even the best of writers by the kind of people you'd cross the town to avoid, so I told her not to get too upset. But Denise had challenged Cat with: "So what are you going to do about it?" The upshot of all this is that, rightly or wrongly, Cat now wants to meet me and do a deal or she has nowhere else to go with this, having tried other writers and then endeavoured to go it alone. So we meet tomorrow. I pray it may be fruitful.

Sunday 30th

Drove to Cat's this afternoon, talked about the film. She gave me a cheque for £700 to put together a new working draft, which is better than a slap with a wet fish. And that's June, that was.

JULY

Tuesday 16th

Continuing with the restoration of *Dark Moon*, the glow beginning again as the script slowly stirs, groggily blinks, and tries feebly but gamely to stand after its ordeal, still pallid and malnourished, but strength returning to its limbs, colour to its cheeks and renewed hope to my heart. Not a good time, then, for Cat to announce that actor Patrick Bergin has "only just read" her now-discredited version, told her she's done 'a great job' with it, and wants to play the part of 'Grimstone'.

Well, praising Cat's writing is an excellent way to get on the right side of her (as Fons Verhoeven well knew) – but I can never forgive Mr Bergin for saying these things at the very moment this script was promising to get back on track.

Friday 19th

Yes, the damage has been done. Since Patrick Bergin's encouragement, Cat's tail is up again, she phones me constantly and it's pretty clear she wants to take over the script again. When today she asked how my new draft felt, I said it was like healing. Yet I know that, however effective my powers of resuscitation might be, Cat and the Belgian, with the perplexing connivance of Denise Cotton, are waiting outside the surgery door – "ready to stride in spraying lethal germs at the recovered patient and chop its legs from under it again?" added my friend. I didn't listen.

Monday 22nd
Howard Pays has been ill with cancer, so I've not wanted to trouble him with the problems I've been facing. But today, knowing he's retired yet feeling a strong need to talk to him anyway, phoned his home number. His wife Lynn answered, and gave me the devastating news that Howard has died. Howard had been a friend as well as a literary agent – of which I now have none. The weather matched my mood: this has been the coldest, wettest, unsunniest summer so far since records began; seaside resorts are deserted, indoor holidays booming.

Wednesday 24th
Met Peter Jaques at the Queen's Head in Pinner – he as usual imperturbable, me all over the place, practically shaking. I need to talk to someone, as they say in the movies. Over a couple of pints of ale and a goodly meal he listened to my ongoing tale of woe, of how this script keeps being wrenched from my grasp just as I start to get control of it again. Peter's advice is to soldier on – apart from walking off and invalidating my contract, the alternatives are limited. Bravo the Britflick! Hoorah for the Union Jack! "Get it as good as you can," he suggests, "then if they decide in their wisdom to screw it up again you'll have done what you can."

Thursday 25th
Finished my new revivified draft of *Dark Moon* last night and am truly pleased with it. Yet now that 'screenwriter Cat' has been re-energised I feel uneasy. Sure enough, not long after emailing my revised script to her she was back declaring that there are "certain bits of dialogue" she doesn't like and that she's preparing revision notes which she'll send to Fons, Denise Cotton and Patrick Bergin. So the game is on again.

This evening by candlelight with a can of beer I realised that the obvious answer is that I haven't a clue about screenwriting and should have walked off long ago and left Cat and the rest of them to put it right. But I have a contract for £52,000 which needs to be honoured in order to collect and by all the great saints and minor ones I NEED that money, especially after all the time I've spent on this project already, the seemingly unending drafts and print-outs of scripts and DHL-ing of screenplays and outlines to far-flung countries of the world, all at my un-reimbursed expense with my finances low and sinking ever lower – sometimes with positive responses that were always somehow brought to nought for reasons beyond my control. So these attempts to 'put the script right' have already been made – they (and others) have already 'put it right' a few times before – indeed, Cat herself 'put it right' with her own version, which Fons applauded but which proved unworkable to anyone else – undisputed fact, not opinion. So, for a fee of £700, Cat invited me back in to 'put it righter' than it was when they'd 'put it right' – and *still* they're making out it needs to be 'put right' all over again, and that Cat is the only one who can do this. And so the madness goes on and on, round and round.

And STILL we have no director since they got rid of John Glen, who had been at the point of shooting the film with main cast in place and finance secured. With Lynda in it too. Oh God.

Unzipped another can…

AUGUST

Monday 26th
Bank Holiday Monday, rainily blowy. Drove Lynda to a country house near Tring to perform at a craft fair. Set up the sound system for her, with mike and amp. She and Janet were doing their thing under a canvas awning in mid-lawn, and had just hit nostalgia time with Vera Lynn's 'White Cliffs of Dover' when a tall bearded man in his 50s comes striding from a marquee, his wife in tow, and goes over to speak to them.

Georgio the ice cream man tells me "That's Dave Lee Travis, he lives near here." It was indeed the 'great hairy monster' of youthtime memory, the legendary Radio Caroline/BBC 1 disc jockey. He talked to the girls for some time, told them he sometimes gives parties at his house and will invite them to perform at one.

Later, Lynda was excited to think where this might lead. Something similar happened to Andy Eastwood when he was entertaining at a hospital and DJ Chris Evans walked in. Amazed by the incredible power and rhythm of Andy's ukulele, Evans rang his broadcaster friend Danny Baker on his mobile and got him to listen, then took Andy's details. Andy never heard from him again, nor from Danny Baker. Still, it made for a happy Lynda, hope-filled again after all the reverses. And you just never know.

'Fashion can be bought. Style one must possess.' Edna Woolman Chase on my diary page today.

Saturday 31st

To Chorleywood in Hertfordshire, an upmarket care home. Coming off the M25 we were suddenly in a sylvan haven surrounded by woodland, a cricket pitch with a game in progress. Lynda in pink silk dress looked svelte as she entertained in the lounge with ukulele, voice and backing tracks. Her opening song was 'Look For The Silver Lining' (the first one I ever heard her sing in that café off Baker Street), after which she told her audience it was once sung by Jessie Matthews, one of Britain's foremost singers and dancers of the 1930s. At this the organiser, a fine-looking woman called Sue Cooke-Angus, said surprisingly, "That's right – and Jessie was my aunt."

After the show Sue sat us down with tea and talked of her Aunt Jessie, her dad's sister, who she remembers well from childhood. Sue also remarked that Lynda's singing voice is technically better than her aunt's was.

Out in the sunshine we parked by the cricket pitch. The players had gone in for tea so we walked into the greeny deeps of an English afternoon. Woods, a golf course. A pond. We could have danced through the undergrowth, wild roses twined in her russet hair, the sun on her smile, a lifetime of romance and plenty beckoning. Pity we're both so broke and have to work so very hard all the time just to stay that way.

Back home I dug out a Jessie Matthews recording and played her singing 'Everything's In Rhythm With My Heart' from 1935. Know what? – Jessie's niece is right. Lynda's voice is richer, note-perfect, greater range, stronger, purer, superior technique. The realisation was exhilarating yet troubling.

Why is a vocalist of Lynda's quality still doing these care homes when the world should be hearing her? Like other things in life, it makes no sense but simply IS.

SEPTEMBER

Wednesday 4th

Cat rang to say the meeting went 'very well' yesterday. What meeting? Whatever, at it Patrick Bergin said the script is ready to go to a director now. Thanks, Mr Bergin. I had to remind myself that a version of this script, written by yours truly, had been 'ready to go to a director' when I redid it last December, so 9 whole months have been lost. Still, let's be positive. Patrick is getting it to Bob Rafelson (who directed *The Postman Only Rings Twice*).

OCTOBER

Tuesday 1st

Patrick Bergin isn't going for Bob Rafelson after all, but will talk with prestigious British director John Irvin this weekend in Dublin about directing *Dark Moon* – Patrick is making a film with him there called *The Boys From County Clare*. The thought of working with the man who directed *Tinker, Tailor, Soldier, Spy* with Alec Guinness for BBC TV a yonk or so ago, also the terrific American military action movie *Hamburger Hill*, is pretty special, but let's not forget that this is Cat's version of the script we're talking about, so my part in it is uncertain.

Tuesday 15th

Have been talking to Lynda about extending her repertoire to include torch songs. She hadn't heard the expression 'torch song' before, which surprised me. So after today's gig I went into a Harrow music shop and emerged with a book with lyrics and backing-track CD titled – you've guessed it – 'TORCH SONGS'.

Back at my place we played the CD and Lynda sang to it – but *softly*, as I coaxed her, not belting the numbers out with that strong rich voice of hers. Cole Porter's 'Every Time We Say Goodbye' was one, and her voice sounded amazing in an entirely different way – smoky and steamy, emotionally charged. Together we've found an additional ingredient to her act, which from now on will have even more warmth, communication and depth. Michael Vine, keen as he was to manage her and her group, never heard Lynda sing like this.

Friday 18th

Was at a gig with Lynda in Blackheath when Cat rang with news that Patrick Bergin saw John Irvin in Ireland – and Irvin has agreed to direct *Dark Moon*, 'script unseen', on his recommendation. He's to sign a letter of intent so Denise Cotton can go to the MIFED film fair next week with a director attached to our project. That's good news, isn't it? And it's Cat's version of the script we're talking about. I'm so pleased for Cat, I know it hasn't been easy for her either, but she keeps on going and that's fantastic.

Tuesday 22nd

Woke refreshed and wrote the final chapter of my novel *French Kisses, English Dreams*. Just have to read it through with the carping, impatient mind of a professional reader, make appropriate amendments, and can send it out to be professionally read*. So while Cat and her associates have been agonising over the countless drafts of *Dark Moon* and whether any one of them is 'quite right' or not before taking it over completely herself, I've written an entire 90,000-word novel, and Lynda has opened her lovely throat to Torch Singing.

Not having written extended prose for so long I felt it best to pay for professional feed-back. The Literary Consultancy is run by Rebecca Swift, daughter of novelist Margaret Drabble and actor Clive Swift, and their publicity states that they don't encourage mediocrity and have a reputation for being cruel to be kind. So I wasn't expecting an easy ride, just needed to know whether or not I'd lost it completely in prose-writing and should waste my own and other people's time no more by trying.

DECEMBER

Friday 13th

Cat rang about the script meeting she's just had with John Irvin. I was fascinated to know how it had gone. She told me he'd begun by saying the story's not bad, but the dialogue and ending need "a great deal of reworking." Yes? So what else is new? As for me, although I still have a legally-binding contract as writer on this project and intend to honour it, in all other respects I'm presumably off the scene completely now. Don't suppose John Irvin even knows I exist*.

*He didn't. But he was soon to know about me and my connection with Dark Moon in an impossible-to-have-guessed way.

Thursday 19th

In the post was the manuscript of my brand spanking new novel *French Kisses, English Dreams* back from The Literary Consultancy with their reader's report. But now, having shelled out £275 I couldn't afford for this very moment, I could only stand staring at the package in dread.

I didn't relish having to acknowledge that Fons Verhoeven, Cat and her friends had been right all along – that in fact I'm a lousy writer and have been desperately trying to deceive myself that I'm not; and why it's not my version of *Dark Moon* being read by this latest world-class director after all my time on the project, but Cat's.

So I just couldn't bring myself to open that envelope. I know I've written bad stuff in the past – maybe all writers do at some time – at periods in my life when I was psychologically screwed up – but such material has long since been destroyed by shredder and fire while I wondered in horror and disgust what manner of person could possibly have written it.

But surely those times are far behind me now? Or *are* they? With Christmas so close and *Dark Moon* angsts hard upon me I knew I couldn't bear to read a frank, caustic, negative report from a no-nonsense professional reader that will dash all hopes of a return to novel-writing. So I decided to leave it unopened until the new year when I might feel more prepared to swallow yet further rebukes regarding my paltry abilities as a scribe.

Lynda has a sore throat, can barely speak, and wonders has she wrecked her voice doing so many low-paid gigs just to survive. So she and I ended the day in dread that the careers we have both sacrificed so much for are effectively over: she, that she will never sing again; me, that the report on my new novel will be so damning I will never write again.

Friday 20th
Steeled myself to stop being such a gutless ninny and to read the report on my new novel, whatever it said. So I took a deep breath, ripped open the envelope and – flinchingly at first, then in increasing wonderment – read what their reader had to say.

French Kisses, English Dreams
by Robin Squire

I found this to be an absorbing novel, erotic, informative, comic, sympathetic to the characters that share their puzzling predilection, and, ultimately, charged with considerable pathos. I also feel that the novel is stylistically very solid.

Story, structure, discourse, humour
In all good novels, the characters and their story or stories develop in tandem, and I feel that, in yours, both aspects are strong. I warmed to the characters and their stories as I read, and consequently felt that the novel became more engrossing as it developed.

Jed's and Tamar's lives move forward through various twists, turns, ups and downs, to their story's shared resolution. I found the denouement satisfyingly powerful.

Of course the discursive, introspective, and gently comic dimensions prove to be far from the whole story of the book: as Jed's and Tamar's dramas unfold and combine, we uncover a degree of pathos that is equally important and equally effective as the novel's comic dimension, and the characters and plot do begin to interweave in engrossing ways around the novel's central theme, to produce a cohesive and compelling narrative.

Stylistic concerns, character portraits

I have no major criticisms of the novel's style or voice. To my mind, the qualities in the writing are consistently strong throughout. There are far too many examples of fine writing sprinkled liberally throughout the novel for me to quote here.

I like the pastichey modulations of register elsewhere. The inserted texts – poems, letters, magazine articles – are always effective, too; and I was very struck by the high flown poetic prose that announces the kindling of new love in Jed's heart, when the troubadour transfers his gaze to his new beloved object. There are numerous strong set-piece passages.

On top of the background material that helps at intervals to flesh out the central figures, the sketches of the novel's adjunctive characters are always made with a lively flourish. There is also a good deal of mordant wit, which demonstrates the level of intellect that informs the words on the page.

Conclusion

As you can see, I have very few criticisms to make of this draft of your novel, and I feel that it is strong in many respects. You convincingly capture the strangeness of Jed's and Tamar's various encounters and shed light on a little-known scene, though this sense of authenticity is by no means the be all and end all of a funny, touching, and tender story that is very well crafted indeed.

Martin Ouvry
The Literary Consultancy
London

This report from Martin Ouvry absolutely made my Christmas, delighted Lynda, and went a long way towards restoring at least some of my badly-battered confidence as a writer.

2003

JANUARY

Thursday 2nd

Will it be a good year, after all the hopes sploshed about around midnight as Big Ben hit the gong? You're always optimistic this end of things, because anything could go, and there's no reason why not, apart from bloody-mindedness on the part of fate, because you yourself are absolutely ready for it.

Rang lovely Kerry. She had a dream on New Year's night that she visited me in a sort of farmhouse property abroad, probably France, and it was mine. I said that's amazing, only yesterday I was saying to Lynda how I'd love a place in the south of France to holiday in and write. And Kerry and her Chris could come there and stay for as long as they wanted any time they fancied.

A beer and Scotch by the coloured lights of my Christmas tree, dreaming of going to France this summer to look for somewhere to buy, imagining Lynda in a big hat with parasol in a fieldful of poppies, chased and ogled by panting Frenchmen.

'Waiting for the German verb is the ultimate thrill' says Flan O'Brien on today's page in this diary.

Which prompted a memory from some schoolday tutorial: *Ich habe soeben erfahren dass Pegasus das zwei-dreissig Rennen gewonnen hat.* Meaning I've just learned that Pegasus won the 2.30 race. The point being that we don't know till the very end of the sentence that the horse won. Funny what completely useless things like that hang around inside your head…

Tuesday 21st

Cat tells me ICM are asking £1 million for John Irvin to direct *Dark Moon*. When I told my producer pal Debi she howled with laughter down the phone. Reality check required? Wish I had an agent like that, though – indeed, wish I had an agent at all now Howard's gone.

Thursday 30th

It started to snow in the afternoon. I got Lynda home to Golders Green after her gig, then set off back to my place around 7. Snow continued falling when darkness did, roads iced up and remained ungritted. Creeping slitheringly through a mass of crawling traffic I finally abandoned the car at the top of Preston Hill which glistened steeply downwards like a ski-jump slope in the streetlights. Walked the rest of the way home, wading through deep snow across the recreation ground, and didn't get in till midnight. 5 hours to cover 8 miles – a journey that usually takes twenty minutes*. I could have walked it quicker, and wished I had. Swigging a Scotch to recover, it came to me that the journey had been like the progress on *Dark Moon*, unbelievably slow and fraught with hazard.

Next day news emerged of the worst gridlock in London in living memory as thousands tried to get home on ungritted roads like ice-sheets. Many abandoned their vehicles or slept in them. The M25 and M11 were at a standstill. 'Road chiefs' (it said) had been given warning of the snow and freezing conditions, but had done nothing about it. I wonder what a road chief is.

FEBRUARY

Monday 17th

The symbol © used to just mean copyright. But from today, painted in red on a road in London, it also means Congestion Zone. A £5 charge if you drive into it, cameras clocking every vehicle that does, and if you fail to pay by midnight they send a huge fine. Do I hear George Orwell sighing? Cameras and computers have taken over the life of the once free man, and at the click of a shutter can make a criminal out of the most innocent and unsuspecting. It makes you want to go far, far away.

Wednesday 26th

More rejections from literary agents as I work through the list. None of them wants to know I've written a potentially best-selling novel, or even that I have a feature film about to be made (who am I kidding?).

MARCH

Wednesday 12th

Still in search of a literary agent, applied to Jeffrey Simmons – once managing director of W.H. Allen who published my first novel. Somehow I thought it might put him off that he'd once published me, so signed the letter with a different name. At the time, Jeffrey also secured a paperback deal with New English Library and changed my life by liking my work.

'You're not drunk if you can lie on the floor without holding on' says Dean Martin on today's diary page.

Saturday 15th

On these Ides of March came a letter from Jeffrey Simmons saying he can't take on any more clients. Said he hasn't read the enclosures I sent, and returns them with his letter*. Those daggers sure hurt.

*So another potential literary agent gone. But wait. With someone like Lynda in your life the rules of the game start to change…

Thursday 20th

In the news, cataclysmic furore as USA and Allies hit Iraq with the power of an Armageddon scourge to remove Saddam Hussein and stop him lighting the blue touch paper on his weaponry, if any. Guess they can't take chances or the western world could become the biggest barbecue known to man. Imagine, just one person being the focus of all this death and destruction. It's hideous.

Saturday 22nd

This evening over a beer sat agentlessly contemplating what to do about the *Dark Moon* situation. So far I've been hogtied, skinned and roasted; now Cat is keeping me in total darkness instead of merely twilight. Have they hired another writer to raise an adequate director's draft, or is Cat handling this herself? My heart sinks when I think of how good that script once was. As Thomas Hardy put it when rueing the death of his beloved cousin Tryphena Sparks, who died three days before her 39th birthday:

> *... whom I knew when her dreams were upbrimming with light,*
> *And with laughter her eyes.*

APRIL

Sunday 6th

Tonight I dreamed of Howard Pays. I was in his office and he was fit and youthful again and was going to help get things moving in my creative life. It was a good dream, and I woke feeling more positive.

Tuesday 8th

Catch-up drink and natter with Peter Jaques at the City Barge by the Thames. Think I'm starting a bug, felt like death with clogs on later in the day. Having the *Dark Moon* virus creeping lethally through my system doesn't help either.

Friday 11th

A message from Lynda when I got back from the doctor, my legs so weak I can hardly walk. Rang her, and what she said astounded me. She's just phoned literary agent Jeffrey Simmons on my behalf! *What?* Yes, she spoke to this tower of my earlier days and asked if he would reconsider looking at my work – pitching me as one of the young novelists he took on when he was a publisher. Jeffrey said for her to give him a few weeks, then phone again.

From then on my health was on the mend. My energy and cleansing rage came back, marvelling at having the support of this extraordinary woman in my life. I begin to feel like the writer in the French film *Betty Blue* whose girlfriend beat up publishers when they turned his manuscript down. And what's wrong with that?

Thursday 23rd

Surprised to get a phone call from Barrie Saint Clair in South Africa saying a French producer called Philippe Martinez wants to film my screenplay of *La Miss*, with a finance group ready to back it. When I said I thought that was dead in the water he said not at all, there's nothing illegal about it, never was – just a few lawyers getting windy for no good reason. Barrie went on to say he met with the finance yesterday – they need to action their money within the next 2 months, $5 million budget. Will John Glen be directing? Probably not, Barrie said – they've already approached a different director but he wasn't sure who.

MAY

Thursday 8th

Rang Cat about what's happening with *Dark Moon* as I've heard nothing for so long. She went a bit funny-quiet, then announced that John Irvin has now been signed up to direct the film. Also, that she's managed to find the £5000 ICM asked to secure him. Really? Now our new director's off on holiday for two weeks (as would I be if someone paid £5000 to secure me), but Cat confided that she's worried because he wants a complete rewrite *and* to change the story *and* eliminate the supernatural content. I could only laugh nervously into the phone, wondering yet again what on earth has been going on while I've been out here festering on the reserve benches. I asked her does John Irvin want an entirely different film, then, in which case I have other scripts I can show him that are ready to go⋆?

⋆*This remark was to prove spookily prescient.*

Monday 12th

Was summoned to Cat's house for 11.30 a.m., first time in ages, for an 'intensive script discussion'. Interesting. After making coffee and talking uneasily for a while, Cat opened up this script on her computer and scrolled through a very different version to the last one I'd seen, put together by herself, with screeds of notes attached from Denise Cotton. As the now sole writer on *Dark Moon*, Cat, after frequent consultations with John Irvin, has been called on to raise a strong director's draft in preparation for the shoot. And now it seemed she was in trouble.

Nothing's easy, life's a bitch. Wanted to put my arm around her shoulder, admiring her courage in taking this on all on her own. We talked story. A few ideas spilled out as she tossed problems at me that John Irvin had brought up and neither she nor anyone around her (including, presumably, Fons Verhoeven and Denise Cotton) had been able to resolve. But why should they? – these were creative problems only a writer could sort out, not production or sales issues. For the main one I visualised a pre-title sequence that would, in the opening seconds, set up a puzzle that the film's story would resolve, grabbing the audience from the word go. Cat stared at me, her face transformed, and she flung her arms round me. "But that does it," she shouted. "It *does* it!"

She now suggested that she and I should share the writers' credits. A screenwriting credit shouldn't be given lightly – there are so many extremely talented writers out there who would kill to get one. "Just let's see how it goes," I said.

Tuesday 13th

Cat phoned, said she was delighted at how things had gone yesterday, that because of it we now have the full back-story and eliminated all 'coincidence' (something I'd already dealt with in my version of the script several months before because I'd known it was a problem – a script John Irvin had clearly never been shown). *C'est la vie.*

I said that for £500, payable now, I could rework the script so it will at least be good enough to go to Cannes. Having spoken to Fons, Cat came back to say he will send £350 in dollars from his company, and she £150.

So here was me, somewhat surprised to find myself back on *Dark Moon* again. By the end of the day had incorporated the new teaser opening, bringing back useful stuff from past scripts, straightened out the dialogue, restored some of the pace and balance and reworked the ending so at least this 'latest latest' draft will be able to look an industry professional in the eye without flinching too much.

I also sent Fons Verhoeven in Belgium my bank details. I bet paying me something from his company's account will be like having a tooth drawn without anaesthetic. So what? – much of this latest crisis is his own fault for 'far preferring' what might turn out to have been not the best choice.

Friday 23rd

Lynda has spoken to Jeffrey Simmons again! What a girl! He said for her to put any material in the post, but she prevailed on him to let her deliver it in person, saying that the writer she's talking about had a novel published. "Who published it?" he asked. '*You* did,' she said. At this he agreed she could bring my package round in ten days, by which time he'll be settled in his new offices. Lynda is a heroine.

JUNE

Wednesday 4th

To Lynda's soon after ten. Out she came in the fawn faux-fur trimmed leather coat, the classy French trousers in pale cream and matching flouncy blouse, vivid hair in coils to her shoulders and framing her lovely face. She looked like a film star. Found our way to Jeffrey Simmons's literary agency in St John's Wood. It was bucketing down with rain, and I'll never forget the flashing grin she gave me from under her umbrella as she went in, with a briefcase containing my CV and other relevant material including the Martin Ouvry crit on my new novel.

I waited nervily in the car as the deluge continued, wondering what was being said in there. Some half an hour later out she came, looking pleased. We sat in a coffee bar on the little square at Belsize Park. Lynda said Jeffrey hadn't remembered me till she took out the novel he'd published and showed him my photo on the back. The upshot was, he'll read my stuff then get back directly to me if he wants to take it further. He was interested that *Dark Moon* looks about to happen, may like to represent me on that, and suggests I write a book of the film (he's predominantly a book agent).

I was so delighted with my fab ambassadress, took her to the Rising Sun at Totteridge for lunch. Can't afford the Ritz just yet. But we will, we will.

Monday 9th

At Cat's by 10.50 a.m., got in her new 4x4 and along to John Irvin's house overlooking a green expanse near Putney. A tall, hale-looking man in his 60s. As I walked in and gripped his hand, his eyelid drooped in an unmistakeably conspiratorial wink, as if to say "don't say anything, let's just carry on as things are for now."

I wondered what that wink was about as we sat in his lounge. The meeting didn't go on too long – a few final notes during which I was introduced by Cat as a writer who was now helping her on the script, and he and I established some sort of understanding. While this was going on, Cat was jotting things on a pad – I imagined her here on similar meetings doing the same, then going off and diligently incorporating her notes into the script. As we shook hands on departure John gave me an unreadable smile and, again, that mysterious wink. A charming and gifted man, I felt privileged to have met him.

Got home to a message on my answerphone from Jeffrey Simmons! That deep distinguished voice, so well-remembered, that had changed my life when I was young. Asking me to phone him tomorrow. I was jumping up and down. Rang Lynda and told her – she was excited too, but said let's wait till I've heard what he says before we get too euphoric.

Tuesday 10th
Rang Jeffrey Simmons. Wonderful and extraordinary to be talking to him again after all this time. He said that owing to the somewhat unusual background of *French Kisses, English Dreams* he would prefer me to have another novel out first to get me re-established. It's never been so difficult, he said, to get a manuscript read, let alone published – all to do with accountants and the cult of 'celebrity'. "If you were Madonna," he said, "I could get you a deal on your new book by the end of the day, and it would make a fortune." He asked me to send an outline of *Dark Moon*. "Write the book of that first," he said. "Then when we've found a publisher for it, this one can follow."

I asked does this mean he's willing to represent me.

"Yes," he replied.

I'VE GOT AN AGENT! GOT AN AGENT!! GOT AN AGENT!!!

More than that, this agent is the hero of my youth.

With love and thanks to Lynda. Words just can't express.

Wednesday 11th
Mainly worked through what is now to be the current *Dark Moon* script, incorporating our new director's further notes. The script has somehow managed to become drained of vitality, light and sparkle again till it's merely

functional, without pace, irony, zest or surprise. Some *lovely* business has been scrapped. It's a tough trick, getting it right.

JULY

Sunday 13th

Lynda and Janet (Red and Blonde) are guests on Dave Lee Travis's programme from 9-till-12 this morning on BBC Three Counties Radio. Amazing to hear their voices coming from my set. DLT said "I can't believe this, but you're about to hear 'The White Cliffs of Dover'," (the song he first heard Lynda singing at that craft fair near Tring). And so it was, among many other splendid things.

Met Lynda after the broadcast and we drove to the coast on this sunbright day, she in wraparound sarong that kept unwrapping as she excitedly talked, showing shapely bare legs. Can this radio appearance lead anywhere? Later, a barefoot walk on the dazzle-wet beach, tide way out, Toby the cavalier spaniel hurtling around in delight and lying on his back, legs kicking in glee. Then a pint at the Bull, full moon rising. It keeps me relatively sane while *Dark Moon* continues to stutter, whimper to silence, then rage into action again.

What *was* that wink of John Irvin's about?

Tuesday 22nd

Lynda gutsing by necessity into the care homes circuit. The pay's not good but she genuinely feels for the folks she sings for. And me, who would rival a mouse when it comes to public speaking, found myself today, extremely nervously, my booming voice on the speaker an embarrassing shock, introducing her on microphone as "The girl with the russet hair and golden larynx." I even told a joke about the bloke in the army surplus store unable to find the camouflage jackets.

Later, at a table in the Rising Sun as I supped an ale, she held my hand and softly sang 'My Funny Valentine'. It would be easy to invent such moments, with Lynda I don't have to.

Tuesday 5th

In sundrenched Dorset by the sea with Lynda and family and dog. They say it could go up to 100F and more tomorrow – hottest weather ever recorded here.

Tuesday 12th

> **From: Barrie Saint Clair**
> **To: Rob Squire**
> **Date: 12 August 2003**
> **Subject: La Miss**
>
> **Good news Rob,**
> **Last night confirmed a deal for me to produce your La Miss to start shooting in April with John Irvin directing. I've pulled his credits off the net and he has done plenty although I don't know him myself, perhaps you do?**
> **Your fee is as agreed but you might just have to throw in a rewrite (with the director I suppose) but I said yes on your behalf.**
> **I will try to get some money upfront as soon as I can, I may even have to come to London for a meeting.**
> **Best, Barrie**

I stared incredulously at the email just received. Then stared some more. So, at the time we met, John Irvin had already read and agreed to direct my screenplay of *La Miss*. *This* was what that wink was about, he thought I knew. No wonder he wants to start *Dark Moon* by November – he should just about finish post-production by the time he's due to start filming *La Miss* in the Kalahari Desert.

> **Hi Barrie**
> **This is totally amazing. John Irvin is to direct 'Dark Moon'. It's a long story, but this script was taken out of my hands for a while, so the version John will direct - of**

which I touched up the final draft - isn't as good as previously. However, it's going to be made and that's all that matters I suppose. I only got to meet him fairly recently.

But, hell, isn't this great news?? You've done us proud! Let's keep the aspidistra flying and the action on the go.

SEPTEMBER

Monday 1st

John Irvin's latest film *The Boys from County Clare* is getting good press in America, which will enhance his profile for *Dark Moon*. And for *La Miss* too – though Cat doesn't know about that yet, and John and I have yet to refer to it.

'He who awaits much can expect little,' says Gabriel Garcia Marquez in my diary today.

Thursday 11th

Was at a gig in East London with Lynda this afternoon when I picked up the call from Jeffrey Simmons on my mobile and went into the reception area to talk. He said he's just had a meeting with Cat and Fons Verhoeven about an Associate Producer fee for the masses of unpaid additional writing I've been called on to do. It seems to have been quite a bloody affair, with Fons insisting I wasn't worth more that £15,000 extra for this. Jeffrey managed to push him up to £25,000, and with that I must be content. There appears to have been some robust speaking, with Fons piping up with "We don't like his dialogue" and "Cat has had to do a great amount on the script re-writing his work." Hence the low fee offered by Cat's Belgian champion, who is clearly still of the opinion that I can't write at all and that Cat could be a contender for an Academy Award.

Jeffrey stuck to his guns and began firing back. He defended my dialogue, saying he published my first novel and the dialogue was one of his reasons for accepting the book. He then said the ex-gratia payments Cat has given me on various occasions to write rescue drafts should be waived, and not set against my writer's fee as she'd planned but absorbed by the £2000 of my original £52,000 fee. To this Cat agreed. Jeffrey then said my new combined fee of £75,000 should be paid in two halves – the first on pre-production, the second on principal photography. They agreed.*

*As Jeffrey said at the time, the film business is like "swimming in muddy water." Only the music business, he reckons, is nastier ('where there's a hit there's a writ'). Glad I don't write songs, then.

Tuesday 14th
Driven by Cat to John Irvin's house, early afternoon. She rang the bell and out he came looking fed up, as if just woken. We sat in his lounge again, but this time I did most of the talking, explaining why I've restored various vital story elements. He gave me time and listened with respect (though still no mention was made of his involvement with *La Miss*). Left the latest draft of *Dark Moon* with him.

Thursday 16th
Visited Jeffrey Simmons in his St John's Wood office. Delightful to see him after all this time. We chatted like survivors from another era brought together by some miracle in the here-and-now. Jeffrey is keen on *La Miss* – an amazing story that will make great cinema. The commander of the Free French/Foreign Legion at Bir Hakeim in 1942 was General Pierre Koenig, and Jeffrey knew him well when he lived in the south of France. Once the film gets going, Jeffrey is sure he can get me a commission to write the book.

Wednesday 17th
Fons Verhoeven has sent a version of *Dark Moon* (let me try and guess which version) to American casting director Meg Liberman, still banging on about getting Hugh Grant for 'Bryce'. But Meg isn't too struck by what she's read. "I like it but don't love it," is how she cautiously put it – a polite way of saying it stinks like a garlic-chewing polecat (said my friend). But which draft has Ms Liberman read?

Saturday 20th
A terrific day on the re-restoration of *Dark Moon*, virtually reaching the

end. Good to know that Casting are waiting for *this* script – let's hope Fons hasn't got any other tricks up his sleeve. Made sure by emailing the result direct to Meg Lieberman myself.

Friday 26th

Was already up when Cat phoned around 7 a.m. – to say I should be the first to know that the American casting *do* love the new version of *Dark Moon*. She sounded so excited. Came back later with one or two notes from them, which I quickly applied.

Still no word from John Irvin about directing *La Miss*. The whole thing's starting to feel a bit odd, and I feel reluctant to mention it to him until we can get together for an unencumbered talk.

Lynda had never given up the prospect of making her group 'Red Hot & Blonde' an ongoing reality. Andy Eastwood was running a weekly ad in The Stage *for his solo act, and working as support to the likes of Ken Dodd, The Krankies, Danny la Rue and Ronnie Ronalde the whistling virtuoso of yesteryear. He and his dad Walt had finally finished putting together the group's CD in June, titled* Running Wild, *and Michael Vine remained keen on managing them. But Andy's constant non-availability meant that no gigs happened, apart from rare ones generated by Lynda (and once by myself).*

I introduced Lynda to Cat, who was wonderfully helpful and supportive. I'll always thank Cat for that kindness. The group played at a party she organised at her house, and went down a storm. Michael Vine made the trip to Barnes and remained enthusiastic to manage 'Red Hot & Blonde'. Yet Andy still said no, no doubt for his own perfectly good reasons.

However, during the summer Lynda had sent the group's CD to Decca Records, and was overwhelmed on getting a phone call from Jackie Schroer, who headed the 'crossover' section of the recording giant. Ms Schroer said she liked the sound and, assuming they were working in the corporate sector, asked to see them in performance.

With Andy otherwise engaged with his brilliant virtuoso solo act, the group had no venues to perform at, but this was too good to let pass. So Lynda and I went out one hot afternoon canvassing restaurants and other likely venues. Most turned down the idea of live music, even for free. But Brown's Restaurant *on Kew Green (now* The Botanist*) were hearteningly helpful. The group was allotted a space to* *play unpaid to the diners, and a date set for September 29th. Jackie Schroer was invited, and promised to be along (Decca's office was just up the road in Chiswick). Andy was great, agreeing to join them on the chance of securing a recording contract, so everything was still possible – or so it seemed. Here's what happened:*

Monday 29th
To Lynda's for 4-ish, cerulean weather. She looked sensational in clingy velvet dress, sister Nicola looking nifty too. Picked up my good friend David Alexander, who lives round the corner in Golders Green, and we all drove down to Kew together.

Andy Eastwood arrived with his dad Walt. Into Brown's Restaurant and set up the sound. Around 6.30 'our' people began arriving – friends a-plenty, including Debi, then Michael Vine himself, highly personable as always. Perhaps strangely, Cat and her friends and associates, although invited, didn't make it. Nor did Robert Young, who lived just across the Green and had said he would be there. The restaurant filled, and diners were surprised to realise they were to be entertained. Towards seven o'clock a very dishy young woman came in, with a youngish trendy male. It was Jackie Schroer from Decca, and her escort was Mark Cavell, influential record producer.

At 7 p.m. 'Red Hot & Blonde' came on. They looked, sounded and were sensational. I've never heard them perform so well – Lynda's soaring voice and uke, Andy's explosive ukulele-banjo, Janet's extraordinary accordion and swinging saxophone. The energy that came off them filled the place and threatened to burst the windows. At one point Andy grabbed his violin and moved about, playing like the prodigy he is. They were fantastic, amazing, the whole restaurant was roaring, Michael Vine their hot showbiz manager was on his feet clapping and stomping.

Afterwards, Mark Cavell★ came up to Lynda, very enthused, and said (quote) "That was just terrific. Exciting! Full of energy! Loved it!" Meanwhile Michael Vine spoke to Jackie Schroer, who said she was impressed, and that she understood the group is to appear in a forthcoming film – meaning *Dark Moon* (Lynda had mentioned it). Clearly Ms Schroer was intrigued by that, and by them. As was Mark Cavell. Excitement was high. Andy himself had had a ball, Michael Vine bought drinks all round and stayed to celebrate what must surely have been a highly successful recording audition, departing late in a taxi. I have never seen Lynda so utterly happy. Tonight 'Red Hot & Blonde' were a triumph. Absolutely anything can happen now!

One of the diners that evening was a QC by the name of Charon who runs a lively website on legal matters which encompasses other subjects that take his interest. On the morning of September 30th this review appeared online:

> To Brown's in Kew (a particular favourite of mine) last night with an old acquaintance – a solicitor, as it happens, which allowed me to put the entire evening down to detailed legal research.
>
> Half of the restaurant had been taken over by a group called 'Red Hot & Blonde'. They were auditioning for the people at Decca. Their short set was superb – a mix of Jazz meets George Formby. Ukuleles were played frenetically. The violin of Andy Eastwood was precise and brilliant and when Janet Beale played the accordion – exceptional. Lynda Styan's voice, rounded and rich, filled the restaurant. As with all good things, they stopped leaving the audience wanting more. I hope Decca sign them. I gather that they are available for corporate events and can be contacted through their website, the eponymous Michael Vine. I was mildly over refreshed and muttered something to him about writing a piece about the group. His eyes sparkled. He asked me what I was drinking. I said I would contact him on the morrow – which I did.

And there, at the height of their collective brilliance, 'Red Hot & Blonde' froze to silence forever. Their first gig having been onstage at the London Palladium to a packed and enthusiastic house, this was only their fifth public outing. But Andy remained adamant about going his own way, for his own no doubt perfectly sound reasons. So, with no group to manage, Michael Vine went on to ever greater success with fresh acts to nurture to stardom; with no group to sign up, Decca fell away. Incredibly, that seminal performance by Lynda's dynamic group was to be their last.

*Mark Cavell had wanted to see 'Red Hot & Blonde' again, said their sound was "unique". I believe he would have signed them (as he'd signed the likes of Russell Watson) and put songwriters to work to create their first album. Lynda did try to find a replacement for Andy, but none could come anywhere near matching that extraordinarily chemistry the three of them had onstage. So that, sad to say, was the end of it. I believe Andy still has a few Running Wild CDs for sale on his website, so any who fancy hearing how the real 'Red Hot & Blonde' once sounded can check in at www.andyeastwood.com and I'm sure he'll be able to find one.

2004

Tuesday 10th

It's incredible how it drags on, as if a giant brake has been applied to my life. Meanwhile John Irvin looks increasingly shaky as director for *Dark Moon* as the delays continue – with *La Miss* on hold so I never got to talk to him about it.

Cat is now at odds with Fons, who continues to await confirmation of 50% funding from a Brussels bank and has stopped returning her calls (again). Looks like it could drag on till June. Feel I'm stuck on a merry-go-round without the 'merry' bit.

'Better to remain silent and be thought a fool than to speak out and remove all doubt.' Abraham Lincoln on today's diary page.

Friday 20th

Email from Barrie – he's blaming 'Black Tuesday', the withdrawal of tax shelter facilities for film investors in Britain on February 10th, on the non-payment of my advance for *La Miss*. Barrie said Philippe Martinez has dropped a film for this year so will be making only 3 – one of which is *La Miss*, which he will now direct himself, and is in talks with MGM about. So what happened to John Irvin?

MARCH

Saturday 27th

Took Lynda to Cat's party at Barnes as she was going on to a gig in nearby Wimbledon to perform with the saxophone player from The Temperance Seven – her hair curled to the shoulders, fawn spangled bodice and those pale pants with floppy flares.

Denise Cotton came over, gave me a Continental-style kiss. Fons Verhoeven was there too, in London 'for meetings'. Also, rather to my surprise, was John Irvin with his BBC director look. He said "Hello, my dear," to me and shook my hand, yet seemed remote, as if unsure quite what he was doing there, guarded by a coterie of confidantes. We still haven't mentioned *La Miss*, and I don't suppose we ever will now.

Lynda and I had to leave around 5. Denise seemed intrigued by her, and Fons was no doubt puzzling over what such a woman is doing with a talentless no-hoper who has to have his work rewritten by Cat. I asked Denise and Fons, when they were standing together, whether they could both now raise 50% of the *Dark Moon* budget. Each said ringingly: "Yes!"

Wednesday 31st

Barrie Saint Clair has spoken to Lucky 7's accountant about the advance for *La Miss*, waiting for publication of the British Treasury's latest 'rules' on film funding on April 5th *. Not till then can monies be released. Jeffrey Simmons wasn't impressed by this latest stall.

*   * Film-makers have welcomed the new tax credit scheme introduced in the Budget to help the British film industry. Sir Alan Parker, chairman of the UK Film Council, described it as "a significant step forward". The new scheme replaces a tax loophole that was closed suddenly earlier this year, threatening a number of productions.*

*   The new tax credit will support new UK films with a budget of up to £15 million, and will be introduced after the current film tax relief system, Section 48, expires in July 2005. No time limit has been placed on the scheme.*

*   Sir Alan Parker called for the scope of the new tax credit to be extended to distribution as well as production. "This," he said, "will provide a major boost to the UK film industry, helping to ensure that many more people get the chance to see British films both at home and abroad."*

Extract from Writers' Bulletin, *April/May 2004*

MAY

Saturday 1st

'On the first of May it is moving day, Spring is here so blow your job, throw your job away' wrote Lorenz Hart. If writing can be called my job, it seems to have thrown *me* away and trusted to its wanderlust. Shall I ever see it again?

No improvement in the lousy weather – a bit like everything else really. The silence is like a great weight. If it weren't for Lynda… What can I say about that sweet, feisty, gentle, compassionate, fiery, vulnerable, gutsy, infuriating, adorable lady with her flashes of fire and brio and moments of immense tenderness? Went to her place for 4 o'clock, out she came bonny and willowy in new jeans. To the National Film Theatre at Waterloo and saw Diana Dors in *Value For Money* (1955). On the way back in the car Lynda played a recording she's made of herself singing to the torch song disc. It was 'I'm In The Mood For Love', sung in a way I've never heard before, using her lower register – as if in a smoky cocktail lounge on a smoochy dance-floor. That style suits her so well. Jackie Schroer at Decca knew Lynda had something special, but never heard her like this. If only…

Thursday 27th

Now they're about to get rid of John Irvin on *Dark Moon*! He's been "very difficult," said Cat. Meaning his agent is wanting large sums of money up front – and he couldn't do *Dark Moon* till next March anyway. The money's still in place, Cat said, but further delays will lose it. So who's delaying?

'I wish people who have trouble communicating would just shut up,' says Tom Lehrer on my diary page today.

JUNE

Tuesday 1st

A new month. Rarely have I felt so utterly wretched about the prospects in my life. Always before there seemed to be some kind of hope, but today that had all drained away. Looks like the magazine journalism work, that's kept me ticking over for so long, is drying up too. What then?

'The mass of men lead lives of quiet desperation.' – Henry David Thoreau (1817 – 1862) on today's diary page.

Tuesday 2nd

Cat rang and changed my day. To keep the funding in place *Dark Moon* MUST be made this year, she said. So John Irvin is off the picture, and a new director urgently needed. ICM were demanding £20,000 up front and the rest of his fee in escrow (he's already had £5000 – more than I've had in my entire time on this film). So it looks like all systems (instead of cisterns) go again, and I discussed with Cat how to fix one or two anomalies some German reader picked up on (how I hate know-it-all German readers who think they speak English better than like what you or me does).

Monday 7th

Drove down Abbey Road past the EMI recording studios and over the Beatles' zebra crossing, perfect weather, and thought this could be a key moment in my life, driving into St John's Wood to my literary agent's office to talk to a film producer keen to make a film of mine.

Jeffrey Simmons welcomed me in and we chatted till the time arranged to phone Philippe Martinez of Lucky 7. On he came, wants he and me to talk revisions on *La Miss*. Made an appointment for next Monday p.m. at his office.

I then put Philippe on to Jeffrey, who did a revised deal: £5000 immediately to option the rights, £7000 for the 'rewrite', £75,000 on principal photography. "A good morning's work," said a smiling Jeffrey.

Tuesday 8th

Cat asked Jeffrey can he suggest a director to replace John Irvin. He said his nephew David Van Eyssen is a gifted director who made a film in South Africa last year. So I emailed a *Dark Moon* script to David's agent in Beverly Hills.

Cat forwarded a crit from Universal sent to Denise Cotton several weeks ago – I'd never seen it before.

> **From: Denise Cotton**
> **To: Fons Verhoeven, Cat Frome**
> **Date: 21 April 2004**
> **Subject: Dark Moon script**
>
> **Here are some comments from Focus Features/**

Universal re our script:

"A gripping script. The pacing is excellent and the writer sustains the levels of tension and suspense throughout. There are some genuinely frightening moments and I liked the Victorian aspects of the narrative which worked well with the contemporary setting. I wasn't entirely convinced by the final reveal as I did not think that enough hints were given throughout the script to arrive at these revelations."

Who was 'the writer', and which version? It's easier not to ask, but it sounded like a much earlier one. Now, if only, at the time, someone had said...

Thursday 17th

Cat in a state about directors. David van Eyssen (she says) wants to rewrite the entire script and take weeks over it*. So really (she said) he's eliminated himself. John Hough in his white suit and bangles, who Cat saw with Denise yesterday, was 'depressingly wrong' for the project (they thought). The only other contender is Gordon Truscott – a friend of friends of Cat – who is dropping another film to concentrate on *Dark Moon* – yet Denise Cotton won't even see him because she doesn't think he's right as he's known exclusively as a horror director.

As I never got to talk with David about this I have no idea whether his intention was to write his own version of Dark Moon. *The impression I got from his Uncle Jeffrey was that he was keen to talk to the writer and work on a fresh script, incorporating ideas of his own. Which would have been fine – if only (again)...*

Monday 21st

Phoned Lucky 7 to confirm my meeting with Philippe Martinez at 4 p.m. today to discuss the director's draft of *La Miss*. Travelled into London to their address at 53 Frith Street at the time appointed – and walked into an otherwise empty office to be told by the only person there – a young Aussi – that Philippe had gone home because he had suddenly felt 'very ill'. In that moment I felt 'very ill' too.

And that was the end of it. I later learned that Martinez's lawyer had warned him off at the last moment because of 'possible legal complications' re the biographical book Susan Travers had had ghost-written – even though my script had been cleared by lawyers as being based entirely on material in public domain.

Tuesday 29th

Cat rang with a load of fresh revisions on *Dark Moon* following a "long script discussion" she's just had with director Gordon Truscott. Felt dismay. Is it worth hanging on? Yes, because I have a contract that will clear me of all financial problems and set me up for the future with one fell swoop the moment this film gets made – in whatever form, or however bad, that turns out to be. So I have to hang on, or be in breach of contract and lose the lot.

'Experience is a good teacher, but she sends in terrific bills.' Minna Antrim on today's diary page.

Wednesday 30th

Quaffed an ale with Peter Jaques at the Queen's Head, Pinner, made him laugh like a drain as I outlined the latest goings-on on *Dark Moon*. I do puzzle why Cat sends me Gordon's revisions to implement, rather than doing them herself, and wonder if she's aware how incredibly irksome it is for me to be called on like this to apply changes I may disagree with but am given no right of consultation about. Is this why Gordon talks script exclusively with Cat, in case I might challenge him? Yet the result of that might enhance the screenplay. Peter says the ideal is to be a writer-director, so when a script meeting's called you only have yourself to argue with.

JULY

Wednesday 14th

The (latest latest) revised *Dark Moon* is urgently needed, but Cat won't talk to my agent about some upfront money. I know how tedious this asking for money must seem to her, but we're at the point where the film could collapse unless I do something.

So, for the greater good (as I see it), opened a new version of *Dark Moon* and began the building, healing and restoring for the umpteenth time. Worked late into the evening, feeling some of the roughness smoothing – but it's like shoring up a sandcastle till the next tide comes in.

Friday 16th

Amongst other things Cat let slip in our conversation this morning is that Fons has included in director Gordon Truscott's deal letter a sum of $10,000 – in addition to his director's fee of $300,000 (!) – to write his own 'script polish'. Which is precisely what I'm engaged on at the moment for no money at all. Does Fons think I don't have the wit to talk to the director to tease out his thoughts and apply them? What a vile insult to any writer this man is.

To my huge surprise, this afternoon Jeffrey Simmons rang to say that Cat has just phoned him, and he asked for £5000 advance on my screenwriting fee for my work on the (latest) revisions. This thought alone made me set to with new vigour, romping through rewritten/new scenes, bringing back subtlety and dimension, new light and colour to a savaged script.

Then Cat rang and said she "might have trouble" finding the £5000, but that if the script is ready by Monday to let her have it "on trust," adding that Fons is away till Tuesday so she won't be able to "talk to him" about the payment till then.

I couldn't help laughing, and wished Cat could see the heap of bills on my table waiting with increasing urgency to be paid. Jeffrey said to let him know when the script is ready and not to hand it over till some money has changed hands.

Sunday 18th

Worked steadily till gone 8 p.m., incorporating Gordon Truscott's notes and ideas and enlivening turgid scenes, clunky sequences and dialogue which have, like an infestation of poisonous fungus, found their way back into this script. No wonder Demi Moore turned it down – so would I have done and I'm not as pretty as her. Worst thing is, my name's on the cover again – now as 'co-writer'. The thought of it chills my bones.

Thursday 22nd

Rang Cat and reminded her (again) that my new draft of *Dark Moon* is ready, and my agent has asked me not to release it until at least a portion of the advance he negotiated with her is paid. She said that she/they "couldn't possibly afford" to pay me anything at all – so as I was being so difficult she was putting a draft together *herself*. Hello, this sounds familiar, have I had an attack of déjà-vu?

'If you're going through hell, keep going.' – *Sir Winston Churchill, on today's diary page.*

Friday 23rd

Woke in the early hours deeply troubled about my financial future. Finally drifted off, to be woken by the phone at 7.15 a.m. It's Cat. She told me that Gordon Truscott *has already written his own draft* of *Dark Moon* (no doubt encouraged by the $10,000 offered by our Belgian producer in the deal letter). This explained, of course, why Cat so staunchly resisted paying me for an alternative version. But why did she tell me she was writing her own version (again)?

While I assimilated this simultaneous double kick in guts and groin, Cat emailed me Truscott's version of *Dark Moon*, which I read not so much with interest as with appalled fascination. It's formatted American style, and mainly he's embellished the ending, making it hard-nosed and wham-bammish with a strong tang of horror rather than thriller-with-supernatural. And he's thrown out the entire point of the story while writing in these new scenes. Also, to my continuing surprise, Denise Cotton has already put in her remarks about this 'new script' and made her own amendments.

So while I was slogging away to create THE draft, they ALL not only knew that this Truscott version existed, but had each waded through it and added their own thoughts.

Saturday 24th

> **From: Rob Squire**
> **To: Denise Cotton**
> **Sent: 24 July 2004**
> **Subject: Last 20 pages**
>
> **Dear Denise**
> **Have now read what Gordon Truscott has put together, and**

Cat asked me to send you the last 20 pages of this version now going forward. She said you were concerned about it, and I sympathise with your feelings and views.

This is not the kind of film I envisaged when I first came on. Rather, I saw something beautiful, subtle, life-enhancing, with a powerfully moving revelatory ending. But all my attempts to achieve this were scotched by rewrites by others, for reasons I never did understand. In earlier days I wrote Bryce as a charming, witty, charismatic and fun man - so that the sinister changes in him as the film developed were all the more telling. Sadly, all that too was wiped out by others when my back was turned, so all that remains is the 2-dimensional bore Bryce now is.

But I have to accept that Gordon Truscott's ending is more likely to attract a mass audience – even though, storywise, he has thrown out the baby with the bathwater. I would rather this film danced like a fencing master, not plodded like a thug with a bludgeon as it does now - but if this is what sells, and Gordon has powerful contacts in the industry who might help get this film away at last, I'm prepared to go with it.

All best

Rob

Monday 26th

From: Denise Cotton
To: Rob Squire
Date: 26 July 2004
Subject: Last 20 pages

Dear Rob

Between you and me, I am also saddened by the way Bryce is now written. I have been pushing for such a long time that I too wanted Bryce to be exactly what you say he should be, but alas, I also find that he is now a 'boring run of the mill'. Like you, I am not at all happy with many of the changes

Gordon has made to the script, and the profanity that now fouls the mouth of nearly every character. Also, he has put in some blatant steals from other films. I agree with you that in Gordon's version the story now makes no sense. In saying this, I can only presume he has not thought it fully through.

While I will go along with a few things for now, please let me say now Rob, as I have said to Cat, I will not invest $6m in a film I do not believe in. Gordon cannot possibly expect me to approve HIS script, despite his (unsubstantiated) claims that he can come up with some 'names'. I am concerned that if Cat keeps playing along with Gordon as she does, he is going to think that his version is FINAL, which would be disastrous for us all, may I say.

However, my view now is to let things move forward, but part of my deal is that I have approval of the final draft. I most certainly need this for my investors, so I do hope that when it is time to start the finance, all will bode well for everyone. I could write a book about "THE ONGOING SAGA OF DARK MOON"!

Let's try to keep in touch
With kindest regards, Denise

AUGUST

Monday 2nd

Into Richmond Park with Lynda after she sang at a care home nearby. Such sweetness and lissome power, russet ringlets and merry grin. Summer and warm, the ferns so high this time of year no one can see and we took full advantage.

There's a heron at the pond near Ham Gate. We sat on a seat afterwards, watching it perch on its branch then swoop around the water on broad wings as if to say this is all mine, and the madness of *Dark Moon* dispersed like smoke into the azure sky. I like the word azure, corny as a cat on speed but more fun than blue, which can also describe sea, or eyes, or films, or emotion. Azure can only be sky.

Saturday 21st

On the coast with Lynda and her family for a brief holiday and thank heaven for credit cards. At the guesthouse I caught the Final of the Coxless Fours at the Athens Olympics – a terrific race with the British crew, led by Matthew Pinsent, winning the Gold from Canada. The medal ceremony was very emotional, with the powerhouse Pinsent breaking into tears. A good start to anyone's day – unless you're Canadian.

Tuesday 24th

Still trying not to brood about *Dark Moon* and follow the Olympic Games in Athens. Delighted to see on the guesthouse TV not only Seb Coe (now a lord), but Steve Ovett, talking with fellow-athlete (now presenter) Steve Cram. The once-dazzling Ovett is now quite bald, a bit saggy and jowly – but it was he rather than Coe who was my favourite in their competition days, surging into an unbeatable sprint on the final bend like pressing the accelerator of a high-powered car, waving airily and grinning as he ripped through the tape.

Saturday 28th

Jumping up and down in the Dorset guesthouse on hearing that Kelly Holmes has WON the 1500 metres Gold Medal at Athens to add to her Gold in the 800 metres – the first British woman ever to win the double. Totally amazing, the stuff of legends. In the playback Kelly's face shows astonishment and the dawning of the most stupendous delight. This news made my day, and suggests that all things really are possible if only you keep on trying and believing (and if you believe that you'll believe anything).
FANTASTIC.

Sunday 29th

The men's Olympic marathon this afternoon, but the ladies want to shop in Arundel while dad Peter stays with the TV. So there we went under black skies, an Irish band playing, people everywhere. Bank holiday weekend. At a little craft fair I buy Lynda an eggcup with a face like a cat. I didn't know she likes cats, it enchants her. When *Dark Moon* happens I'll buy her a litter of them. I *know* it will happen now – somehow, sometime, somewhere. Kelly Holmes has inspirited me.

An Italian called Stefano Baldini won the marathon. The young Brit Indian boxer, Amil Khan, was outpointed in the lightweight final, got Silver, put up a terrific fight. This evening I ran Lynda, Nicola and mum Joan to Littlehampton. The river was unusually high, flowing fast and choppy. Drove back by the sea, full moon in a clear sky making brilliant the surgy water.

In the Olympics closing ceremony at Athens Kelly Holmes carried the British flag. A brave and good note on which to end this holiday.

Now back to reality…

SEPTEMBER

Monday 13th

Cat on the phone telling me how our Belgian producer is being "rude" to everyone, agents included (well, agents won't notice, being rude themselves as a default mode), and now the Belgian bank he hopes to raise production money from has delayed its decision by another week. Cat dear, ever since this man got on to *Dark Moon* by 'far preferring' your script, and we've had all these directors and agents, actors and actresses, one after the other and sometimes collectively, turning down our increasingly compromised project, with me consigned to the furthermost outfield never to be spoken to, let alone consulted, this project has been cursed.

Tuesday 14th

Blustery and getting cooler – and not only the weather. We now learn – NOW, mind you – that Fons Verhoeven's elusive €6 million from the Belgian bank is conditional on stars being in place 'as is the case with all independent productions'. Er… yes? Today Joseph Fiennes is reading for 'Bryce'. Ha ha. Filming now is more likely for January '05, with pre-production in November. Trouble is, the part of Bryce has been reduced to a piece of woodwork so no actor will take it. Same goes for all the other parts now, including (even more heartbreakingly) 'Laura'. If only they would ask the humble, overlooked writer to fix it I could make the roles stand up again, but they never do because they believe the script is great the way it is now that it's been 'fixed' by whosoever it/they might be and I'm afraid I've forgotten or never knew.

'Life is a matter of passing the time enjoyably. There may be other things in life, but I've been too busy passing my time enjoyably to think very deeply about them.' Peter Cook on today's diary page.

Friday 18th
To the Reform Club on Pall Mall in London this evening, invited by Peter Jaques who is a member and on the committee. Phileas Fogg began and ended his journey round the world in 80 days from these hallowed premises in Jules Verne's vivid narrative. I got done up in tuxedo and bow tie, Lynda looking like the recipient of a major award at the Oscars in shimmering silver-and-white figure-clinging dress with matching high heels and clutch-bag, Titian hair curled and brightly flowing. It's another world in there, the food and drink melt on the tongue, urbanity and wit sparkle around the tables. "It'll do you both good," Peter said. It did indeed, Lynda's eyes shone like lamps as she drank the refined ambience in and dreamed that money was flowing through our lives so that evenings such as this could be the norm rather than such a treasured rarity. Thanks, Peter.

Tuesday 21st
Fons Verhoeven has sent Cat and Denise Cotton a strange message expressing bewilderment as to why all the 'names' are passing on this project. If he ever bothered to speak to me I could tell him.

> **From: Fons Verhoeven**
> **To: Cat Frome, Denise Cotton**
> **Date: 21 September 2004**
> **Subject: Food for thought...**
>
> **Dear Cat and Denise,**
> **Why is happening oh what is happening...???**
> **I have been contemplating, thinking, dreaming, night and day**
> **during the last many weeks, to try comprehend what is happening, and I know well that most of the time, if not constantly, it is extremely difficult or impossible to have cast attached to a movie.**

Why have once more so many passed on this film, and why is it others do not come back with even a reply...? i.e. Even Emily Mortimer...no reply, Daniel Craig, who has no job at this moment * *(* Yes, I know!)*, saying no, Olivier Martinez why is he also passing...

When asking to many people, the question always come back...: "Gordon Truscott is very much related to horror-movies, why is he chosen by you? Why does he do it...?"

Could this confuse the cast we approached so far, because all those actors is NOT into horror, could it be they do not want to involve with a "horror film director"...? Is the image of the director working against the film we would like to make and deliver, is his image working against "quality-actors" and "quality-actresses"...?

Is it that the package (script-director-budget) is just not suitable to interest this A-level cast ?

At what time are we going to, OR having to decide to make smaller our ambitions...? Could it be that, in spite of the positive responses, we still have a problem with the script*?

An innocent reader lately made the remark:

"I have a problem, because in the script is a continuous change of perspective, from Laura, to Bryce, back to Laura & Grimstone, back on Bryce, etc... And, when one learns to know a bit about Laura, the script is focusing on Bryce...and as an audience, you are asked to follow Bryce, but why would one have sympathy for Bryce...? And this is happening at the wrong time...so it is unclear for the audience who should be followed, with as result, that one always has a distant emotional link with both Laura and Bryce...Why is it not possible to completely focus on Laura, so that the complete audience is emotional linked with Laura, all the time, always..."

Can it be that actors-actresses have the same "feeling"...?

So, Cat & Denise, again, as mentioned, it is because we are in this situation, which is becoming confusing, because I am confused, that we have to completely re-think about this,

talk about this, maybe share our problems with Gordon Truscott, have a strategy...
DON'T MISCOMPREHEND ME !!!! I AM NOT LEAVING THE SHIP, ON THE CONTRARY, BUT THE FUEL IS AT THIS MOMENT NOT IN ACCORDANCE WITH THE SIZE OF THE BOAT.
Best regards, Fons

*Sympathetic to Fons though I perhaps ought to be on re-reading this rather odd message (again addressed solely to Cat and Denise), my feeling is that the reaper was only reaping what he had sown. Having dismissed the original writer in preference to Cat as the screen-scribe on this project, he was possibly puzzled why I was still floating around his 'ship' like a sour ghost.

I can only say, Fons, that if you hadn't 'far preferred' a possibly-promising-but-nonetheless amateur version of this script to a professionally crafted one in order to ease your way on to this project almost three years before, this film might have already been made and doing well at the time you sent this plaintive message.

You asked why so many were now 'passing' on the present Dark Moon. But all the problems you specify in the above email had already been dealt with in the script you regarded as inferior to Cat's. The question 'whose story is this?' is elementary to any writer approaching a script. It's Laura's, of course – always was – but the balance between the characters had by now become so confused and distorted by the input of others over the last 3 or 4 years that it would have required my working on the screenplay without interference to bring everything back into balance – as I offered Cat to do but was declined because she thought it unnecessary. So I had to sit back and watch the Dark Moon bus rumble on past me towards the gaping hole in the road just round the corner.

Hope the driver spots it in time. Who's the driver? You tell me.

Friday 24th
'Sometimes the appropriate response to reality is to go insane.' – Philip K. Dick on today's diary page.

This quotation intrigued me, because on last night's TV I caught A Beautiful Mind with Russell Crowe as Nobel prize-winning mathematician John Nash, who suffered from paranoid schizophrenia. The thought bugged me that I too could be suffering from a delusional disorder in believing that I can write. Could the reality be that I'm actually a lousy writer who only *thinks* he's any good? With Fons turning and tossing his nights and days away wondering what's still wrong with the script, can the truth be that my early drafts of *Dark Moon* really were so bad that Cat was right to have me rewritten again and again (including letting her non-writer lawyer pal have a go at the whole thing, then taking over the writing herself)?; that Denise Cotton was right to bring in that Hollywood scribe to rework me completely (with negative results)?; that Fons was right in 'far preferring' Cat's draft to what I'd thought was my own carefully crafted piece of screenwriting? Have I given up my life for nothing more than a delusion so strong – like John Nash's – that I believed in it totally but must now wake up if I'm to save my sanity – or am I already insane and don't know it?

Saturday 25th

Cat has received a forwarded email from Fons offering Olivier Martinez the part of Bryce in *Dark Moon* at $3 million (!). And his agent has accepted. So we have our main male lead, do we? But (shyly puts up hand) excuse me, er, isn't that more than half the budget of the entire film? Well, it's not for me to say, must leave this sort of stuff to the experts. But Gordon Truscott is querying the validity of this too, I'm told.

'If you sometimes feel depressed or let down, if you're suffering from the pressures of life, or simply having a plain old grey day, my advice is to roast a chicken.' Quote by Delia Smith on today's diary page.

Went out and bought a chicken.

Thursday 30th

Cat suggests that she and I should get together next week to enhance the script by 'going through it very slowly'. Well it's nice to be asked, but I don't think so – it would be like walking through a haunted graveyard with cadavers rising on every side. Doesn't she know it doesn't work that way? Not for me it doesn't, anyway (shambles off into undergrowth, muttering).

OCTOBER

Monday 4th

Script meeting for 11 a.m. in Soho tomorrow. I was genuinely surprised to (a) be told about it, (b) be invited, so routine has this sidelining of the writer become.

Tuesday 5th

Arrived at the address on Meard Street just before 11. Cat was already there, looking surprisingly nervy. We went up together to the 4th floor in the lift, an editing suite. Gordon Truscott arrived – so *at last* I get to meet my (?) director – quite short and stocky, 50ish and losing his hair, which is black with grey strands where the scalp hasn't taken over and decided to broaden its territory, face somewhat like that of an ancient pharaoh, olive complexion, lips thick and sensuous, expression spoiled and autocratic. He could be crouched on the floor yet still appear to be looking down his nose at you. I wouldn't want to cross this man, meet him in a dark alley or see him on the arm of my daughter. He's made a fair number of movies of a certain genre, some good, some very good. Written them too. He's good at what he does, and knows it. He blinked tetchily at me, unsure who I was or whether he cared. Then in came Michael Weymouth the production designer – a grey-head of the old school who also looked at me as if to say 'who the fuck are you?' Me? – only someone without whom none of you lot would have a film to discuss, pal.

After we sat down I brought up several vital elements now lacking in the script since the director's rewrites. Truscott looked surprised. "Oh yes," he said vaguely, "put that back in." He then told off Cat for having herself deleted, without discussion, what he considered to be some important lines of his own (I could almost hear Cat thinking 'Oops, sorry, I thought they were Rob's').

Towards the end of the meeting I asked Truscott will it be okay to include Lynda in the party sequence, to help put colour into the scene as in the current script it needs a lift – pointing out that she's a professional singer, drama-trained. Again he agreed with a vague "Cool."

Wednesday 6th
Another somewhat weird email was forwarded to me by Cat.

> **From: Fons Verhoeven**
> **To: Cat Frome, Denise Cotton**
> **Date: 6 October 2004**
> **Subject: Soap-opera**
>
> **Dear Cat and Denise**
> **I always disliked soap-operas, because they are dealing with betrayal and manipulation...**
> **And so, I also dislike the soap-opera which has Gordon Truscott, Olivier Martinez in the leading parts, with plenty additional roles...**
> **Episode One:**
> **We send a firm offer to the agent of Olivier, and get instant response...but...in the darkest moment of the night, Gordon is calling to question the offer...and the only beneficiary is the telecom-company...**
> **Episode Two:**
> **We send a deal-memo to the agent of Olivier, have a few decent phone calls with the agent, who is responding that they agree with the deal-memo, proposing to move forward with the longform agreement...**
> **but...again...in the darkest moment of the night...the same leading role, performed by Gordon...is creating more panic following a dinner somewhere in a haunted house, questioning the role of the agent of the other leading role, performed by Olivier....**
> **Episode Three:**
> **During the night of Wednesday, October 6.................**
> **Viewers can take part in a game to win a ticket for entering the haunted house by answering the question : who is to be shot tonight?**

After Cat kindly forwarded this on to me, I went through it two or three times. Was the $3 million offer to Olivier Martinez real? This seemed to say yes, yet Fons has raised no money, and won't this hugely inflate the budget? I wasn't surprised to hear that Gordon had questioned it, but this response was something else. Cat says Fons has gone into hospital with a 'muscular condition', though the suggestion is it's a nervous breakdown.

'Any man who goes to a psychiatrist needs his head examined.' Sam Goldwyn *on my diary page today.*

Friday 8th
Drove Lynda to a care home gig at Reigate in Surrey and set up the sound equipment in the lounge. Today I tentatively sang with her in public for the first time, duetting the Gershwins' 'Nice Work If You Can Get It' on the second mike. To my surprise I didn't choke. Fred Astaire did that one in *Damsel In Distress* (1937). I just lo-o-o-o-o-ve old movies. Because scared I phrased the song like Fred did, as if hiding behind his mighty monochrome image. I think it may have helped (you can fool most of the people some of the time…).

Cat called me on my mobile and told me about this morning's production meeting (which I hadn't been told about). Denise Cotton brought with her a possible new producer, Phil Hunt, who was "seriously young" (Cat said). Michael Weymouth was screaming at him, and Gordon Truscott almost walked out when Phil said "my only solution is to sack everyone and start again from scratch" (hey, I *like* this boy…) – including telling Olivier Martinez he can't have $3 million but no more than a third of that, and only then if he's extremely lucky. At the end Phil, overwhelmed by the negativity and abuse of the others, mentioned another producer "who knows the ropes and is available." Cat said she'd like her and me to meet him next week and 'check him out'. His name is Saul Wilson. Felt honoured, if not a little surprised, at this sudden elevation in status.

Monday 11th
With Cat, met Saul Wilson in the Foresters pub at 11.30 a.m. in Hampton Wick. 40ish, relaxed, successful producer of several movies. Over coffee we set about convincing him to come aboard, despite the funding not being in place, notably the money Fons promises to raise from a Belgian

Bank which never comes to fruition and can Saul replace this? Saul said not to worry, he has access to funds from Germany and feels sure he can help.

An hour and a half later we parted with handshakes and smiles. Pleased with ourselves, Cat took me to lunch. With Saul Wilson now on the case, the other 50% to match Denise Cotton's proposed funding could be provided from fresh sources and this film will be away at last.

Tuesday 12th

Saul Wilson is meeting Denise Cotton at Groucho's in Soho today. Pray it all comes together and the money gets sorted. Rang Jeffrey Simmons and told him the latest 'news' – he said he'll believe it when he sees it, being utterly fed up with all this messing about, non sequiturs, interferences, blind alleys, stalls, stoppages, barriers, blockages, stymies, tripwires, bottlenecks, impasses, cul-de-sacs, hindrances, handicaps, obstructions, wipe-outs, strike-outs, bike-outs, freak geeks, moronic meddlers, lie-peddlers, shackles, hackles, stalemates, fail-states, traffic jams, daffy-whams, logjams, encumbrances, stitch-ups, botch-ups, scotch-ups, hold-ups, hang-ups, muck-ups, fuck-ups, hiccups, clog-ups, storms-in-teacups and dead ends on this film.

Tuesday 19th

Such relief to get away on a gig with Lynda. To Mile End Hospital in the East End, driving through all kinds of traffic. Set up in the Robinson Ward for dementia patients. Lynda was a delight, empathising with her audience, half-dancing with one lively woman called Nancy, feeding energy and vitality with every note.

Afterwards we found our way to the nearby preserved Victorian music hall, Hoxton Hall – on the beat my grandfather Harry Floyd when very young once trod as an East End copper, swinging his heavy cape to clout trouble-makers. Now a smiling black girl showed us into the empty hall. High galleries looked down on the little stage once graced by so many legendary feet. Lynda stood up on it and sang 'The Boy I Love Is Up In The Gallery' in her Marie Lloyd voice – which rang unamplified around the walls as the queen of the music hall's voice must once have done here, and brought the amazed girl back in.

164

"Hope you don't mind," said Lynda apologetically.

"Oh no," said the girl, "it's lovely." She stayed and listened with a rapt expression as Lynda sang 'If You Were the Only Boy In the World'. Not a dry eye.

No roughies outside to swing capes at.

Hi Grandad.

Wednesday 20th

Met Saul Wilson at Cat's, and had a discussion re *Dark Moon*. He suggests double-egging the ending by having the seemingly dead 'Grimstone', who has manipulated 'Bryce' all along, getting up and attacking again. Hello? This is a cliché of course (e.g. *Halloween*), but I went along with it for now. A full implementation of Saul's idea will have 'Bryce' innocent all along, instead of psychologically destroyed in childhood and coming good at the end.

For me Saul's idea is a stultifying cop-out, and weakens the role of 'Bryce' and the dynamics of his relationship with 'Laura' even more drastically. However, the only one to talk sensibly about this with is director Gordon Truscott – and he wasn't there, and he only ever talks to Cat anyway, so what's the point of even *thinking* about it?

On today's diary page, by David Mamet: 'A good film script should be able to do completely without dialogue.'

Friday 22nd

Just when I felt things were starting to go right, got a phone call from Cat this morning of chaos and disaster. Saul Wilson has found that the main actors have not had their deals closed financially. So William Hurt (Grimstone) has gone, also Olivier Martinez (Bryce) – and Julia Ormond (Laura) looks about to go too. Denise Cotton was "vilely rude" to Cat on the phone, having received an email from her; Fons is unobtainable by anyone, still possibly languishing in hospital somewhere. So Cat is now keen to switch to a new sales agent, delete Fons and let Saul Wilson take over completely as producer.

From: Cat Frome
To: Denise Cotton
Date: 22 Oct 2004
Subject: Dark Moon

Dear Denise,
Our entire operation is one of absolute chaos. Thank God
Saul is at least professional and efficient.
As producer and creator of this film, I would like to know
whether you are following up on my suggestions and what
the next positive move is to be.
I feel dreadful for my various friends who have trusted me
with their monies and also for leading Gordon Truscott and
his team up the garden path with promises of being fully
funded + false filming dates.
I am absolutely committed to getting this film made come
what may, with a great deal less hindrance and encumbrance.
Cat

To which Denise has spiritedly replied:

From: Denise Cotton
To: Cat Frome
CC: Rob Squire
Date: 22 Oct 2004
Subject: Dark Moon

Dear Cat
What in hell's name is this all about?? Why am I being
attacked like this???
I am extremely angry that you are suggesting it is my fault
that you have led your friends and also Gordon and his
team up the garden path. And that you are committed to
getting this film made with less hindrance and
encumbrance!! How dare you say these things to me. I have
worked hundreds of hours on this film and spent more than

£25,000 of my own money over the last 5 years, all in good faith and trust. How dare you talk to me in this manner.... I just can't carry on with this, I can't tell you how distressed I am with your attitude.
Denise

Saturday 23rd

Oh dear. Looks like the what-not has hit the proverbial. Gordon Truscott has a sales agent contact in America called Keith Bearman who might come on if Denise Cotton blows up. I was surprised and touched that Denise had copied to me her unhappy broadside against Cat's 'chaos' email. Will reply tomorrow. I do have sympathy for Denise – I believe she genuinely cares about this movie.

Meanwhile the man from Ghent continues to be unavailable – and I wonder how much he muddied my name along with Cat's when he and Saul Wilson had drinks at Groucho's the other day. Certainly Saul is no longer responding to Cat's phone calls. And if Saul feels qualified to come in from nowhere and tell me that the story is hopelessly flawed and how to put it right, his opinion of me as a writer can't be any higher than Fons's.

'One is never too old for romance.' Quote by Ingrid Bergman on today's diary page.

Sunday 24th

Thinking it's time to put my head above the parapet again, sent an email to Denise Cotton. On the rare occasions I've spoken to her I've really liked her and felt that here might be a mind to engage with.

From: Rob Squire
To: Denise Cotton
Date: 24 Oct 2004
Subject: Dark Moon

Dear Denise
Thanks for copying to me your response to Cat's email.
Rightly or wrongly, fairly or not, you are seen, with Fons,

as being the two prime movers in raising the funds to make *Dark Moon*. No one questions that you have done your job admirably, and worked supremely hard and consistently in your efforts - with ours - to get this film to happen. You have done all you can, we know, and are continuing so to do.

Cat's email to you simply reflects the extreme frustration and anxiety over the future of this film that we are now all acutely feeling, especially with this latest blow that the lead players who agreed to the roles seem about to fall away because their deals have not been safely sealed.

For even at this incredibly late time, with good professionals working on spec at all hours to help *Dark Moon* reach its intended shooting target in January, the producer who came on board at your instigation, Fons Verhoeven, has still failed to deliver his part of the bargain. It is, I think, your continuing support of this man which has led to Cat's frustration.

Thanks to Cat keeping me informed of what's going on, I'm aware that you, too, share her and our bewilderment as to why Fons continues to deliver nothing. As you know, it is his now deeply worrying pattern of giving plausible promises that lead only to further delays which made it necessary to bring in Saul Wilson, for – again rightly or wrongly - few of us any longer have confidence (except, it seems, you), that Fons will come up with the goods in time. And it's far too late now to simply cross our fingers and hope for the best.

By the by, I managed to get Gordon Truscott's attention for long enough to discuss our great concern that he has deleted vital elements from the script. When I explained what they'd been there for he agreed they should be re-incorporated - though with the current free-for-all on the script I can't guarantee how long they will stay.

With best personal wishes

Rob

Friday 29th

Jeffrey Simmons is marvellous, a calm mind and clear eye, advising and helping and trying to make sense of the tumult. He had a good talk with Cat, persuaded her to give the present set-up a chance to breathe – with Denise Cotton off to the American Film Market with a script revised by me to bring it up to date with our notes, the current team still in place.

NOVEMBER

Wednesday 3rd

George W. Bush is American President for another 4 years. So what else is new and where can I hide?

Wednesday 10th

Was exploring strange blue lights with Lynda in the graveyard by Denham church in the pitch dark when Cat rang my mobile to say Denise Cotton has a distribution deal for *Dark Moon*, which is going well at the American Film Market! She has also found 35% funding from Hungary, which will replace Fons's non-existent Belgian finance. Don't know why I didn't feel more excited, have reached the point where I hardly believe a thing anyone says any more.

Coming closer, we found that the blue lights were little lanterns, each burning by a recent grave. The last place I saw photos of the dear departed was in southern France in blazing sunshine, and found them rather spooky. Now here, vaguely lit in the dim glow, were photos of a lovely girl, a handsome youth, a smiling child... The sadness of it was choking, these young lives cut off, and without their brief term on earth their particular light would not be burning through the blackness on this chill November night and alarm Lynda with its ghostly hovering.

Tuesday 16th

Fons Verhoeven would appear to be back. He now tells Cat that the Belgian 40% hasn't happened because the bank requires pre-sales first, and *Dark Moon* has none (er, did he not know this before?). Also, Fons is keen to drop Denise as sales agent and go with Keith Bearman the production company/sales agent in Los Angeles. So the scene seems in as hopeless a mess as ever.

Denise Cotton being back from the AFM, a meeting is arranged at her place tomorrow with Cat, Saul Wilson and a lady called Kenteas Brine (who claims access to American funding) – to get the money sorted out once and for all. Also, there's a billionaire called Topper who knows Gordon Truscott and might invest in *Dark Moon* too. It all begins to sound like something out of a novel by Thorne Smith.

'The thing about performance, even if it's only an illusion, is that it's a celebration of the fact that we do contain within ourselves infinite possibilities.' Daniel Day-Lewis on today's page of this diary.

Saturday 20th

Cat is now castigating the Denise Cotton/Saul Wilson combo for ganging up and keeping her out of things. Well, as long as they're hitting the right action buttons what does it matter? And it really does looks as if they are; they get on well, it seems. Excellent.

During a chat with my producer friend Debi Nethersole I learn that Denise Cotton is currently perceived as being 'weak' on the international sales scene, the rumour being that she's about to retire. So is this drive for the line with Saul Wilson to be Denise's last hurrah?

Gordon Truscott tells Cat he's made many films, but never has it reached this stage and still the money's not there. Could the rumour about Denise be why investors draw back? She's claiming 10% of the budget for her fee – even with the reduced budget of £5 million it still makes £500,000. My God, with that kind of money I could buy one of those new flats by the river at Kew, marry Lynda and live happily evermore.

Thursday 25th

Lynda's artist sister Nicola is exhibiting her work at a studio on the Harrow Road W9. I really like her 'Self Portrait' – a thumbprint in red done up like a sort of portrait – clever and very appealing. Had a beer and strolled around. The moment I turned my back Lynda was being chatted up by a bearded poet.

Then I took these two flame-haired lovelies to a party at my old mate

Paul Cowan's flat in Holland Park. Amazing to see Paul again, we embraced like long-lost brothers. Met his wife and family, and business partner Chris Wheeldon. Paul's a hot producer and line producer, knows everyone in the business. We had howls from yestergone, memories of beers and birds, Portobello Road on hot Saturdays, Hampstead parties in crammed flats...

Friday 26th
In Denise Cotton's last conversation with Cat before going to Spain on holiday she was pretty dejected with "I just can't see how this film can be made." But according to Cat we potentially have: 42% from Ingenious, 25% via Kenteas Brine, 25% from Hungary, leaving only 8% of budget to find. It put me in mind of a limerick I once heard:

> *A mathematician named Hall*
> *Had a hexahedronical ball*
> *And the cube of its weight*
> *Times two-sevenths, plus eight*
> *Was four-fifths of five-fourths of fuck-all.*

Saturday 27th
American sales agent Keith Bearman is keen to come on *Dark Moon* at once – knows he can 'sell it big'. Cat suggests we see Denise Cotton this week and tell her she's been relegated. Sounds to me more like a way of getting World War 3 to begin.

DECEMBER

Saturday 4th
To the National Film Theatre with Lynda this evening. Watched *Missing Believed Wiped* – rediscovered BBC TV footage from the 1960s: an *Out of the Unknown*, part of a Troy Kennedy Martin play, and an early *Z Cars* written by Alan Plater. We were surprised at how slow-moving they were, and how under-characterised the women – who played wives and/or office functionaries with no strong characters of their own.

Tuesday 7th

Cat wants to go to Thailand for Christmas, but worries about leaving with this film unresolved. She was introduced yesterday to a producer of sorts called Jason Craine, who apparently impressed her with his air of assurance. He insisted on a legal document tying him to *Dark Moon* – upon which he promises to sort out the funding and get rid of the 'dead wood' as he calls it. Denise Cotton might have to go, he declares, and unless Fons Verhoeven does something useful he'll be off too. It's as if Cat is hiring an executioner. But hang on, Saul Wilson's our producer, isn't he?

Looked Craine up on the Internet. Has executive-produced several films – the last one being in 2001. Rang Paul Cowan and asked if he knows this man. "Yes," he said. "He's never produced a film, only been involved with funding." Paul said he'll call a couple of people in the business and get back to me.

Wednesday 8th

Paul Cowan has spoken to producer Nik Powell, also Rodney Payne, about Jason Craine. Word is currently good on this man, he's well-placed to find funding – so it's okay to bring him on as Executive Producer – but on no account sign him as main Producer – he has no hands-on experience of putting a film together.

Finally reached Cat on her mobile in a taxi and told her this. She was pleased to hear that her latest find appears to have access to funds. But I also told her about Paul's warning not to use Craine as a full-on producer, he doesn't have that kind of experience. A glitch cut off our call and we spoke no more.

Friday 10th

Cat phoned me from Thailand – 7 hours ahead so it was 2.30 a.m. there. She said Jason Craine has phoned Denise Cotton to tell her of the change at the top, and Denise apparently swore down the phone, bad-mouthing Cat and declaring that *she* (Denise) was producer of this film. "No you're not," said Craine, "*I* am." I asked Cat what she meant, this man is only Executive Producer, isn't he? But she rushed on to say that Craine will be visiting Denise on Monday, and if she has any pre-sales she can stay on, if not he'll pay her off. Craine also says Saul Wilson's budget wasn't good –

exchange rates were wrong and so forth – so he'll be told *he's* off the project too. Put down the phone more baffled than ever.

Saturday 11th

Opened my emails this morning to find one from Saul Wilson addressed to Cat, copied (unusually) to me.

> **From: Saul Wilson**
> **To: Cat Frome**
> **CC: Rob Squire, Denise Cotton, Richard Broxbourne**
> **Date: 10 December 2004**
> **Subject: RE: Dark Moon**
>
> **Dear Cat**
> **What a pity. Just yesterday Denise and I found the final piece of the funding for you and were looking forward to announcing that we now have all the money lined up to get your film made.**
> **However, Denise received a call from Jason Craine today, declaring himself to be the new producer.**
> **For the record:**
> **You approached me to produce Dark Moon, saying that you were fully financed. This turned out to be entirely false.**
> **Despite that, I worked on trust, without payment, to help you get this film away. I raised finance, production and finance plans, budgets and so on, and worked long hours with Denise Cotton to attempt to structure the film.**
> **The fact is, as of yesterday your finance consisted of precisely zero, mine and Denise's between us making up 100% of the mix.**
> **Especially I worked on the script, requesting vital changes which not only substantially improved the screenplay but made it one which had a chance of attracting funding.**
> **I now declare my right to be identified as co-author of the screenplay Dark Moon and I caution you that for as long as I continue to do so you cannot claim clear chain of title**

without legal repercussions.

It had puzzled me to understand how a script with potential could possibly have languished for more than 8 years without resolution, and now I know.

I will ask my Attorney to contact Richard Broxbourne next week.

Saul Wilson

Sunday 12th

Had a ponder over a glass of wine last night about Saul's email. At times felt so angry I could hardly breathe. This morning I felt it was head-above-parapet time again.

From: Rob Squire
To: Saul Wilson
CC: Cat Frome, Denise Cotton, Richard Broxbourne
Date: 12 December 2004
Subject: RE: Dark Moon

Dear Saul

Many thanks for copying to me your email to Cat. As she is currently in Thailand, I'll reply without prejudice as Writer and Associate Producer on 'Dark Moon'.

To deal with your points in turn:

a) As I understand it, we don't have a new producer, but a new executive producer, which is a different position altogether as you know. If you and Denise now have 100% of the funding in place, this is wonderful news with which the EP will be delighted and we can all celebrate. As I understand it, Jason will be seeing Denise on Monday December 13th, so will no doubt hear this marvellous information from her in full and welcome detail.

b) To speak up for Cat here, when she and I met you for the first time on October 11th this year she certainly did not claim that this film was fully financed. Indeed, the whole purpose of that meeting was to explain to you that she had

174

no trust in the promise of 40% funding from Belgium, and we therefore asked if you had any contacts which might make up this anticipated (and now proven) shortfall. You said that you would do what you could to help find this alternative funding, and it was on this basis that you came on board. That you later chose to disregard what was said to you at that meeting is hardly Cat's fault.

c) You say that "especially I worked on the script." Forgive me for contradicting you, but you simply didn't, Saul. You may have read it and talked about it (who hasn't, of all those involved?), but "work on it" you never did. Nor did you suggest "vital changes" as such, but a single key change. To be specific, it was to have Grimstone as the 'baddie' throughout the film so that Bryce could emerge clean at the end. This amendment took me about fifteen minutes to implement, without in any way altering the structure and main thrust of our story nor affecting a single line of dialogue, apart from a couple of brief scenes which I can furnish details of if required. Re my notes dated 20/10/04 citing ideas for tweaking the script, most of the points were clarifications of my own thoughts which had already been suggested to, and approved by, the director.

d) Your assertion that your (quote) 'changes' "substantially improved the screenplay" is simply untrue. 'Substantially' implies something far more fundamental and far-reaching than your idea was. So your claim to be identified as the co-author of the screenplay of this film is not only preposterous but insulting to me, as writer, who has put so much time, genuine talent and energy into making this film work while at the same time having to satisfy so many disparate ideas and influences from various sources over the past eight years and more. Currently Cat would seem now to have some claim for co-authorship, and perhaps Gordon Truscott too. But you most certainly do not, and I would caution you in return. You know, I'm sure, that you cannot copyright an idea - which was your sole input into the current screenplay. I am prepared to stand up in court and swear that on the Bible. Even had you written your thought down and presented it as a suggestion for a story 'improvement', I doubt that this would have been sufficient for you to claim co-authorship of the script which incorporated it, and was in any case no more than any producer would do in the course of discussing a screenplay in preparation for filming.

e) That these 'changes' of yours somehow "made it a script "which had a chance of attracting funding" is again pure sophistry. You must know that such a statement is groundless. The suggestion that you have in some way, with your great creative input, made this a film which didn't otherwise have any chance of finding finance is sheer nonsense. Fifteen minutes of brief adjustments to a script simply doesn't make for the transforming quality of organic change you imply. I'm not suggesting that you are attempting to deceive others by making out that it does, but you are most certainly deceiving yourself.

f) You know perfectly well that if everyone who had an idea or story/character suggestion during the course of a script's development - most of them without an ounce of writing talent - were to claim co-authorship of a screenplay, the screenwriter credit list would be so long as to be a travesty, and would constitute – as does your spurious claim to co-authorship – a gross abuse and cynical underestimation of the professional screenwriter's craft. As a Full Member of the Writers' Guild of Great Britain I am more than happy to put this situation to their arbitration committee.

g) As for waving lawyers at us, I find this contemptible.

Rob Squire

To which, minutes later, Saul replied:

To: Rob Squire
From: Saul Wilson
(copied to no one)
Date: 12 December 2004
Subject: RE: Dark Moon

Rob
Clearly we have different recollections. As does my agent.
Without even as a telephone call, let alone a meeting or
consultation, the first Denise and I knew of Jason Craine
was when he called here and announced himself as the new
producer, and that he has a contract that proves this.
I think you'll find that my input on the script is more than
enough to interrupt chain of title.
I have never been treated remotely in this way in my entire
life, and I certainly have no intention of putting up with it.
This is simply not how it's done, Rob

Here was an unfair casualty. Saul Wilson is a decent, effective, hard-working
producer who got in the way of a howitzer shell. Had he stayed, I honestly believe
that he and Denise would have got this film away at last. Looking back, I'd like
to say I'm sorry, Saul – you're a good man.

Monday 13th
Cat rang from 'a fabulous white beach' (as she described it) in Thailand
to say I must bring Lynda out there when the *Dark Moon* money comes in.
I told her I'm looking like a real fool here – they all seem to think Jason
Craine's the new *producer* – he's not, is he? – not after Paul Cowan's
warning? "Only for 6 months," she said in a slightly smaller voice.
    While I made like a goldfish Cat said she's spoken to lawyer Richard
Broxbourne, who says "Tell Rob not to worry, Saul Wilson hasn't a legal leg
to stand on with his claim for co-authorship." I felt sick in the stomach.
New producer? Legal leg? *Six months*??? My God…

From: Denise Cotton
To: Rob Squire
CC: Saul Wilson, Cat Frome, Richard Broxbourne
Date: 13 December 2004
Subject: RE: Dark Moon

Dear Rob

You appear to be going a bit 'overboard' regarding the Script situation* and not fully addressing the fact that Saul was indeed employed to work and raise finance for this film and did so in good faith without a contract.

I would like to point out that I also could claim rights to the screenplay, which you definitely know is correct. I've worked with Cat for hours on end on many scenes throughout the script, and at one time was told by Cat that I would have an "in association with" credit on the screenplay. This promise lasted for about 5 minutes and was then conveniently forgotten.

The fact is, it was totally out of order for a new Producer (and I say "Producer" because this is what Jason Craine informed me he was, and that he has total and unencumbered authority to do whatever he chooses with this film) to have been signed up by Cat without so much as a mention of it to either Saul or myself beforehand.

For the record, I would point out that I received verbal abuse from Cat on Saturday evening for not having seemingly done what I said I would do. I have done everything an Executive Producer and Sales Agent can possibly do, and more, and have always insisted on a Real Producer being in place. This I felt Saul was more than capable of doing.

The problem with this project has been the fact that Saul should have insisted on a Contract when he was employed by you and Cat during your meeting. Then he would have been clear to handle the finance as well as the Cast and Director. Instead, he worked in good faith knowing that he was unable to interfere with the Actors or Director because Cat insisted that this task remain with Fons - even though she well knew that Fons was not going to come up with his money.

This project has been the hardest I have ever been involved with. I have been committed and loyal to Cat for the whole 5 years I've been on this. Cat and I have seen personnel come and go on this film and I am the ONLY one who has stayed faithful to her. However, she now seems to be telling everybody how much I have let her down.

Anyway, I have to close now - Jason Craine is on his way here.

Regards
Denise Cotton

After this email from Denise I realised with surprise that no one on this project appeared to understand what a professional screenwriter is, or does. Does the act of holding a pen automatically make you a writer? Does suggesting amendments to a scene give rights to a screenplay credit? Does inflicting backstory changes which are then implemented (possibly under protest) by another give right to a chain-of-title claim? Sympathetic to Denise as I was at the time, despite the many abuses to which I had been subjected as a writer, I remained proud of my hard-won craft and was weary of non-artisans claiming public acknowledgement (and money) for skills they did not possess.

Wednesday 22nd

Unsure quite what to do, thought I'd better phone Jason Craine and introduce myself. He confirmed that we are still on course for a March shoot, but that he inherited "quite a mess" and needs to "implement a new funding strategy." Said he's spoken to Fons and given him (as with Denise) a final chance to deliver. Okay though Jason sounds, I just can't focus on him being the main producer – there's an air of tactical game-playing about him, like he's controlling a flight simulator rather than an actual flight.

I then rang Jeffrey Simmons, who sees the whole thing as a bad joke now. He's utterly fed up with it all, as well as the way his nephew was treated when he ventured briefly into the firing line on this project. So thanks to the whole mess I'm almost back without an agent, as well as being potless again for Christmas.

Sunday 26th
Heard with horror that a massive tidal wave has hit the west coast of Thailand – the worst natural disaster ever to strike there, with waves higher than a house towering terrifyingly in and inundating the coastline. Thousands are dead.

Rang Cat and left an anxious message. She phoned back to say that she and her family only just avoided the massive *tsunami*. She must lead a charmed life, could so easily have been swept away. When you touch into that kind of devastating reality it makes our own concerns look puny.

Friday 31st
An early New Year's Eve gig with Lynda at an upmarket Elstree care home. Afterwards, drove down to her parents' place in Sussex along roads oddly empty, as if some scourge had vanished the population so we were alone in an uninhabited world. An hour and three-quarters later were walking in to a buffet meal, low lights, a happily barking dog and smiling sister Nicola, smart-looking mum Joan and beaming dad Peter, in Santa hat, offering me a foaming pint of the excellent beer he brews in the garage.

So as disappointing old 2004 vanished we toasted fresh hopes in champagne, then joined hands and sang *Auld Lang Syne*. Rang Kerry and we wished each other a wild and happy New Year. So that's another one done – which saw *Dark Moon* drag desperately along for a further 12 months, the inglorious death of my once-gloriously-promising *La Miss* film following that of the lady herself the previous year – and continued to keep my career pickled in aspic.

What 2005 has to offer I shan't hazard a guess. It can't be like 2004 or I'll have had it.

Author as Auton in Doctor Who

Red Hot 1940s babe

Kerry and Dad go boating

Lynda with frozen yoghurt at Eastbourne

Lynda with Rob (and Toby)

With young Kerry

Lynda by the sea

Kerry in the poppies

With Kerry more recently on the London Eye

Father's Day drink with Kerry

2005

Saturday 1st

Woke in Lynda's parents' bungalow at Goring-by-Sea to a new year fraught with possibilities. Watched *The Loneliness of the Long Distance Runner* from the Alan Sillitoe book. He tells in the foreword how he saw a jogger through his window, and the title came before the story did.

I've enjoyed the break, but feel like the captain of a sinking ship who would rather be on the bridge pretending to steer than out on deck screaming while it goes down. If nothing happens this month the sea will be pouring down the companionway by March and I'll have to take to the lifeboats. To strike another terrible analogy, if *Dark Moon* falls away again I shall be a lone distress signal booming ever more faintly through the fog.

Tuesday 4th

Jason Craine our 'new producer' is en route to Paris to meet film funders called The Wild Bunch. If they come on, the German/Russian fund Craine claims connections with will underwrite the rest of the money. If Wild Bunch fail, Craine will see a contact at Pathé. If either of those companies is involved, pre-sales won't be required. Sounds good if you say it quickly.

Monday 10th

Cat says that all agree that the 2-page synopsis for the *Dark Moon* presentation pack, written by Kenteas Brine, isn't right. Rewrote the synopsis so it did a tap-dance instead of sitting on the floor looking tired. Craine's publicity colleague used it without changing a word, and sent me polite thanks.

Monday 17th

Cat angsting that now Jason Craine isn't returning her calls! She said all the producers on this project have in time ceased to communicate with her, even though she regards *Dark Moon* as still very much her own 'baby'.

"By-the-bye, what became of the baby" said the Cheshire Cat. "I'd nearly forgotten to ask."

"It turned into a pig," Alice answered very quietly.

Wednesday 19th

How it looks on *Dark Moon*: 40% confirmed by Ingenious, 30% from France. The last 30% either from Jason Craine's Russian source – or 30% tax shelter funding from Hungary. Line Producer will be Paul Ritchie (who worked on *Bend It Like Beckham*). Denise Cotton could be a problem – Craine's 'take-it-or leave-it' attitude could result in eruptions of emotion and writs, but he's 'dealing with her' (as he puts it) via her lawyer.

This is a lousy foul-breathed business with warts all over its ugly face and a ghastly black-toothed evil grimace. You wouldn't want to take it home to meet mother.

'Few great men would have got past personnel.' Quote from Paul Goodman on today's diary page.

Thursday 27th

The people at sales agent Content don't like the revised ending. I've forgotten what it is, or who fiddled with it and when. Am not being approached by anyone to advise or attend to the matter, so what can I say?

It's Holocaust Day – terrible images from the past, the last of the survivors revisiting Auschwitz. Absolutely harrowing. Last Saturday was a TV programme of music played in the derelict camp. They had orchestras at Auschwitz at the time – musicians and singers plucked from death to engage in music. An incredibly evocative experience, surrounded by that awesome grey concrete.

Monday 31st

The Iraqis have turned out in huge numbers to vote for a democratic government, despite being threatened with death by insurgents for doing so.

FEBRUARY

Friday 4th

Met Lynda in the carpark behind Harrow-on-the-Hill station. She came down the steps towards my car carrying her ukulele, with that puzzled troubled look I remember from our first meeting outside Baker Street station. Drove to a nearby care home where she performed with her usual dazzle, though many are hardly aware she's there. Yet she puts on a party dress and special shoes, engages with her audience afterwards for maybe half an hour. Most are quiet, doomed folk, almost always sweet, with only rarely a curmudgeon who reads a newspaper throughout her act, shaking his head as though in dismay at the awful noises assailing the air. A very few others will cover their ears to block out the music as if it's devil's noise, trapped in their physical and mental incapacities, all of whom once led full lives, fell in love, brought up children. Now they just sit silently staring, wheeled in and out by nurses, rebelling now and then but soon put down by the young and strong. And any one of us could become like that in the blink of an eye. It keeps us sober, Lynda and me.

Friday 11th

Cat tells me she went with Jason Craine to Denise Cotton's house yesterday. On their arrival, Denise broke down in tears and had to leave the room to recover while it was explained to her husband that investors won't go with her any more as it's generally known that she's retiring this year. Denise came back in somewhat brighter to announce that a £750,000 pre-sale from Italy for *Dark Moon* has just come in. Honour thus satisfied, she announced that she is standing down as sales agent. During the discussions, as wine began to flow, Craine declared that Gordon Truscott wasn't anyone he could sell as director for this film, his credentials rest on horror movies while this is a psychological thriller with supernatural overtones.

Saturday 19th

Cat's birthday party at her big house in Barnes. She agreed Lynda could 'do a turn' for the guests in the lounge, so I set up the mikes and sound equipment in an alcove. Just as the party was starting to flag, on came Lynda till the place was recharged with energy, the walls rang with singing and the room was roaring. Cat's wealthy mother, accustomed to the finest cabaret entertainment, was gazing astonished at this flame-haired performer who cheekily sang George Formby's 'When I'm Cleaning Windows' with ukulele one minute, and then, with infinite tenderness, the Gershwins' 'Someone To Watch Over Me' the next.

Cat, too, was so amazed she not only wrote Lynda a healthy-looking cheque from her own account (instead of asking her mother to pay, as she'd intended) but added a bonus. Lynda had made her evening.

By now I was Lynda's regular roadie, taking her to an ever-increasing number of gigs as word got around how good she was. She did lunch clubs and occasional revues and stage shows, but much of her bread-and-butter work was on the low-paid care home circuit. At the venue, while she changed into something glamorous to perform in, I set up the sound system with a speaker (one spare) and two mikes, introduced her in a 'warm-up' sort of way and joined her on the occasional duet, surprised that our songs went down well but due no doubt to her superior technique that somehow made me seem better than I was. Lynda was transcendent, as a kid she'd been winning all-England school singing competitions from the age of eight. Jackie Schroer of Decca Records had recognised the extraordinary quality of Lynda's voice, as did would-have-been-manager Michael Vine.

However, with Janet recently married and Andy doing his own thing, she'd had to craft her own one-hour act. Now she was buying a flat in Finchley with her sister and needed to keep her mortgage paid because going on benefit was not an option. Meanwhile the big break continued to elude her, though not for lack of trying on her part.

Tuesday 22nd

With Lynda this afternoon at an upmarket retirement home in Bushey – once some landowner's mansion, with rolling green views beyond the great windows. Among the genteel audience of elegantly dressed residents was Rebecca Graf, whose sons have diamond shops in Mayfair and New York. So Lynda sang 'Diamonds Are A Girl's Best Friend' for her in breathy Marilyn Monroe voice and Rebecca loved it. Also in the audience was another stylish lady called Elsie, aged 96, who graciously congratulated Lynda afterwards on her professionalism and talent in an exquisitely bygone era way.

Elsie told us her husband had been chairman of Republic Pictures* in London in the 1930s and '40s. They travelled often to Hollywood and knew all the greats such as Humphrey Bogart, Clark Gable, James Cagney and Judy Garland on a personal basis – and all of them liked to be treated as ordinary mortals and nothing special (Elsie said).

Also watching Lynda was a handsome gentleman in a wheelchair who put me in mind of Peter O'Toole. He was Colonel Rampling**, who I later learned was the father of actress Charlotte. As Lynda sang today and the colonel joined lustily in, a snow blizzard whited out the great windows and I imagined us being snowed up there playing a real life version of Cluedo, with a British colonel and elegant ladies from the 1920s and '30s. And, of course, our own Miss Scarlett complete with ukulele. But the snow didn't stick and we were soon on our way to seek out tea and cakes in a nearby café.

*The first film Republic Pictures made was Westward Ho in 1935 starring a 28-year-old John Wayne. Kids attending Saturday morning cinema in those years would have been familiar with the company's logo as they made mainly Westerns, with titles like Riders of the Whistling Skull, starring the likes of Gene Autry, Roy Rogers and Kit Carson. They also made titles like The Adventures of Captain Marvel (1941) and, perhaps curiously (do I hear Elsie's refined British husband stepping in here?), a screen version of Macbeth in 1948 with Orson Welles.

And here was me, the great galoot, a-hobnobbing with the chairman's wife all these goshdurned years later. 'Time thou thief who love to get sweets into your list, put that in' (as Leigh Hunt wrote when marvelling that 'Jenny' had jumped up from her chair and kissed him).

**Another example of 'time thou thief' came when I spoke to Colonel Rampling. Although in a wheelchair he still gave the appearance of being tall, lean and limber. Quiet of voice, with steady eyes and an air of unostentatious authority, he impressed me enormously – so much so that I Googled him later to see if I could find out what manner of man I'd been conversing with that afternoon. And was staggered by what I found.

Godfrey Lionel Rampling (born 1909) had been a world class athlete. At the 1936 Olympics in Berlin he ran second leg for Britain in the 4 x 400 metres, and the team won. These Games, presided over by Adolf Hitler, are more famous for the *feats of black American athlete Jesse Owens, who won four Gold Medals and cocked a snook at Nazi racist beliefs that 'Aryans' are superior. So while Jesse was doing his thing to the fury of Hitler, the man I spoke to in the wheelchair that day was winning a Gold Medal for Britain in the same Games.*

Thursday 24th

Cat emailed me director Gordon Truscott's latest amendments and tells me he's a 'technophobe' who never works with computers (nor with his writer, so perhaps he's a 'writerphobe' too?) but handscrawls his notes on the printed-out script and faxes the pages to Cat, who incorporates them into an updated draft on her computer – so none of the director's ideas or changes get debated with me at all. The result looks a shambles. I phoned Cat back – does she want me to straighten it out and sort out the spelling etc.? "Only," she said guardedly, "if you don't change a word of it." My teeth are stumps from being gnashed.

Monday 28th

Peter Jaques took a while to speak after I'd finished outlining the latest, he was laughing so much. I suppose if you look at the *Dark Moon* situation in a certain way it *is* funny – unless you happen to be in the middle of it. We lunched at the Queen's Head in Pinner again, one of our fave hostelries. "So how long do you think Jason Craine's going to last?" he asked, polishing his glasses. "You do know, I suppose, that he's never produced a film in his life?" "Yes," I said, "and now we don't even have a sales agent."

MARCH

Tuesday 8th

Today was sweet. Performed at a dementia care home at Edmonton with Lynda. A Pearly Queen called Marie was visiting, as she does nearly every day, in full sequinned uniform, sprightly and still pretty at 84. When Lynda closed with *Lambeth Walk* this amazing lady showed me the steps and we strutted up and down the room together, side-by-side, thumbs in imaginary braces, thighs thumped with fists, air punched with out-thrust thumb on every "Oi!" It was great. Afterwards, she said Lynda was lovely, and that I was 'lovely' too. Oi!

Friday 11th

Extraordinary news about Lynda's mum, Joan Styan. Husband Peter posted her written reminiscences of being a child in the London Blitz on the BBC's 'Wartime' website. Now the BBC are in touch with her, will bring camera and crew to their Goring-by-Sea bungalow for a filmed interview, to be edited into a 4-part wartime reminiscence programme for the 60th anniversary of D-Day in May.

Thursday 17th

At a day centre in Golders Green, Lynda and I duetted Hoagy Carmichael's (and Frank Loesser's) 'Two Sleepy People' for the first time. "Here we are out of cigarettes..." The backing track we sing to is the same that Dean Martin recorded to with Line Renaud, and by some bizarre fluke I pitch the same as he does (which is where the similarity ends) – but if I moan into the mike and quiver the larynx it surprises everyone, dogs in earshot start to bark and cats flee.

When I told Kerry about this latest addition to our 'repertoire' she surprised me by saying I used to sometimes sing those same opening lines when putting her to bed as a kiddie. Some kind of strange long-term prescience at work?

Friday 18th

Sunny warm, first really decent day this year. Gordon Brown's Budget yesterday had good news for film investors, tax shelter stays.

Meanwhile the Jason Craine not-so-merry-go-round continues. He is now 'forbidding' Cat to talk to anyone about *Dark Moon* (might as well forbid a mother to pick up her crying infant), and seems set on getting her mega-wealthy family involved in creating a great pool of spendable dosh. Sounds dodgy to me, and he still hasn't locked down his German/Russian fund.

Petrol is on the up again – unleaded is 81.9p per litre locally (at Tesco it's 2p more and as high as 86.9p elsewhere). Bring on the hydrogen car. Is E-Day approaching sooner than expected, when all the world's oil runs out? With China buying cars in their millions it shouldn't be long.

"In Hollywood, if you don't have happiness you send out for it" – Rex Reed on today's diary page.

Wednesday 30th

Lynda gig at Ascot. On our way home came a call on her mobile from Dave Lee Travis inviting her to perform at his 60th birthday party in May. It put an exciting zing into her day. If *Dark Moon* would hurry up and get funded, and she and her ukulele get a part in it, she'll really be starting to motor – or 'get on the engine' as Ros Hubbard used to say in the long ago before this film developed canker, whiskers and a permanent limp.

Thursday 31st

With Lynda to a care home on The Bishop's Avenue at Hampstead – once the house where Gracie Fields lived. So when Lynda sang in strong high soprano 'Wish Me Luck As You Wave Me Goodbye' to close her act, the rafters rang as they must once have done to the tonsils of the lass from Rochdale. Doing this work we find ourselves in some intriguing places. I heard that our Gracie was so unpretentious she would roll up her sleeves and help the servants out in the cooking, cleaning and other household chores because she hated 'putting on airs and graces'.

APRIL

Tuesday 5th

A residential home gig in Rickmansworth with Lynda. A tiny lady called Agnes was in the audience. Afterwards I spoke to her, holding her hand, which was light as paper. Born in 1896, she was 18 when the First World War began, will be 109 on June 19th this year. She told me in a frail clear voice that she never married because her 'intended' died at Passchendaele in 1917 and she never wanted anyone else. Her old eyes filmed as she talked about him. Yes, it was a long time ago, but to Agnes it's only yesterday, and the boy she loved is always young*.

This conversation gave me the idea of incorporating into a film script of mine, The Pond, a meeting in the present day between a very old lady and the spirit of her long-ago lover who had served in World War I and died young.

Wednesday 6th

A Day Centre gig at Hailey in Hertfordshire this morning. Joined Lynda on 'Nice Work If You Can Get It', and the place was jumping, if those with arthritis and conditions ranging from creaky joints to elephantiasis could be said to jump. While talking to folks afterwards a woman called Pam said she used to go out with singer Matt Monroe when he drove a 27 bus from Highgate to Teddington and was called Terry Parsons. When Lynda asked what she thought of my singing Pam looked doubtful, as if I should be the one driving the bus. "Fares please!"

I'm feeling silly – this ever-more convoluted *Dark Moon* business is getting to me. It does seem a form of crazy, but really that's word-play. How does *real* crazy first show itself, and is the afflicted person aware of it? To me the thought is more terrifying than a stroke or accident that leaves me dependent on others. When I see folks with Alzheimer's or Elderly Mental Illness it rends the heart when these once-dignified people amble up to Lynda while she's singing and stand grinning at her, or try to take her mike, or trip over the cables, or forget what they've said moments after saying it, don't know their own names or where they came from. A visiting daughter, unable to stop weeping at her father's unknowing stare, showed astonished delight when Lynda's voice and manner brought a smile to his expressionless face, a flash of her old dad like a sudden sun-blaze.

Monday 11th

Cat tells me her cat's had kittens and the household is very excited. Well, it's good to know that at least HER CAT has successfully produced something.

Monday 18th

"Technically," said Cat during this morning's phone call, "we are now fully funded." It sounded like a pronouncement by the Duchess in *Alice in Wonderland*. Jason Craine (who seems to have been in hospital) was phoned there to urge him to action the now-vital 40% fund he's been promising since before Cat invited him on, also not to rely on her family to make up any shortfall in the budget. Denise Cotton's Italian presale 'has been confirmed*' (she claims).

It hadn't.

193

Tuesday 19th

A new Pope is announced: Benedict XIV. A German, aged 78, Vatican insider, likes Sauerkraut mit Schnitzeln. White smoke showed he'd been chose. How important is this? – discuss.

Wednesday 20th

Cat tells me that Jason Craine tells her his 40% funding is dependent on her family fund getting implemented. As for the facilities deal, normally they invest 20% of budget to make it worth their while – but Craine's putative 40% stipulates that we must film in Russia and…

"Oh, don't bother me with figures, I never could abide them!" cried the Duchess in a hoarse growl. "And the moral is, 'Be what you would seem to be' – or put more simply – 'never imagine yourself not to be otherwise than what it might appear to others that what you were or might have been was not otherwise than what you had been would have appeared to them to be otherwise'."

Sunday 24th

After a Chislehurst gig down in Kent, Lynda and I drove to her mum's childhood home at Clapham. It was from here on VE night 1945, aged 15, that Joan and her mother crossed the road to Clapham Junction station, took a train to Victoria and joined the crowds massed before Buckingham Palace to see on the balcony King George VI and Queen Elizabeth, Princesses Elizabeth and Margaret, and Winston Churchill. Joan and her mum joined in the revelries and ended up in the early hours on the milk train home. She wrote about it for her U3A biography class, posted to the WW2 BBC website – and tomorrow the BBC are coming with cameras to interview her outside her old home and retrace her steps to the Palace, for primetime TV in May. Magical, amazing, Lynda still can't believe it's happening. "Mum's doing better than *I* am!" she says.

Thursday 28th

Our director Gordon Truscott wants *per diem* expenses at £1000 per week! Cat is asking her mother to put up the money, returnable when the film is cashflowed. Meanwhile I stumble potlessly on, our main producer scarcely knows who I am, and to the director of *Dark Moon* I continue to remain a shadowy stranger.

MAY

Monday 2nd

Clear-skied and sunny warm. Cat tells me Gordon Truscott has made 'more amendments to the script' and faxed them to her. I can't help feeling that if Gordon were to fax direct to me (I *do* have a fax machine) it might inspire fresh thoughts to enhance what he's done and we could create a new professionally competent draft ready formatted for him to take to Cannes. But if this is the way he wants to play it there's not a lot I can do. Even Alexei Sayle's increasingly bemused scriptwriter in the Comic Strip's *The Strike* didn't have anything like this to contend with.

Wednesday 4th

Joan Styan is the subject of a 2-page spread in today's *Evening Standard*, photos of VE Day 8th May 1945 outside the Palace, Joan aged 15 with background of wartime London and Trafalgar Square, with her recollections. I bought a copy and took it round to her daughters Lynda and Nicola. Great excitement.

Friday 6th

A production meeting yesterday for *Dark Moon* was a disaster (sez Cat, I wasn't invited). The stress on this movie-that-never-happens has become so unbearable that Messrs. Craine and Truscott were actually screaming at each other, Craine saying he can't 'sell' the latter because he's known strictly as a horror director. Also, Craine's German/Russian fund appears to be in jeopardy

Watched Lynda's mum interviewed on *Richard & Judy* this afternoon – THEY asked HER on to their show. Joan looked great and came over well.

Sunday 8th

VE Day 60 years on. Watched on TV the big celebration 'party' in Trafalgar Square, with singer Katie Melua among others, but not one of those female vocalists could hold a candle to Lynda's presentation and voice and the feeling she gets into a song. In a fairer world she would have been there too, singing soaringly to overshadow the rest and their puerilely poppish "And a nightingale sang in Berkeley Square, woh-woh…"

Wednesday 11th
Lynda's mum has a pre-filmed spot on BBC TV's Breakfast programme this morning, introduced by Dermot Murnaghan and Natasha Kaplinsky. Joan is seen playing piano at home in Goring-by-Sea, then outside her old home at Clapham, at Buckingham Palace remembering, then walking their cavalier spaniel Toby on the beach at Ferring – all most effective and memorable. Dermot described her as "the wonderful Joan Styan."

Monday 16th
Drove to Brighton with Lynda, weather fair. Jeffrey Simmons phoned my mobile while we were on the front – he says that however high the budget goes I can't expect more than £75,000 for *Dark Moon* as it's a done deal, advised me to take what's on offer then make for the hills. He also said I have every right to write a novel of the film's story – if it's strong enough by the time they've finished messing with it (which I really don't now believe it is – strong enough, I mean). I looked at the dazzling sea and said how about, instead, a book of ten years mismanagement and confusion on a heroic scale, based on diaries I've kept? Jeffrey was intrigued. Perhaps I could call it, with suitable irony, *The Making Of A Britflick*, or something like that.

Wednesday 18th
At Cannes things seem to be going well, though at the distribution company Peace Arch Jason Craine is known as 'Smoke and Mirrors' – suggesting they see him as an illusionist. Quote from film lawyer Richard Broxbourne to Cat: "Fifty percent of the producers and money people at Cannes should be in jail."

Thursday 26th
Weather hot for first time this year – in England, at least. To my surprise am invited to a meeting in London with Jason Craine, Gordon Truscott and Cat – a rare event indeed. I walked through the heat to the address on Long Acre, Covent Garden and, being a bit early, waited outside. In time there came shambling towards me a man looking a bit like an actor playing Napoleon on St Helena, with an aloof expression as might befit an exiled emperor craggily brooding, an incongruous-looking baseball cap clamped

over his baldness. It was Gordon Truscott, clearly steeped in great thoughts that took no heed of mundane things.

He stopped outside the door, but seemed not to see me. Crossing to where he stood, I wondered if a spell had been cast that made me invisible as well as inaudible to everyone else on this film, for even when I stood directly in front of him he seemed oblivious of my presence. When I waggled fingers in his face he focused on me with reluctance, as if annoyed at this disturbance, yet still seemed not to have any idea who I was (aw shit, man, I only wrote the fucking movie, hey, the subtle one you filled up with a shit-bucketload of fucking profanity), but soon we were talking, albeit monosyllabically. Then this burly chap comes bustling up, 50ish, determination tinged with bafflement, white linen jacket and trousers. I didn't have to ask if this was the White Rabbit... er, I mean Jason Craine. He looked oddly at me when I introduced myself as the writer, and blinked – as far as he knows, even though I did speak to him once on the phone, Cat has written this script entirely herself with a bit of help from Gordon Truscott, so who the hell am I?

Cat arrived in her chauffeur-piloted 4x4 and up we went to a first floor office where we met line producer Paul Ritchie, young, smart and civilised. I sat next to Jason Craine, facing Cat and Gordon. We all asked Craine why the continuing delay. He said airily that he's waiting for the Russians to agree to the recoupment proposals he's put to them and they can't be pushed, so what's the fuss and why this meeting? I asked are these people aware of the extreme urgency of the situation, with a director stuck here doing nothing for six months on *per diem*s of £1000 per week, and cast waiting?

At this Craine turned his back on me in a calculatedly insulting way, lit a cigarette and puffed it out of the open window. I reckoned that if I got my arms under his fat thighs and straightened up I could just about heave him out on to the street below. Instead I came round and sat next to Cat. "I can see you better from here," I told him. He turned and said, "Oh, I didn't mean..." Then we both stood up and shook hands. It was okay.

The meeting was over with an impasse that satisfied no one. Out in the sunshine again I winced, beanless as I am, while Cat wrote our director out his weekly cheque for £1000 (donated by her mother). Then jauntily off he went, and down the road in the heat went the rest of us for a beer.

In the bar I found Jason Craine to be a charmer, with a sense of humour entirely lacked by everyone else on this project – the type women go for. His imitation of producer Avi Lerner had me howling – it reminded me of actor John Forgeham doing a wonderful Harvey Keitel take-off when I met him once. However, although talking in millions every day, Craine is tormented by lack of personal finance and desperately needs this film to happen, as do I. At times, with troubled eyes blinking through specs, plus a touch of angry yet never venomous bluster, he put me in mind of Robert Newton's 'Pistil' in Olivier's *Henry V*. Hell and damnation, I liked him.

Sunday 29th
Delivered Lynda to Dave Lee Travis's house at a village near Tring, where she's performing at his 60th birthday party. She was excited and tense. I set up the sound system in the main party area and left her to 'break a leg'.

Returned towards eight in the evening to collect her, and was invited in. The party was over, DLT really friendly. He gave me a drink and showed a video he'd taken of the day's events. Lynda had done a 30-minute cabaret spot in front of his celebrity guests, and had gone down well. On the video I saw her make the announcement: "My next number was recorded by Anita Harris in the 1960s," and clocked Lynda's amazement when a voice in the crowd called out "That's right!" and Anita herself appeared, came up to the microphone and duetted with Lynda the 1931 Wayne King song 'Dream A Little Dream'*.

Other veteran disc jockeys like Kid Jensen and Mike Read had been there too; John Bly the *Antiques Roadshow* man played spoons to some of Lynda's numbers. Ruby Wax had been there, Jeremy Beadle, Art Malik plus plenty more – and they'd all cheered Lynda's performance. Mary, wife of actor Cyril Cusack, told her how Cyril had been offered the part of Doctor Who when it began in 1963, but had turned it down.

Munched DLT's birthday cake and talked to his lovely mum aged 84, her accent wistfully evoking my own northern upbringing. She told me how in 1941 she went out in Manchester with a man who took her into a pub where the air was so thick with cigarette smoke that she insisted they came out again – to find themselves dodging bombs in an air-raid, during which the pub they'd just left had a direct hit and all inside were killed. So if she'd stayed for a drink there would have been no Dave Lee Travis.

In time Lynda and I came to duet this too on performances in the care homes.

JUNE

Thursday 2ⁿᵈ

Lawyer Broxbourne says that if Jason Craine fails to deliver the required paperwork this week he is deemed to have broken his contract and the 'other funding' can come into play. This involves a company called Fretwork – Denise Cotton's set-up with Larry Chandler and, er – wait for this… Saul Wilson.

Wednesday 8ᵗʰ

Jason Craine is off the film. In a conversation with Cat yesterday he agreed to step down as he "cannot get the Russian 40% as long as Denise Cotton remains." Why? Because, he said, her copyright claim in the *Dark Moon* script makes chain of title unclear. Yet Denise has no claim. Apart from ideas for discussion while poring over it for long hours with Cat she has given no input to the actual script. But Gordon Truscott is now in a negative state, his argument being that any producer is better than no producer, which is what we now have.

Friday 10ᵗʰ

Drove Lynda to a new care home outside Romford in Essex. Afterwards we went to Southend-on-Sea for fish and chips overlooking the prom. Walked a bit, wind on the chilly side, then drove along the coast and parked atop a rise overlooking the estuary. As the sun set it tinted houses, a distant church, the beach, becalmed boats and the water itself with a pinky blush. Soon enough, in the almost midsummer twilight, it was ten o'clock and all around us was dusky under a pale strawberry sky. Away we went, at peace with each other, talking of going away somewhere together – if I can afford the petrol, which I won't be able to if *Dark Moon* doesn't happen soon.

Saturday 11ᵗʰ

Cat says American producer/sales agent Keith Bearman has come back with an offer to take the whole film over. He plans to reduce the budget to $8 million, generate another $3.5 million with two UK tax shelter schemes – to double up on the $3.5 million already available (20% GAP finance + 10% Italian sale), shoot in Dublin with Irish producers and get a further $1 million from an Irish fund. But this can't be implemented until October – so filming this summer will be out.

Monday 13th
Collected lovely Kerry from her place of work late afternoon and we sat on the towpath edge by the Thames outside the Bull's Head at Strand-on-the-Green in the warmy dazzle, drinkily a-chat as the tide came up and the sun went down. She and her Chris are off to America on Saturday, starting at San Francisco. We don't talk *Dark Moon* any more, it's become a bad joke best not referred to.

Friday 17th
Lorraine Ross has agreed to come on as UK producer for *Dark Moon* – thanks to an introduction from a contact of Jason Craine's. Feel excited again, as the film seemed to have run aground. The lady is rather prestigious, with a heckuva track, she's read the script (heaven knows which or whose version) and thinks she can help make it happen. Her CV is strong, with producer and executive producer credits as long as your arm. So we have a 'real' producer again at long last. Allowed myself to celebrate a little, and Lynda was so relieved that someone's come on who knows what they're doing.

Thursday 23rd
Weather humid hot. All's well, it seems, for filming on the Isle of Man thanks to an approach by Lorraine Ross who has worked with Hilary Dugdale there before – though the Film Commission's computers have been down so no one's heard for sure. Cat tells me Gordon Truscott is 'depressed' and she had to 'gee him up' last night. He's getting £1000 a week from her, poor chap, and he's depressed. Wish I could afford to be depressed like that.

In the Barnet care home where Lynda performed today was a man called John Newman who I'm told used to be George Shearing's drummer. He's had two strokes, can hardly pick up a spoon now, let alone a drumstick, and watches Lynda with bright eyes as she sings. I imagined the mighty venues he has played at, it's beyond sad to see him like this.

Tuesday 28th

Michael Vine, who Lynda has stayed in touch with, kindly put 3 tickets aside for her, Nicola and me to see his protégé Derren Brown at the Cambridge Theatre in London. Michael found Derren doing table magic in a café, and built him up from there – as he would no doubt have done with 'Red Hot & Blonde'. Derren was amazing, it's impossible to know how he does it. He throws a large toy monkey from the stage, and whoever it lands on is invited up to be the subject of his astonishing psychological magic. A couple of rows in front of us were Stephen Fry and Ben Elton (Fry is a huge fan). On one throw the monkey landed in Ben's lap, but he tossed it elsewhere. Just as well, or Derren would have had motor mouth to contend with. A great evening.

Wednesday 29th

Am told by Cat that Hilary Dugdale at the Isle of Man Film Commission has come back to Lorraine Ross (who knows and has worked with her) with a 'yes' – but wants changes to the script. *Quelle surprise*. I've no idea which version Hilary has been shown this time round (before the re-writers got busy, she and Steve Christian had been happy to run with the script as it was *eight years ago*, which I had written solo and unencumbered). But now, who knows? In the heady days of Hollywood scriptwriters were referred to as 'schmucks with typewriters'. Has anything really changed (apart from we work with computers now)? All I know is that this 'schmuck' is pretty darned good and sick of the whole scenario (whoever it was who last re-rewrote it).

However, as all my information is derived from Cat and I've long since been put outside with the dustbins, this is what I gather: 'Laura' should be American, and England should be Scotland because of potential Scottish investment (10%). Also 'they' (is this Hilary Dugdale talking, or our new producer?) don't want 'Laura' working (i.e. doing a day job) *at all* once she gets to the house, hence we lose the shock effect at her place of work when her psychological degeneration first takes effect and she feels forced to leave and thereby become fully a victim to the house's malevolent influences from which there is now no escape. While Cat talked on, not saying from where these high-handed and misjudged directives were emanating, I found myself laughing in a brittle sort of way. Why not have 'Laura' Chinese, to attract the ever-growing audience in China, joshing charismatically with 'Bryce' in subtitled Mandarin?

Thursday 30th

This being a relatively simple geographical transference in the script, Cat gave the job of doing it to me. So, leaning forward at my iMac and thinking of England – I mean Scotland – set to. By coffee break had finished transferring London/England to Edinburgh/Scotland, avoiding jokes like "Ye've taken me fancy, Nancy" "Aye, Jock – I c'n see the tilt in yeer kilt" – which might not have been appreciated by the po-faced lot awaiting this, for already I'm divining that Lorraine Ross isn't exactly a barrel of laughs either. Anyway, emailed the finished result to Cat, and that was my good (?) deed for the day.

Well, the dialogue for Johnny Weissmuller's first outing as the jungle swinger in *Tarzan The Ape Man* in 1932 was written by 'We'll Gather Lilacs' man Ivor Novello, so maybe I shouldn't protest about Cat giving me this job. Perhaps I should feel honoured. I don't suppose Ivor felt too stretched penning lines like "Me Tarzan, you Jane" but just picked up the money and scarpered. But in my case there is no money to pick up, only more and more debt as this latest producer begins to take us on her own particular voyage into God-knows-where-and-do-we-really-want-to-go-there-anyway?

JULY

Sunday 3rd

Today I travelled into my family's past. Lynda was booked to sing with a couple of musicians on a sunny pitch outside Southwark Cathedral in London's Borough Market. Although great on sax and keyboards, both men were rather old and scruffy, in contrast to Lynda who looked vibrant, young, clean, willowy and all a-dazzle in floaty blue French outfit with medieval-style hangings on skirt and sleeves, russet coils clustered around her head and the loveliest smile.

I looked around at the ancient girders and brickwork, trains rumbling across the metal bridge above my upturned phizzog, and realised that my dad's dad, Walter, would have known this whole place intimately – he worked on Borough Market in his youth. A cockney, he sang in pubs and won races with a column of baskets on his head. For a while I felt him at my side, cor-blimeying the cor-blimeyers, enjoying a salg of reeb in backslang and watching his favourite performer Harry Champion at the music hall, a growing family at home to feed. He died when I was a child – and I found myself anxiously wondering what he would have made of his grandson now. Then I felt the ghost of his arm around my shoulder and was oddly comforted.

Cathedral bells chimed, street acts abounded, Lynda's voice swooped and soared and her ukulele rocked, taking possession for a while of all Grandad Squire once knew here in this very same place, drawing a crowd like once he would have done – including a little black boy who found Lynda fascinating, gazing up at her as he jigged and jerked to the rhythm she made. Magic happens.

Monday 4th

Cat forwarded me the script notes – written by one Jennifer Knight, Lorraine's Ross's business partner/colleague apparently, and (of course) addressed solely to Cat. Like John Irvin before them, are they even aware that the writer exists (other than as some unfocused irritant whose function is obscure)? However, at last I have the privilege of seeing the notes passed down from on high. Worked all day on them and into the evening.

Tuesday 5th

Towards 10 a.m. emailed the notes-incorporated script to Cat – wishing I could send it direct to Lorraine/Jennifer, but Cat insists that she 'must see it first'. Later got a phone call from her which niggled strangely. She'd just lunched with Gordon Truscott, who had been through the newly revised script. He said to "tell Rob he's done a good job." Well, it's good to know that, but why am I not dealing with the director myself? How uncomfortably familiar this strange situation is, and I wonder what creative insights remain unborn for lack of fertilisation because of it?

Wednesday 6th

A gig with Lynda in a Surrey care home where she went down a storm and was booked to appear twice more. Again we duetted 'Two Sleepy People'. On the way back we passed a newsstand – the headline read 'WE'VE WON!' – and I knew that London has won the bid to stage the Olympic Games in 2012. "Who cares?" said Lynda. "We'll both be past our sell-by date by then." "*You* certainly won't be," I told her. "You'll be kicking in in full sound and colour in the wider world out there. They might even make you an Olympic sport: 'Out-Singing The Lynda'! They'll lose, of course – all of them – you'll be Gold all the way." Couldn't help wondering, though, whether it will be pouring with rain all of the time or only for some of it.

Back home to a rare message from Gordon Truscott on my answerphone saying he's absolutely FOR what I've done, that it's (quote) 'clever and subtle' in just the right places, and all the notes are taken account of, that he really enjoyed reading it and has made very few changes. He kept saying "Well done" and ended by saying "Let's get this frigging movie made now!" Thanks, Gordon *. Celebrated with a beer.

This was as close as director and writer ever got to talking one-to-one about the script (forever afterwards referred to as 'the good script'), which from then on continued to get remorselessly 'improved' by others, including Jennifer Knight – herself clearly no writer but who worked closely with Lorraine Ross.

Thursday 7th

Dental appointment in Chiswick today, so left at 10.15 to give plenty of time. All along the M25 signs were lit up: TURN ON YOUR RADIO. Which I did, only to get Ken Bruce playing pap. Approaching the M4 the signs changed to: INCIDENT LONDON, AVOID AREA. Then the radio announcements began, about a series of terrorist attacks on tube trains and buses this morning; several killed, many injured. As I approached London on the M4 the traffic had slowed to an immense crawl, ambulances and police cars weaving through the jams. Tried to phone the dentist to tell them I'd be late, but constantly got 'network busy'.

Didn't reach my destination till just before noon. They were surprised to see me. On their TV screens were pictures of a bus blown apart and London in chaos in the City area; the underground system and buses shut down, streets in gridlock. Several people on their way to work by tube and bus have been killed, others maimed and lost limbs from the various blasts. It's just horrible.

Got home by avoiding the choked motorways, and back into the *Dark Moon* madness. Learned that Gordon Truscott's few amendments are being incorporated into my new script by Cat herself via hand-scribbled notes faxed to her by him. Around 5 p.m. she emailed the results to me, and I was relieved to see that by and large my stuff had been left pretty much as it was.

Tonight the roads in and around London are eerily deserted. How will tomorrow be?

Friday 8th

To a care home in South Croydon with Lynda this afternoon. Once more she performed terrifically and looked great. Among the residents were Burma veterans from the 2nd World War, a bomber pilot called Mack (Malcolm) in a wheelchair being visited by his friend Bob, once his navigator on bombing sorties. Another, Tom Green (who reminded me of John Glen to look at and in manner) was an RSM in the 8th Army who pushed the Germans and Italians to Tunis, and he said the entire Italian army surrendered and they didn't know what to do with them all. "A lot of shouting went on," he said with a grin.

How different my afternoon conversations are to my morning ones.

Saturday 9th

After my having got the script of *Dark Moon* right and satisfied the director in the process, Lorraine Ross has sent Cat an email saying that this latest draft is 'disappointing' and 'doesn't address the problems still there.' This really got to me! What problems are being referred to? No one told me about any 'problems'. You might have thought they'd want to refer to the writer to deal with this, whatever 'this' is – unless they're continuing to assume that Cat is the writer. But Cat doesn't know what 'the problems' are either. I only know the script works like a Swiss watch again now, and that our director wholeheartedly agrees. It feels like working in thick fog in the dark with insufficient light filtering through to formulate a route ahead.

Wednesday 13th

Finally got to meet our new producer today. Tubed to Tottenham Court Road and, being early, sat in sunshine on a bench in Soho Square and called the Isle of Man Film Commission on my mobile – needing to find out exactly *who* is saying the script needs changing so drastically. Hilary

Dugdale came on and I got it from her straight. *Dark Moon* isn't for them, she said: "It's overfull, reads like an airport novel, is too densely plotted." She said she only agreed to read it because she's worked with Lorraine before, and unless the script can be considerably simplified it's not a film they'll want to be involved with. I reminded Hilary that she's seen this project before and had wanted to go with it, when I was sole writer and Robert Young director. "It's not the same script now," she said. "It's lost a lot, or gained too much." I thanked her for this sorely-needed clarification, and we wished each other well.

Met up with Cat, and we went into Lorraine Ross's poky office on Carlisle Street, which has an adjoining room where Jennifer Knight works. Lorraine is blonde and tall with pleasant enough face but hard eyes which brook no nonsense. Madame wasn't pleased to hear I'd just spoken to Hilary Dugdale, and tried to freeze me with headmistressy disapproval: it wasn't my 'place' to have made such a call. But I told her I've met Hilary before and was extremely glad that she and I had just talked because, having been kept in the dark for so long, I now know exactly where we are with the Isle of Man, and why.

When Cat and I re-emerged I didn't fancy joining her for a coffee to 'discuss things', but headed back to Euston on the tube with a tense feeling that less than a week ago four young men with bombs in rucksacks had detonated them on just such a train – British-bred suicide bombers, Islamic fundamentalists.

After that ghastly meeting it was sweet relief to escape to a gig at a Hampstead care home with Lynda. Weather muggy hot. Lynda looked edible in red Spanish-style figure-caressing dress. While waiting for her to get changed I got a call from Cat sounding terribly depressed. Said she's made notes on this morning's meeting (I certainly hadn't) but wonders why she bothers, that nothing ever works out for her. I've never heard Cat like this before, and really felt for her – whatever else she's been, she's always been positive.

Said what I could to reassure her that we'll get this film made somehow, with whoever and whatever it takes. Frankly, I'm pretty sick of the patronising attitude of certain people I've met recently and their toffee-nosed one-way misdirected injunctions.

AUGUST

Sunday 7th

Woke in the Wheatsheaf Inn at Warwick, Lynda still a-snooze. Heartening views of blue sky beyond the curtains. We made suitable tendernesses to greet the new day when she gently woke; then down to a hearty full English breakfast before nine and out into the cerulean morn.

There were throngs at Warwick Castle. I certainly hadn't expected the rip-off price of £16.95 each to get in. The figure didn't seem credible and I wondered in my innocence whether someone had made a mistake. A mercenary pall hung over the place, the waitresses in the café were sour – those knights of old would have lopped off the organisers' heads for levying such obscene charges on the common people and hiring such miserable wenches to serve them.

So we didn't go in, but instead drove off along sunny lanes to Henley-in-Arden where we bought ice cream (for which the little town is famed) and sat on a sun-drenched bench outside the shop to eat them. Continued on to Wootton Wawen village where we lunched at the Bull. It was dreamlike, sitting with my beauty who eats twice what I do and never puts on an ounce around her ever-trim waist.

On then to Stratford-on-Avon, the town teeming with visitors in the blazing sunshine. We broke free from the crowds and strolled along the River Avon, coming on a small plaque set in the grass beside the path: 'To Vivien Leigh, *an unparalleled lass*'. On we walked into a quiet part of this place famous solely because *a writer* once lived here. Passing the old Grammar School we were invited in by some smartly-uniformed pupils, at £2 each, and shown round by one of the boys. The building goes back over 400 years yet is still a working school, with the original Elizabethan paint and décor. Took photos in the old schoolroom, including one of a desk, at which Lynda obligingly sat, once occupied by a pupil called William Shakespeare. This stuff you can't invent.

To tea at the Thistle opposite the Stratford Memorial Theatre, but the cream tea was stale and tasteless, Lynda complained and we got a refund. This incident put us squarely back into the don't-care-fuck-you-grungy-mobile-phone-infested-bare-midriffed-floppy-bellied present day and we knew it was time to head for home, our little idyll over.

But it wasn't quite. We headed south along the now little-used A3400, spectacular scenery, greeny hills and fields, hay-bales gleaming as if Rumpelstiltskin had just passed along there and touched them all to gold. Through Oxford, where once we saw Andy Eastwood's triumphant performance on ukulele for his music degree final – it still gives Lynda a pang to think of it, and that huge chance for the bigtime she feels was lost, though she's happy of course that he's doing so well now. And so on to Dorchester where three men and a dog once drifted in their boat along the river as evening gilded the surroundings and took us into Henley – on Thames now, not in Arden.

Not till we reached Beaconsfield and joined the M40 to London did we feel that our little jaunt was truly over and reality was back with all its grimness and challenge.

Friday 19th
With Lynda and her family in Dorset on a shoestring with credit cards. This morning we went to the village of Moreton where T.E. Lawrence, aka Lawrence of Arabia, is buried. Above his grave is written: 'Dominus illuminatio mea'. It means 'the Lord is my light', and I realised it was ideal for the closing scene in *The Pond* script I'm writing. Mourners there in 1935 included Winston Churchill, Siegfried Sassoon, Mrs Thomas Hardy, Augustus John and other luminaries.

After lunch in a drowsy country pub we went to Thomas Hardy's cottage at Higher Bockhampton. I stood with awe in the room where the jollifications in *Under The Greenwood Tree* took place (I've been in love with Fancy Day since I was 15 on first reading the book in the English lesson at Sale Grammar School), marvelling at the room's smallness (how thrillingly close a lad must have got to a girl in such a confined space); sat on the window seat where the great man wrote *Far From The Madding Crowd*; stood at the little window hatch through which the bucolic workers he wrote about so memorably once received their pay.

Then on to the ghost village of Tyneham, the restored schoolhouse with its blackboard and oil lamps from the 1920s; long-abandoned houses open to the sky. It's said to be the most haunted village in Dorset: on a quiet night children's voices can be heard...

Wednesday 31st

The strategy from on high is getting clearer – cut budget to bone by trimming the script till its pips squeak. Who will do this extremely delicate and difficult task is unclear, but it isn't me. Seems like a recipe for disaster on a production in which the writer is given zero value.

Now Cat tells me a 30-word précis is required for the application to Scottish Screen. To those 'in charge' I don't exist, except as a vague nonentity somewhere in the far background, so it wasn't me who was approached to do this exacting job, but Cat. "I tried, but it's impossible," she said, passing the buck to yours truly. It took 20 minutes, like weaving search engine optimisation keywords into a compelling, colourful mini-narrative. Anyone can do it...

Terrible scenes on the News of flood and devastation in New Orleans in the wake of Hurricane Katrina.

SEPTEMBER

Monday 5th

Humid hot again. In weather like this the body craves peaches, sweet vine tomatoes, milk, iced orange juice, with hardly a thing to eat. Phoned Cat around 9 a.m., she says she's had a rough time getting all the documents in for Scottish Screen – refusing to sign her rights away during this process as had been suggested by certain people. Canny lass.

So am I nearly out of the financial quicksands? Jeffrey Simmons wants the book rights – they represent my way back to published authordom and a break from this soul-rotting screenwriting where respect and appreciation are so low, quality and painstaking care are swept aside with apparent contempt and mediocrity so often seems to get its way.

Friday 9th

Cat mentioned an email sent to 'everyone' (except, of course, to me) by our producer, which gives the current funding strategy. I begged Cat to let me see it.

From: Lorraine Ross
To: Richard Broxbourne; Robert Birtles
CC: Cat Frome; Studio Eight; Jennifer Knight; Stanford Bridges; etc.
Date: 8 September 2005
Subject: Dark Moon

We are approaching rapid closure of the finance with a view to starting preproduction late October. The film's structure will be as a UK/Hungarian/Italian (finance only) co-production.
The finance plan is:
Budget £5.4
financed 2.16 PE
1.5 Studio 8
    5 Presales Italy/Spain
    6 Hungarian tax credit
    64 Bank gap
It is presumed that the Scottish Screen money will not now come through, with a resultant possible modest reduction in the budget.
We believe the mix of GAP money, EIS and Section 48 production finance should present no problem, but this must be confirmed asap.
We should then proceed rapidly to confirm recoupment and bank arrangements (with Bank of Ireland) and to close our deal with Mark Horowitz the sales agent who is BOI approved.
Best wishes
Lorraine/Jennifer

Again it was good of Cat to forward this to me – as she did throughout our association with so many other emails from which I was excluded. I was fascinated how the finance was structured, though there did seem – in my supreme ignorance of such matters – to be a few holes in the plan, and I could only hope that a mathematician named Hall wasn't lurking somewhere.

Monday 12th
ENGLAND'S CRICKET TEAM HAS WON THE ASHES FOR THE FIRST TIME FOR 16 YEARS!!!! JUMPED ABOUT LIKE A FOOL AND UNZIPPED AN EXTRA BEER – WELL, IT'S VERY HOT AND… AND THEN ANOTHERRNN\$\$£%???!!

Wednesday 28th
After Lynda's gig at a community centre in Paddington today we made our way under a grey sky to Hampstead Heath, then took umbrellas and walked. At the top of Parliament Hill from where you can look right across London we couldn't believe what we were seeing on the grass below – a massive table and chair, big enough for a fairytale giant to sit at. We went down to look at it, towering above us. It's called 'The Writer', by an Italian artist. I felt that certain key personnel on *Dark Moon* would have appreciated it, because 'The Writer' had neither profile nor substance and was easy to disregard, being invisible, absent or consigned to outer darkness never to be discussed or even thought about.

*Its only reference was a note saying 'rolloart.com', and we wondered if it was now a permanent feature of the Heath. But the next time we went there the table and chair had gone.

OCTOBER

Sunday 2nd
After Lynda's twice-yearly meeting with the Ukulele Society of GB at the village hall in Digswell in Hertfordshire, we and a few of the ukulele enthusiasts ended up at the Harvester restaurant on the A1. A mad air prevails after these bashes. Lynda brought in her ukulele and sang 'Leaning On A Lamp Post' to a group of diners who watched amazed, then clapped and cheered. The only sour one was the manager: "this is against the rules" – or, to paraphrase George Formby, 'We Don't Have A Licence For That'. Why do I so often feel with Lynda that I'm taking part in a movie?

Tuesday 4th

Lorraine Ross has given the Isle Of Man until this morning to say if they wish to be involved with *Dark Moon*, as she has a meeting with Irish funders this afternoon. Pre-production is not now expected till November, with a January 2006 shoot. But if this goes the Irish route, Cat has offered to borrow £400,000 on her house to make up the shortfall*.

*When Cat told me this I felt a chill. For the first time this whole set-up didn't feel strictly ballroom, and reminded me of something producer Barrie Saint Clair once said in an email:

Golden Rule Number One: Do not put your own money into a movie, it clouds your judgement.
Number Two: Do not let friends or family put money into the movie, it clouds your judgement.

Wednesday 5th

Hilary Dugdale phoned Lorraine yesterday to say they will come in with 25% of the budget for *Dark Moon*. So a pre-production date in early November is anticipated, filming early December.

Did a gig with Lynda near Harrow this afternoon at the care home with the woman who went to school with Vera Lynn and tells us her real name was Vera Welch. Afterwards, having tea at a new café near the boys' school which Winston Churchill and Byron attended, a CD was playing a female singer who sounded like a cat being strangled. I asked why was she allowed to do that? It's Mariah Carey, Lynda explained patiently. While agreeing with me about the strangled cat quality of the singing (or a baby with teething pains), all this divinely gifted but under-paid and under-used songstress could do was shrug and say "That's what they want these days."

"Am I getting old?" I asked in Maurice Chevalier tones, hoping for a sympathetic 'of course not' reply as Ms Carey caterwauled on.

"Yes," said Lynda. "And maybe I am too."

Monday 10th

Drink early evening with Peter Jaques at the Case Is Altered at Old Redding near Harrow and gave him the latest lowdown on *Dark Moon*. W.S.

Gilbert used to live just across the way – I wondered to Peter over the second pint whether the great librettist had ever had people say things to him like: "Look William, we've had a libretto meeting and, well, these lines of yours, we all of us agree they're not quite right: Stuff like 'I am the very model of a modern Major-General, I've information vegetable, animal, and mineral…' Trouble is, y'see, my friends don't talk like that, so how do you expect anyone to understand? – so, anyway, I've changed it to: 'I'm a smart senior soldier with all kinds of gen.' See? Says it much better. Less says more. The director agrees…"

Friday 14th
Am told that Gordon Truscott has already storyboarded up to 1000 shots/images, thinks the Isle of Man perfect for the exteriors; the house Hilary Dugdale suggests is ideal. Well, I'm glad that at least Gordon's happy; the bottle of Lanson champagne I bought three years ago to celebrate the making of this film still waits to be opened, its contents getting increasingly flat and the paper it's wrapped in slowly taking on the appearance of ancient parchment.

Sunday 16th
Cat says "they" want the script location changed back from Scotland to England. Er… why? Because Scottish Screen have dropped out (after all that Edinburgh business). Er… why? Because the application wasn't presented by a Scottish person. Hoots and awa', is everyone a wee bit addled in the heid? Once more I feel how naff it is to be given such information in this third-hand way. Cat said she was 'doing the changes' herself. Ah, we're all right then.

Friday 21st
Cat has borrowed another £10,000 from her wealthy mother, and the same from her friend Lisa to keep the pre-pre-production phase going. Cat says Stanford Bridges's investors from New Zealand are flying in this weekend. Hello? I thought they flew in weeks ago – and if they did, what happened? Perhaps they flew out again and are flying in once more – let's hope to greater effect this time so far as this film is concerned. Lorraine has decided to forget filming in Hungary and go for Ireland. I asked Cat that if

this happened would the script have to be changed to Dublin? And what about the Isle of Man? I mean the house, Hilary Dugdale, the storyboards Gordon's done there, 25% of the budget? It was only a week ago I heard all that. Confused? (being fed scraps of information like this can get to be like Chinese whispers...)

It's Trafalgar Day. 200 years ago Nelson and our navy defeated the combined French and Spanish fleets with a firepower almost 3 times greater than theirs, even though numerically inferior in ships. The 'Nelson touch' won the day. Big celebrations on the *Victory* at Portsmouth – and a display by the Royal Navy of the incredible speed and loudness of the cannonfire which blasted out of that amazing ship.

Tuesday 25th

Lorraine has herself changed the location of the script to Ireland on her computer. 'Bankside Lodge' will now be in the Wicklow Mountains, an Irish Art Director has been appointed. Er... (tiny voice) but what about the Isle of Man, Miss? – didn't Gordon Truscott just fly out there at Cat's mother's expense and do thousands of storyboards and get all excited and hasn't Hilary Dugdale just found the ideal house, and...? "Silence, boy! Don't ask aggravating questions! Off with his head!"

Feel thoroughly emasculated as the writer of this movie, and have to keep reminding myself that without my work over many years they would have nothing to tweak, take out, replace or generally bugger up. I now learn that the script is 'too long' for a supernatural thriller – should be 90 minutes rather than 120. The budget is extremely tight, need to do it on a 36-day shoot (not 39). All of this I could fix if someone would only TALK TO ME.

When Cat then said, "We're all having to take deferred payments" I went cold. "Not you," she added hurriedly – but the suspicion was planted. Doing my bit, I went through the script cutting scenes not absolutely essential. It's amazing how a script can be trimmed – the trick is not to throw out baby with bathwater like Gordon did on his first rewrite. Sent the result to Cat.

Later, she emailed me the cut/amended Dublin script concocted by Jennifer Knight, Gordon, Cat and Lorraine Ross, and I saw with a freezing sensation that every single one of my suggestions had been entirely ignored. It was a mess. Clearly, I am regarded as nobody* on this production.

Nevertheless, this 'nobody' worked all evening straightening up this garbled dog's dinner of a script, then sent an additional file making a case for the maimed and missing scenes. "I'm the director," says Truscott. "What I say goes!" Yes, that's all very fine, mate, but this director never consults with his writer, ignores all his suggestions, and if this grand attitude means (apart from anything else) that the core terror scene of *Dark Moon* is reduced to a pastiche of scenes from other films we are ALL affected and the quality of our film will be reduced and its ultimate saleability could be disastrously compromised.

This despairing entry marked what I saw as the gradually-accelerating descent of the quality of this script, and a new low in its prospects of ever being worthy or memorable.

*It occurred to me when first thinking of putting this book together that it could be called The Diary Of A Nobody *– but that's already been done!*

NOVEMBER

Tuesday 1st

With me feeling ever more confused and Cat borrowing ever more money from family and friends, seemingly to feed operations in Ireland, I'm on a treadmill into nowhere, depleting my resources as I sink deeper and deeper into an ever-spreading mire of debt.

In morose mind this evening I worked out that I'm actually worth more dead than alive. If I could go into deep-freeze for a few months and have no need to consume food and drink to survive it might help. Or the answer might be to simply hibernate like a hedgehog. I wondered if there are any pills I could take that would put me quietly to sleep till *Dark Moon* has been made and my fees are in. I unzipped a can of strong beer, looked on the Internet and made a few text amendments as the beverage kicked in:

'Hibernation is a state of inactivity and metabolic depression in writers wishing to buy time without having the immediate wherewithal to achieve this. It is characterised by lower body temperature, slower breathing, and lower metabolic rate, to conserve energy during seriously penurious time-periods when to retain consciousness and activity would result in poverty, starvation and possibly death. During hibernation, unpaid scribes can slow their metabolism to a very low level to allow them to use their energy reserves, stored as body's fat, at a slower rate.

Although Pliny the Elder thought that swallows hibernated, and even a keen observer like the Rev. Gilbert White (*The Natural History of Selborne*) believed so, birds typically do not hibernate, instead using torpor, but an exceptional bird known as the Poorwill does hibernate. The unwinged species, known as the Poorwriter, has also been known to do this, and many experts believe that the processes of daily torpor and hibernation form a continuum'.

That will do nicely, sir.

Wednesday 2nd

Apropos of not a lot my agent Jeffrey Simmons says that had the project gone with his nephew David van Eyssen he would have got Screen Gems to do it and avoided all these crazy delays. Great, well don't blame me, chum. Out of interest I looked Screen Gems up. They've produced 505 films, starting in 1926 with a silent titled *Watery Gravy*. And have distributed 294 films, starting with a TV *Dracula* in 1957. Now there's a title – 'Watery Gravy'. Well, at least it got made...

Cat tells me we're now in the 14-day hiatus called by our producer, by the end of which the money is intended to all be in and pre-production (and half my desperately-awaited fee) can be funded by a financing company called Freewheeler.

Friday 4th

Larry Chandler's German investor, who was sent the package yesterday, is looking positive – Jenny Knight left an upbeat message on Cat's phone to 'expect really good news'. This is for 30%, maybe 40%, of the budget. But Denise Cotton's Italian 10% presale is still seeking closure (don't the Italians like psychological thrillers with supernatural content, or is it because there are no salami scenes?) (getting silly now)

"Hey Rob, could you write in a couple of scenes featuring salami?"

"Why's that, Cat?"

"Denise feels it might help to secure the Italian pre-sale."

"Okay. Would it help if I added some fettuccine with Gorgonzola?"

"Fine, fine – whatever you feel is right – I'm going to change it anyway, and if I don't, Gordon or Lorraine or Jenny will."

"Consider it done, then. I might even throw in a spot of insalata di cavolfiore e gamberi with a side-dish of tortellini."

"No, over the top! Definitely O.T.T.! – all of us agree. Look, don't worry, Gordon and I will do it. (pause) Are sardines Italian, and how do you spell that...?"

In fact Cat was in sombre mood today, says she feels completely drained out, can't get excited or enthusiastic about *anything* unless/until *Dark Moon* is funded and away. I know how she feels. Gordon Truscott tells her that in Los Angeles they're saying that this film is 'cursed'.

Sunday 6th

Lone drink by candlelight in the lounge that will no longer be mine if *Dark Moon* doesn't happen pronto. And I started to laugh. And laugh. Lynda? I can't believe your face and form, soaring soprano and husky low-tones, nimble fingers a-strum on uke-strings, lips like loving limpets and eyes that dance. Will you be gone too if this film doesn't go?

That's when I stopped laughing.

Tuesday 8th

To save on the budget Gordon Truscott has agreed to take a 50% cut in his director's fee – from £300,000 to £150,000. Now, I call that real generous. Wondered if this was a hint that I should make a similar noble gesture and halve my fee to £37,500 now I've been permanently relegated to the creative outfield with a myriad other tormented souls nobody ever listens to.

Thursday 10th

A wildly-excited call came from Cat to say that Karl Brinkmann, head of the German fund, has just phoned Lorraine Ross to say *we have the money*!! He's finalising paperwork for 26% of the funding. A quiet, positive glow that the road is clear for full funding on *Dark Moon* after ten years of crazy began in my soul★.

★*Poor soul...*

Monday 14th
Windows frost-white first thing. This is the day given for pre-production to start, but there's certainly no sign of it. Gordon Truscott has some Indian investors called Crossover in reserve if the Germans fall away, confided Cat. I asked her will the film have to relocate to Mumbai if that happens, with 'Bryce' sporting a dark moustache and playing sitar? "Oh no," she says seriously, "I'm sure it won't come to that."

But do we have a film or do we not?

"Have some wine," said the March Hare.

Alice looked, but there was nothing but tea. "I don't see any wine," she remarked.

"There isn't any," said the March Hare.

"Then it wasn't very civil of you to offer it," remarked Alice*.

**By this point the whole set-up was reminding me more and more of Alice In Wonderland – hence bits of it began spilling over into the diaries.*

Tuesday 15th
Cat is worried about Denise Cotton's 10% Italian sale (still not secured); also the 10% from Stanford Bridges's EIS (Enterprise Investment Scheme) fund is now looking shaky (er, sorry, excuse me, but what happened to the New Zealand money and all those investors flying in and out then back in again? "Don't ask foolish questions, boy!" Lorraine suggests again that Cat remortgage her house to cover the 20% they're worried about. Another way to cover this last 20% is to go back to American producer Keith Bearman, who would put this amount in and take over as sales agent – but Lorraine refuses to work with Bearman for some reason it's probably best not to enquire into too deeply. So what happens now?

"Would you tell me please, which way I ought to go from here?" said Alice.

"I don't much care where –"

"Then it doesn't matter which way you go," said the Cheshire Cat.

"– as long as I get somewhere," Alice added.

"Oh, you're sure to do that if you only walk long enough. In that direction," the Cat said, waving its paw around, "lives a Hatter; and in that direction," waving the other paw, "lives a March Hare. Visit either you like: they're both mad."

"But I dont want to go among mad people," Alice remarked
"Oh, you can't help that," said the Cat: "we're all mad here. I'm mad.
You're mad."
"How do you know I'm mad?" said Alice.
"You must be," said the Cat, "or you wouldn't have come here in the first
place."

Wednesday 16th

New German Chancellor, Angela Merkel, has removed all tax incentive investment schemes retrospectively – so the German 26% now looks stricken and a lot of films will collapse. On the other hand, Studio 8 are showing up again, and Gordon Truscott's Bollywood company is standing by. Am preparing to change 'Bryce's' name to Jitin or Yogi. And 'Laura'? Well, let me see, there's Usha, Misha, Neeta...

This evening dear Kerry rang. She has a cold, sounded wan but cheery – she always sounds cheery – we'll get together next week when her cold is better, and let's hope I'll have some positive news about the film so she won't see her dad as such a failure all the time. Afterwards, the sound of her gentle voice stayed with me and I felt so moved with love for her. Cue for some schmaltz before unzipping a beer...

> 'Kerry Melanie
> Isn't well, hope that she
> Gets better soon to chase the moon
> And sing the tune she knows quite well.

> 'Kerry Melanie
> When she's asleep on our settee
> Dreams will come of fairy nooks
> And nursery books and wishing wells

> 'And then it's five o'clock
> And time for tea and kids' TV –
> I'll get some evening soon
> When she doesn't fall asleep in the afternoo-oon...'

But that was long ago, as a rather more famous song put it. I used to warble it to her on guitar when she was ill off school snoozing under a blanket on the settee during the day.

Time, thou thief…

Friday 18th

Gig with Lynda at a convent care home in Chiswick run by nuns. "Do you think I ought to sing words like 'Lover when you're near me and I hear you speak my name, Softly in my ear you breathe a flame'?" Lynda asks in concern before we go in. "I'm not sure," I say. Yet most of her audience are very ill. Some are actually asleep. And life is life, and none of them would be here at all if their parents hadn't breathed into each other's ear at some time or another. So Lynda did, and eyes opened, and rapt looks transformed tired faces as her caressive voice warmed them through and quietly illuminated their day.

Later I rang Cat on my mobile to ask what's going on. It's been a terrible week, she said, with the Germans folding like that. The Bollywood fund was complicated and it looked as if *Dark Moon* was finished. However, at 6.30 this evening our producer got a call to say the German government has reversed its decision – so the original fund is available again.

'If at first you don't succeed, try, try again. Then quit. No use being a damn fool about it.' W.C. Fields on today's diary page.

Monday 21st

Lawyer Broxbourne has sent Cat a £17,000 bill for work done on *Dark Moon*, presumably because he feels the film is about to collapse. Stanford Bridges's fund has proved to be about as real as a bank manager's smile and the giant called Stark Truth is stomping the territory with his club. Stand by to hit horizon, kids!

Yep – HERE comes Starky and that club of his:

From: Karl Brinkmann, President Outreach
Entertainment, Germany
To: Larry Chandler (Fretwork)
CC: Lorraine Ross, Jennifer Knight, Cat Frome
Date: Mon, 21 Nov 2005

Subject: *Dark Moons urgent*

Hallo everyone

It is a shame – but this project "Dark moons" has been shopped around since years – to all investors – all European buyers I spoke to today know of the project – and the most astounding thing is: always with a total different budget – different producers – different version etc. *It is a shame.*

I nearly fell over when Cat forwarded this little gem, because not so 'most astounding' is to realise that Fretwork are part of the German funding set-up, Saul Wilson being a business partner in it. Not that I'm suggesting Saul has murmured into someone's shell-like about the shoddy treatment he received from the 'Dark moons' set-up, and to give it as wide a berth as possible on pain of forcible removal of molars without anaesthetic, but my suspicions are strong. Nice one, Saul, I think you may have done for us – *if* it was you, of course – and I'm not saying it was, mind...

From: Karl Brinkmann
To: Lorraine Ross, Larry Chandler (Fretwork Entertainment), etc.
CC: Jennifer Knight, Cat Frome
Date: 21 November 2005
Subject: *RE: Dark moons urgent*

Dear Lorraine
As Jason Craine tried to make with German funds through Rainer Schmidt, who shopped it to maybe 40 production and European investment companies and European sales systems, nearly all equity funds know of this project, at that time with a budget of around 10 Mio, then suddenly it became 15 Mio, and two years ago announced with Denise Cotton as a 5 to 6 mio TV film (with possible theatrical upside).
Please understand that in the last ten years almost 70% OF ALL FEATURE FILMS HAVE BEEN FINANCED

THROUGH THE GERMAN TAX FUNDS.
Clearly not just the wider market place knows of this product, the *whole place* had it in their hands sometime. The problem is that I did not know the complete history of this - but I should have been told.
You will understand I don't want to lose my name in the investors scene.
Karl

To which Lorraine briskly replied:

From: Lorraine Ross
To: Karl Brinkmann, Larry Chandler (Fretwork Entertainment), etc.
CC: Jennifer Knight, Cat Frome
Date: 21 November 2005
Subject: *RE: Dark moons urgent*

Karl, there was never a budget of $5m - it was over $10m when we came on in June.
Earlier producers include Fons Verhoeven and Jason Craine - and Denise Cotton was selling it for some while. But the present script is very much better than it was then. The investment we require is for the project as it is now, with the budget you currently have! We feel confident in saying that with our track records for producing award-winning films, *Dark Moon* now has the chance to be both creatively and commercially successful. Do we still have a chance of a deal, would you say?
Best wishes
Lorraine

Out of the woods, would you say? If so, one (plus several) up for Lorraine Ross. It's at moments as tenuous as this that her reputation wins hearts and minds where lesser producers would get egg-on-tie awards.

Friday 25th

Stand up and salute Karl Brinkmann, the man we thought had pulled out on us. And congratulations to Lorraine Ross who won the day after all. Now *that*'s a producer! – who cares what she thinks about the silly old writer? Karl has made a £490,000 pre-sale of the as-yet-unmade *Dark Moon* to Telepool in Munich, which is 10% of the current budget.

When I try to tell Jeffrey Simmons what's going on he's amazed at how the funding story constantly changes – a strong contender one day has vanished the next. He keeps careful tabs on what's happening, and said today that if the 'certain' funds could be locked down we could see a cheque next week.

So another Friday and still not fully there, but feeling optimistic. Christmas is in the shops and streets, flashing with coloured lights and sparkle, but my little home remains frozen and waiting, wondering if it will have to be sold to keep me going.

George Best died today. Mostly it's the legend of brilliance combined with glamour; perhaps the brilliance alone might not have had George so remembered and mourned by so many had he not been the 'fifth Beatle' in the 1960s, laid Miss Worlds by the dozen and had the kind of looks that might have had Tyrone Power running for a plastic surgeon.

DECEMBER

Thursday 1st

Am told 92% of the *Dark Moon* funding is now confirmed, but Cat is increasingly anxious as she has now personally borrowed £43,000 so-called 'seed' money from her friend, plus a further £10,000 from her mother, just to keep things going.

Later Cat sounded more cheerful, having spoken at length to Jenny Knight. Here's the current plan according to her: Isle of Man Film Commission – 37%; Bank of Ireland, 20%; Irish Tax Subsidy – 15%; Telepool – 10%; Stanford Bridges's EIS – 10%. Denise Cotton's long-promised Italian pre-sale – now worth 8% of the total, is the only one considered shaky. Lorraine is off to Dublin to further lock down money, and see the Irish Equity Fund. This has become an edge-of seat white-knuckled thriller in its own right.

Sounds good – or is a mathematician named Hall still doing the books?

And why is the Isle of Man still in it?

Why don't I understand these things?

Wednesday 7th

The Tories have a new leader – David Cameron. He looks young and went to Eton – will transform the party's image?

Friday 9th

This morning my doorbell rang, a Romany woman on my step. She peered at me then said a lot of good luck is coming my way, and that I will soon be fully 'with' someone, that I shan't need to live alone any more. She said this gazing at me with quiet eyes and talking in a light gravely voice. I gave her £2.50 for a lucky stone.

Next came a call from an increasingly worried Cat. The Telepool pre-sale still hasn't sent confirmation. No word either from Ireland re the equity fund of £400,000 Lorraine had hoped/expected to be confirmed by now. So unless something drastic happens in the next few days it looks as if *Dark Moon* will collapse again. I stared at my lucky stone and nearly chucked it through the window.

It was the last journey today of the red London Routemaster buses with the jump on/jump off open back.

Thursday 15th

The moon tonight is the brightest it's been for many years, at its highest point – but the sky too cloudy to see it.

Thursday 22nd

Tonight with Lynda at my little abode, coloured lights strung up over the closed curtains, my Victorian Father Christmas figure benignly watching us, carols quietly playing. And, despite the angsts and vicissitudes elsewhere in our lives, bliss visited us.

Sunday 25th

Came yesterday with Lynda and her family to Worgret's Manor Hotel near Wareham in Dorset. Weather brilliant this Christmas Day. It's Nicola's birthday as well as Jesus's, and she wanted to go to Lulworth. So we did, and strolled with Toby the cavalier down to the Cove.

Leaving the parents below, the girls, me and dog slogged up a long steep track to the ridge-top overlooking the sun-dazzled water. Up here was warm as Spring. Lynda said she wished we could stay here forever if only it would remain exactly as it is now and none of us got any older.

Back to Christmas lunch at the hotel, mulled wine then all the courses. Excellent – with no cooking or washing up or getting half-blasted on sherry in the process till your head nearly spins off and you lose one of your slippers which is never found again. And thank the good Lord for credit cards or I'd be more stuffed than the turkey.

Monday 26th

Text on my mobile phone from Cat said Happy Christmas and 'here's to a fabulous year for us all with *Dark Moon*.'

To the Royal Norfolk Hotel at Bognor this evening to celebrate Lynda's Boxing Day birthday (after her sister's on Christmas Day). She looked sensational in the gold-sequinned top I bought her (on credit card) from Frank Usher and the cream French trousers that show off her fabulous nether assets. We danced to the disco till half eleven. Came out happy to frost on car windows and freezing air, and midnight passed as we drove back to Goring.

Saturday 31st

Tippling down with rain when midnight struck. Drove the girls and their mum Joan to Worthing pier, but it was too wet to get out of the car. Tried phoning Kerry, but the mobile network was jammed. Didn't get through till one in the morning in a thundering downpour by the water at Littlehampton to wish each other a Happy New Year.

Back at Lynda's parents' for a Scotch with dad Peter. According to the last information from Lorraine Ross via Cat, pre-production on *Dark Moon* is due to start on Jan 3rd, filming Feb 10th – but no matter how hard I wish I can't seriously see it happening unless somebody waves a wand of exceedingly magical quality or I fall down a rabbit hole.

2006

JANUARY

Wednesday 4th

Jeffrey Simmons has caught up with Cat – she's in Barbados, the poor broke thing, and told him that all on *Dark Moon* looks good. Seems they're 10% short of the full budget and Lorraine Ross is off to Ireland to secure it. Shooting on the Isle of Man may be delayed a week till Feb 17th. Whatever, the prospect of payment looms at long last.

Buoyed up by this, loaded up the car with prezzies, luggage and festive left-overs and drove away back to London with Lynda and Nicola, passing through villages with Christmas lights still in them like girls stood up at a dance. Okay, the new year has begun, so now let's get this flick MADE.

Wednesday 11th

Here it comes. At 10.30 this evening Cat phoned. *Dark Moon*, 'for its own good' must be postponed for 2–3 months and will now be filming June/July on the Isle of Man once the Renée Zellweger film there (*Miss Potter*) is finished. Pre-production is to start April/May this year. Also, a 'sexier' cast must be found. Casting director of the BBC TV serial *Bleak House*, Kate Rhodes James, will replace Jeremy Zimmerman. The end result will be a better and more profitable film, says Lorraine – who also says the script is 'fabulous' now.

Good. Yes, it is – it's, er, fabulous... isn't it? Lorraine says she/they want this film to be an 'A' one with 'A' quality cast and distribution. *Fabulous*?? To be honest, I've forgotten what it looks like now, if I was ever shown it, that is, which I probably wasn't (vanishes muttering "fabulous?" to himself in puzzled sort of way).

Thursday 12th

What's happened to the Bull and Bush at Hampstead? Went for a drink there with Lynda and found the place boarded up. So much for the last

227

owner's idea to tart it up with bare floorboards, glaring lights and chrome, and remove all the Florrie Forde music hall memorabilia. People deserted in droves.

'Come, come, come and make eyes at me
Down at the old Bull and Bush, tarr-ra-ra-ra-raaa...'

Sorry Florrie (hey, that rhymes!), the place closed down because present day philistines drained it of the life with which you once imbued it*.

*It has since had a revamp and a large picture of Florrie Forde now graces the restaurant room.

Friday 13th

I asked Cat why do we have to wait for the Isle of Man when Hungary and its money are apparently ready waiting? She said Gordon Truscott asked the same question. That way *Dark Moon* could be filming by the end of March and in the can by June. I said this seems to be a delay too far, something feels *wrong* about it – my instincts say we are now being misled or duped, though by whom, or for what reason, is a mystery.

Monday 16th

It's been suggested that the *Dark Moon* title is changed as it's been around too long – possibly because of Karl Brinkmann's 'Dark moons' email in which he says every financial set-up in the world knows about it. I suggested *Precipice* (surprisingly, the title has never been used) – but Cat shunned this in favour of her own *Blade In The Grass* – which I found so funny it made my solar plexus tremble. But she tells me our director thinks it's a 'wonderful' title. Okay. Also, her idea is to change the characters' names too. 'Laura Claridge' becomes 'Annabel de Vere', her brother 'Miles' becomes 'Garth', and so on. Stopped it trembling for just enough time to say "great." *

*These changes were never implemented, which has to be seen, I suppose, as a mercy of sorts.

Friday 27th

Had a long concerned talk with Peter Jaques on the phone, it's always good to get his take on things. He's had a look at the current script – at least, the last one I saw before Christmas. He says it looks drained of the incident and cross-cutting of storylines that gave it depth and pace before, and the characters lack individual identity now and what he calls the 'lift' and 'energy' the script once had have gone. I can't be sure what the script looks like at the moment, of course – several weeks have passed since – but his remarks are interesting because when Jeffrey Simmons saw the latest depleted storyline he finally gave up any thoughts of my doing a book of the film because there's no longer enough substance to engage a reader.

FEBRUARY

Wednesday 1st

The Isle of Man can't do the end of March! If I had a sword I would fall on it. So we're looking at a May shoot in Ireland, pre-production some time next month. Felt pretty down, but it's only a bit longer... isn't it?

Friday 3rd

Things are awesomely tense now. Cat has borrowed more from her friend Lisa, who lends in good faith that the film will happen. But Cat will now be personally liable for around £80,000 if *Dark Moon* falls away (quite apart from her lawyer's bills). The Isle of Man's lost input could be guaranteed by Cat's wealthy mother, while our producer seeks replacement funds. Meanwhile Jenny Knight is being lacklustre and negative, telling the director he might as well go back to America for a while as long as he doesn't mind swimming the Atlantic because there are no funds to pay for his flight.

Tuesday 7th

At Lynda's care home gig this afternoon an infirm lady resident told us she was once secretary to the Marketing Manager at Harrods before the Second World War and remembers the Chairman in top hat, tails and pinstripes with his retinue doing the rounds. Another man, Joe, had a cabbie brother who regularly gave lifts to entertainer Jack Buchanan. Joe also saw Harry Champion perform at the Kilburn Empire in 1939. 'Boiled Beef and

Carrots'? 'Any Old Iron'? Never 'eard of 'em? – get art of ere!

Once there was another world, and those who inhabited it thought – as we do in this one – that it's the only one that exists and will go on forever.

Tuesday 14th

Valentine's Day gig with Lynda. Out she came in gorgeous get-up and we drove to a new care home in Stevenage where she treated the gathering to a glamorous and feelingful performance – including her peerless *My Funny Valentine*, and we did *Two Sleepy People* together. It was moving to see those people listening to love songs and looking wistful. Who was it said "always, everywhere, there is great courage"? In these places it's very strong.

Wednesday 15th

Was shaken this morning to realise, with the humiliation that goes with it (an apologetic phone call from a company whose little standing order has been dishonoured), that the Halifax Bank has stopped both my Halifax *and* Bank of Scotland credit cards – though each still has credit on – in what is evidently their latest move, having refused me more overdraft, to sever my lifelines so I will die more quickly. I wonder if this is fair banking practice, and can't help feeling that someone may have perpetrated an illegality in his or her zeal to play grim God over the hapless writer whose account is in their ghastly control.

Saturday 18th

On BBC TV's *Film 06* saw Jack Cardiff being interviewed almost fawningly by the usually flip and corrosive Jonathan Ross. I met Jack at a West End production office when he wanted to direct an earlier version of my screenplay *The Pond*. Afterwards we walked down the road together, and he was nimbler than me. An amazing man, in his 90s, still looks great, sharp-minded as a 20-year-old. When I think that he photographed Bogart and Hepburn in *The African Queen* it bends reality.

Sunday 19th

Cat phoned from Tunisia where she's having a break – back tonight. She says her mother has put up £180,000 towards the film, accessible now, so that will be our pre-production money (and my leap to freedom from what the Halifax Bank clearly believes to be an assisted death-plunge on their part?) as soon as all the funding's in place.

Thursday 23rd
A terrible shrilling woke me. Inky dark. Floundered for the light-switch. My God, it's 6.40 a.m. and Cat's on the phone wanting to share her anxieties. Her mother's accountant is urgently trying to persuade her not to risk her home and capital on her daughter's film.

Also, Cat continued in agitation, we'll lose the funding Prescience are putting up if we don't shoot by the end of March. Yesterday Gordon Truscott rang Jenny to ask why things are so slow. She told him it's because 'no one likes the script'. I've often thought this might be the case – there's nothing profound, soul-searching, intriguing or challenging in it any more, and I've had to give up as pointless any further endeavours to bring it back up to speed myself (all suggestions to this end having been brushed aside), so Jennifer's remarks left me feeling detached and uninvolved.

Saturday 25th
Have been pondering about the script that 'nobody likes' for the past couple of days. In the end had to virtually beg Cat to send me the latest so I can try to assess what the problem is. Rather to my surprise, Cat sent it. I opened the file in trepidation, and proceeded to read with dismay. It was like seeing an acquaintance after a lapse of time and being shocked at his gaunt, debilitated appearance. Got working at once on a new draft, bringing it slowly back to life. By midnight had had enough and crawled into bed.

Sunday 26th
No Sunday paper today, was too busy trying to repair the damage inflicted on *Dark Moon* since I last saw it. Finally finished around two o'clock. Its legs and lungs are working again, it even manages to dance a little. The scene-to-scene transitions flow more excitingly once more and the terror bits actually scare me. Felt I'd done a fair job in the time allowed, and emailed the result to Cat with a feeling of relief.

Monday 27th
Cat rang. "Gordon and I were working on the script till three o'clock this

morning," she began.

"Doing what?" I asked, pretty amazed and a bit alarmed, because what I'd sent back was tight and pacy again.

Cat: Gordon wants Laura and little Jason to arrive at the house at night.

Me: But Cat, you won't see anything, and would a mother send her small son off to play in the grounds of a strange place in total darkness?

Cat: Gordon wants it to be mysterious.

Me: It'll be that all right if no one can see anything.

Cat: (smaller-voiced) Dusk?

Me: Yeah, the house etched against the evening sky. Okay. But not night – *please* not night.

I suppose Cat must find me 'difficult'. I put down the phone and said to myself just make the film, pay me and let me get away from this never-ending writer's nightmare in which, as my friend says, the monkeys appear to rule the roost and metaphors get mixed willy-nilly ad infinitum.

MARCH

Thursday 2nd

Cat emailed the latest *Dark Moon* with Jenny Knight's clumsy deletions, directorial amendments and heaven knows what else. I checked it over anxiously. My heart has sunk so often on occasions like this it's grown its own coral reef. If this latest example of a mauled-about script were a girl at her first ball no one would be asking her to dance; indeed, the area where she was sitting might need to be cordoned off and the fumigators brought in. The draft I'd worked on so assiduously and cleansingly and sent to Cat had been ignored *in its entirety* – Truscott had stayed with the dodgy that one no one likes, and now it was even worse. Never has the expression 'I don't know why I bothered' resonated with more meaning. When Cat rang, she asked what I thought if it. Weary now and just wanting to get on I said it's okay. "I want it to be more than okay," she said anxiously. I admitted that, okay, it's a reasonably commercial script, but that we've long since lost what made it special in the past.

"It's got to end on page 97," Cat added.

'What?'

"Gordon is superstitious," she said. "All his scripts must end on an odd number. Unless it's page 100, in which case it's all right."

"You're joking, yes?"

"No."

This little beauty finished on page 96, so I had to spread the last few pages to make an extra one. Well, I'm all for a bit of superstition. Martin Scorsese is apparently like this too, only more so. And if it works for him who am I to quibble? Or even giggle?

Kate Rhodes James has sent the script to Gillian Anderson for 'Laura'. Gillian played Lady Dedlock in the BBC TV production of *Bleak House*, so this isn't exactly inspired casting, and Ms Anderson will be used to looking at quality material, which is certainly not what this script is any more. What we sorely need is a 'Bryce', too. Charles Dance looks good for 'Grimstone' – he played Tulkinghorn in *Bleak House* so this would be another dodgy lawyer to add to his portfolio. If we stay with Ms Rhodes James the entire cast could be made up of ex-*Bleak House* actors, perhaps with Johnny Vegas playing 'Braithwaite' the heavy? Hey, we could have him spontaneously combust just at the moment when...

Friday 3rd

A frosty car-window-scraping sort of day. Met writer pal Alan Wightman in Parliament Square. Alan has written for top comics including Bruce Forsyth and Jimmy Tarbuck, authored a book featuring Joe Pasquale, pens pantomimes. From a BBC contact he's acquired tickets for Ronnie Barker's memorial tribute in Westminster Abbey. In we went, the entrance lined with photographers waiting for celebrities such as Stephen Fry, Jimmy Tarbuck, Barry Cryer, Michael Palin and other big names – and actually looking *through* us as if we were invisible. Fair puts you in your place, it does.

My place was behind a huge pillar so I heard rather than saw Richard Briers reading the speech from *Henry V* "Now entertain conjecture of a time..." It had been Ronnie Barker's favourite film as a lad. Mine too, I still know that speech by heart, so felt a kinship with the great actor and comic as I whispered along with Briers: "Fire answers fire, and in their paley flames each battle sees the other's umber'd face; steed threatens steed in high and boastful neighs, piercing the night's dull ear..." Comedian Peter Kay gave a lengthy tribute in a very loud voice, followed by the remarkably tiny

Ronnie Corbett who was moving as well as funny. Both Alan and I felt a connection with the brilliant departed man: Alan wrote sketches and gags for *The Two Ronnies* and I was once a walk-on in the show as a wounded soldier in a Crimean War sketch (about which experience I wrote my first published magazine article). Mr Barker, we salute you.

Saturday 11th

Cat is very troubled by the *Dark Moon* finances and her part in them. Scare stories of her going bankrupt if it all collapses – and our producer constantly pushing her for more money, reminding her how increasingly in debt she (Cat) is getting, so the film "must go now" or she (Cat) "will be personally liable." When I told Cat that I'd rather this film stopped right now than she lose her home over it, she went quiet then said something strange – she said "Lynda is very lucky."

In the end Cat was doing what she's never done before, crying into the phone at how tense and stressful it all is. She's heroic, doing what she's doing. If I'd had the energy I would have cried right back.

Monday 13th

The Hubbards are now sole casting directors on *Dark Moon* – Kate Rhodes James having withdrawn. I wonder how much the lady was paid to end up giving sod-all to this increasingly benighted production while I do battle with banks and credit card companies who are trying to terminate me with increasingly malevolent determination.

Wednesday 15th

Cat tells me Gordon Truscott in Dublin has had the script converted to Final Draft and added more bits and pieces, while some important scenes have been deleted. But knowing Cat doesn't have Final Draft, they converted it to a pdf file and sent her that. I asked would she be kind enough to forward it to me? Which she did.

Saw at once that the draft I'd spent hours proofing and correcting (again) has been completely ignored (again) – it's still their *previous* draft they're running with, with all the mistakes and spellos, with stuff like *mantlepiece* instead of *mantelpiece* and *it's* instead of *its*. Weirdly, 'THE END' was all on its own at the top of page 91. Never in all the snubs and slights

I've endured as a writer in the years since this project began have I felt so ignored and isolated. This version is a shameful disgrace – it's imperative that no actor should see it. Gordon Truscott hadn't noticed anything wrong (maybe he's dyslexic?), nor presumably has Lorraine Ross, but I've no idea what our 'script editor' Jenny Knight was doing to save us all from looking like prize prats by sending out this abomination.

Unable to interact with the pdf file, I went through the script (yet again), raising a long list of corrections to be made. This took till nearly midnight, but at last I emailed it* to the production office in Dublin saying 'power to your computer and all who sail in her'.

*This too was completely ignored. It was as if no one wanted to acknowledge that I existed. Even as I write this now, it makes me shiver. In this country we have a practice of 'sending to Coventry' anyone considered to have violated the social or moral code. No one speaks or communicates with them; if they walk into a room everyone turns the other way or leaves. It felt exactly like that. Hard to think what I could have done to merit such vile treatment – my only 'crime' was in wanting to make this film as fine as it could possibly be, which started, of course, with the script. Yet 'they' seemed intent only in reducing its quality in the most cynical and cavalier ways – and here was the latest example of that.

Thursday 16th
Had been wondering about that widowed 'THE END' on page 91, and it occurred to me that when Gordon Truscott got the girl in the Dublin office to convert to Final Draft he must have insisted that the script should end on an odd-numbered page. Thinking, no doubt, the request as odd as the number, she gave as crazy as she got by doing this. Nice one.

Friday 17th
St Patrick's Day, and auditions for the parts of 'Laura' and 'Bryce' take place at the Hubbards today. At Lynda's gig this afternoon I sang 'Molly Malone' complete with accent. Two of my great-grandmothers were Irish, so I feel a kinship. My nephew Tim designed the footbridge over the Liffey at Dublin, and if oi were goin' there oi wouldn't start from here.

Towards eleven this evening Cat phoned. At the auditions today no 'Bryce' was found, but Andrea Corr – of the Irish group 'The Corrs' – blew all the others away for the part of 'Laura'. So I fell asleep to the thought of Andrea's lovely face and sweet searching tones in my mind speaking words I'd written (if any of them remain) – which was a lot more interesting than counting sheep.

Tuesday 21ˢᵗ

First day of Spring, yet felt on waking: '...Why doesn't my heart go dancing?' Cat rang towards 7.30 and managed to depress me further. Lorraine Ross tells her "I'm climbing Mount Everest at the moment," so let's hope she makes it without losing her oxygen mask. Throughout the day, call after call came from a troubled Cat, her family relationships are in disarray – she's worried about losing her home. I told her it should never have come to this. Then the latest blow – Prescience have just pulled out. But, says Lorraine, Scotts Atlantic have come on to replace them, with 16% sale and leaseback + 7% equity.

I then overheard Jenny Knight saying to Cat on the phone that they need a further €100,000 (about £60,000) *now* or will have to 'lay people off' (what people?). Also, that the loss of Prescience has been covered by reducing the budget further – now down to £2.9 million – by cutting even more from the script.

From: Lorraine Ross
To: Nigel Danvers
Date: 21 March 2006
Subject: Re: Dark Moon

The revised plan is:
We are looking at a budget of £2.9m - cut to the bone it must be said, but Jennifer and Gordon the director are confident this is worth going for.
375 Goldcrest
250 Telepool
499 Scotts Atlantic - see below
1375 Equity - includes 100k circular fees with the 1275 agreed
320 481

81 gap - to find
Recoupment will work as follows:
375 to Goldcrest + sales exs and 5% comm
375 to 1st tier deferments (to have been paid by Bank of Ireland originally, but easier this way) also on 5% comm - this represents basically all the fees on the film, with top-ups due in 2nd tier, then the balance worldwide, after a 15% commission, is available to the equity and second tier deferments which will give us space to restore people's original quotes.
You have the sales figures to run these numbers.
I have just heard from DCMS with a few minor queries, but nothing issued yet.
Best, Lorraine

Not sure who Nigel is, but on seeing this accidentally intercepted gem via Cat I wonder if I'd wandered into mathematician Hall territory again. The word 'deferments' sent a chill to my coccyx – a bit like the first intimations of a charge of heresy against a lapsed Protestant in the court of Henry VIII and what horrors might now creep up on him leading to the torture chamber, decapitation or burning at the stake. But other than that the latter part of Lorraine's text means as little to me as four-fifths of five-fourths of whatever-it-was.

Thursday 23rd
Had just arrived at Lynda's dementia care home venue at Whitechapel this afternoon when Cat called with disastrous news: Goldcrest have pulled out! But, says Lorraine, calm in the storm's eye, Pathé are 'very interested'.

Then came a worried call from Jeffrey Simmons, who had just spoken to Cat – he's very doubtful if this film will ever get made (though Cat can be very discouraging to talk to when she airs her angsts). Ah, that's all right then, just what I wanted to hear right now.

Lynda's Whitechapel gig went well. So did Jack the Ripper's.

Friday 24th
Keith Bearman of Bluebird Pictures in Los Angeles, friend and

supporter of Gordon Truscott, has offered to come in to save the film. Yet Jenny Knight (says Cat) was 'very rude' to him yesterday – these ladies don't want to work with him. Can't imagine Jennifer being rude, can you? Talk about biting the hand that wants to feed you.

They haven't heard from Pathé yet. Why do I feel we never will? Lorraine has now called a 4-week hiatus to give time for 'due diligence' to be applied in legally confirming the various funds, and to get the cast fully in place. So the team in Ireland (what 'team', and why?) has been laid off till after Easter, despite Cat having found the money to keep them going.

We're told that Goldcrest pulled out, as did Prescience, because they didn't like Andrea Corr in the main part! But Keith Bearman, having checked out this beautiful and gifted actress/songstress, is happy with her.

Tuesday 28th

Cat phoned to say Lorraine has applied to the UK Film Council for finance, and Lip Sync have been approached for post-production. Keith Bearman replaces the lost Goldcrest money (£450,000). It's hoped that the 15% sale and leaseback lost when Prescience pulled out (£400,000) can be replaced by Lip Sync. While producer Alan Latham (yes him) can come in with money from the government's new 20% tax credit scheme. Lorraine has also approached BBC Acquisitions, who are interested.

The Hubbards are having trouble casting 'Bryce' – Rupert Friend is latest to say no. Again I told Cat it's because that character has too little to do now – in the script they insist on running with, this role has been rendered a plodding bore with no tumult in him nor an ounce of wit. A sensitive actor could play the role with his eyes and make it work, his inner bewilderment explored until the explosive realisation – but such an actor has yet to come forward, and it needs a director with this quality of understanding to direct him.

APRIL

Wednesday 5th

Thick frost marks the end of the tax year, in which I again earned a disconcerting zilch. Cat informs me that Daniel Brühl had turned down the part of 'Bryce'. Again (and I grow so tired of saying it) my argument remains that in chopping off 'Bryce's' balls the re-re-re-writers have also reduced the potency of 'Laura', so the power of a woman's love for her man is never explored and the story loses tension because the key characters can only interact with each other in mundane ways.

Friday 7th

The film's budget is now down to £2.8 million as Jenny Knight continues stripping the script to save money – or so I'm informed by Cat, not of course being privy to this distressful activity.

Saturday 8th

Watched the Grand National on TV, identifying at first with the horses who ripped their forelegs through the brushwood fences and crumpled on landing – but then, with surging heart and nimble limbs, my name was Numbersixvalverde and I was romping home to win in a rousing finish. One can dream, but this triumph shows that dreams do come true if you stoke up enough energy and commitment behind them.

Thursday 13th

This evening, playing a Harry Connick CD and wondering why his delivery is so slow, the candle in the patterned metal holder Lynda once gave me cast a wavery mellow light on her face in the photo I took that summer in the Grimsdyke woods near Harrow, her Jean Harlow expression faintly mystified by life's vicissitudes, yet defiant and ethereally lovely. Even her hair glowed in the shimmer, and it seemed that her lips moved. I'm not sure what she was saying, but I hoped it wasn't "goodbye."

'Being defeated is often a temporary condition. Giving up is what makes it permanent,' says Marilyn vos Savant on my diary page today.

Wednesday 19th

Apparently Gordon Truscott left a vehement message on Lorraine Ross's phone asking why has she not locked down the actors or any of the finance? Her answer is, "Can't lock actors down till all the finance is in place and definite dates given." So on it drags. The UK Film Council meet on Friday re *Dark Moon* – but they're not sure whether Gordon Truscott is 'big enough' for them as a director.

Friday 21ˢᵗ

Cat tells me Lorraine has informed the crew in Dublin (what crew, and why?) that *Dark Moon* starts filming on May 22ⁿᵈ, with official pre-production in ten days time. Which makes it May 1st. So will it really be 'On the first of May, it is moving day'– or "May Day! May Day!" as our storm-battered vessel goes down with all hands save those who manage to scramble from the wreckage?

'Remember that there is nothing stable in human affairs; therefore avoid undue elation in prosperity, or undue depression in adversity.' So says Socrates on today's diary page.

MAY

Sunday 7ᵗʰ

Keith Bearman is arranging a party on his yacht at Cannes to promote *Dark Moon*, to which press and distributors are invited. Andrea Corr will be there, delaying a world tour to promote her new album in order to star as 'Laura' in *Dark Moon*. Should be good publicity, with plenty of photos and mentions of the film. Cat emailed me the poster Bearman has had done for Cannes. Looks good.

Wednesday 10ᵗʰ

Woken at 6.40 a.m. by Cat on the phone – still on the hook and can't get off it without bringing *Dark Moon* down, finding herself the main investor in her own movie. Our producer has persuaded her that the alternative is no film. Keith Bearman flies into London today, an inter-party agreement is being signed tomorrow by all investors, which will officially greenlight this film and enable the main actors to be locked down.

Found myself feeling a bit sorry for Cat, though she *did* see it coming. She tells me her fee is now down to £30,000 + expenses – but she still has no legally binding agreement. Andrea Corr's theatrical agent expects a deal for their client imminently.

Saturday 13th

Lynda performed at the Star and Garter home for ex-servicemen in Richmond. Duetted 'Together Wherever We Are' with her. Afterwards a man in wheelchair came over. His name is Louis Pengelly-Phillips. He still looks tough and resourceful and gave us a booklet he's had printed of some of his experiences in World War 2. A Royal Marine Commando, he escorted Churchill and the D-Day plans in the liner Queen Mary to the Quebec Conference, and shook hands with Churchill, Roosevelt and Stalin; came hazardously ashore under fire on Gold Beach during the D-Day landings; went on to fight the Japanese in Burma under Mountbatten. This man, chatting pleasantly to us, had done all this! I looked at him in awe, seeing the dashing young commando dodging German bullets and picking off Japanese snipers. Now he sits in a wheelchair, his mind alert and restless, embracing age and infirmity and determined to make them work for him.

Sunday 14th

Drove to Cat's house to meet Gordon Truscott before he goes to Cannes on Wednesday. A useful discussion, after which I pitched Lynda to play 'Jocelyn' if he'll let her read for the part. Yes, Gordon said. If not, he added warily, she can sing/play ukulele in the Irish bar scene. Certainly Lynda's hair fits the bill, even if her accent doesn't – though southern Irish isn't hard for a trained actress. When Truscott made his farewells to Cat he left the envelope behind in which were Lynda's photos and CV. I stopped him at the door and handed it to him, and he made as if he'd merely thoughtlessly forgotten it. And maybe he had…

Wednesday 17th

I wake to another bleak 5 a.m. Cat spent the afternoon with Lorraine yesterday. Apparently Jenny Knight is cutting back on the script even more – sounds as if there won't be much of it left to film, like peeling a potato to the size of a peanut. Again I protested to Cat that I should be consulted about deletions, but it's like coughing into a hurricane.

A call from producer Debi Nethersole, back from South Africa. We talked positively of making films, she wants a list of every screenplay I've got, at what stage and who it's with. Not counting *Dark Moon* (which can't be said to be my script any more) I have TEN feature screenplays ready to go, plus a pilot film and series for TV. It's hard enough getting them actually *read* by anyone, let alone produced.

'Courage does not always roar. Sometimes courage is the quiet voice at the end of the day saying, "I will try again tomorrow."' Mary Anne Radmacher on today's diary page.

Thursday 18th

At last, the producer of *Dark Moon* is in touch with my agent. Jeffrey Simmons phoned me – has spoken to Jenny Knight, who offers me £5000 'imminently', with deferred payments at some unspecified time later. Jeffrey managed to crank this amazing offer up to £6000, at which point she squealed "it's utterly *impossible* to make it any more."

She got back to Jeffrey with some very unsatisfactory dates for my 'deferred' fees. After ten years of slog on this project, it's a bit much – or, rather, the opposite.

From: Lorraine Ross
To: Jeffrey Simmons
Date: 18 May 2006
Subject: Dark Moon

Dear Jeffrey,
Following our phone conversation this afternoon, here is our proposed schedule for Robin Squire's fees on Dark Moon.
The film has attracted investments from the UK Film Council and from Cat Frome, also a sales advance from Bluebird Pictures who are selling the film in Cannes.
£5k paid from the budget on latest of principal photography (June 26) or financial closure, the balance as follows
i) collection agent fees (1%) and expenses
ii) Bluebird sales commission 20% (10% regarding France)
iii) allocation of sales expenses (overall cap $165k)
iv) Bluebird recoupment of up to £300k
v) "Second tier" delayed payments to include

£25k Robin Squire
vi) "third tier" payments to include
£500k equity repayment
£20k Robin Squire
vii) Further equity recoupment
viii) Deferments to include
£25k Robin Squire

Monday 22nd

This starts to look not so good. 'Delayed' and 'payments' are not attractive words when placed side by side – especially when related to the long-awaited recompense for the masses of work I've done over many years on this project, during which I've constantly battled against the odds to have my voice as a writer heard. After Jeffrey spoke staunchly to Jennifer Knight yesterday about the measliness of their initial £5000 offer to me, I'm now offered £7500 up front (10% of my contracted fee).

Cat asked whether I've had an invitation to Keith Bearman's party on his yacht at Cannes, as everyone else on 'the team' has. No, I said, feeling like the fat boy no one picks for their side, and wondered if Bearman even knows I exist.

Saturday 27th

Opened up the front cover file which Cat sent. When I saw what was on it the breath went from me.

Screenplay by
CATHERINE FROME, GORDON TRUSCOTT
and ROBIN SQUIRE

I sat down, sort of in shock. A valid screenplay credit is of vital importance to me, opening the way, I fervently hope, to professional recognition and more writing work after years in the shadows. Yet here I am pushed to the back yet again. Is this why our producers consider I'm worth no more than shelled peanuts in the first pay-out? – because, on the basis of the main credits Cat and Gordon have awarded themselves, they believe me to be no more than Santa's little helper?

Even though I know the script is now a feeble echo of what it once was, this latest smack in the teeth really got to me. Got Cat on the phone. I don't expect all that much in this world, I told her, but am sick of being undervalued and sidelined on this film, given no respect as a writer, being belittled, ignored, insulted, misapprehended and abused by the kind of people I would climb high walls studded with broken glass to avoid.

It was really was quite a paddy I got myself into. In the end Cat said she would put my name at the head of the credits, then emailed the amended front page to Jenny and Lorraine – copy to me:

> **From: Cat Frome**
> **To: Lorraine Ross, Jenny Knight**
> **Date: 27 May 2006**
> **Subject: Dark Moon screen credits**
>
> **PLEASE MAKE SURE THE CREDITS ON THE FRONT COVER APPEARS LIKE THIS.**
> **ENJOY THE WEEKEND.**
> **CAT**

Attached was a revised front cover showing:

Screenplay by:
ROBIN SQUIRE, CATHERINE FROME
AND GORDON TRUSCOTT

And then I thought, my God, will people now think I'm the *main perpetrator* of this scriptic concoction and assume the muddled mess to be a true representation of my work? That didn't feel good either. There seems no way I can win on this now.

Sunday 28th
Gig with Lynda at Bushey. We duetted 'Together Wherever We Are', after my gag that Gypsy Rose Lee's dress code stipulated that she always wore at least two feathers on stage. They go for it, we get cheers. But Lynda's solos are supreme, the swingin' Sinatra stuff, the transcendent 'Nightingale Sang In Berkeley Square', the soaring Gracie Fields songs, breathy Marilyn

Monroe with the little ukulele, heartwrenching torch numbers that bring the handkerchiefs out. Why isn't this girl famous? Why didn't the group happen? Michael Vine would have had them on national tours by now, TV spots, maybe we could be making that wild and wacky little musical film Andy Eastwood and I once dreamed of doing.

To Grimsdyke and strolled in the woods together. The May blossom is still out, heavy on the air. Inhaling the perfume I thought how good it would be to enjoy this latest Springtime with my career revived and Lynda with me for life, smiles and ease instead of unending tension wondering all the time whether we're sunk or gloriously relaunched.

JUNE

Friday 2nd
Jeffrey Simmons is a tower of power on my behalf, constantly pressing for more serious recognition of my input and pushing for a more substantial upfront payment. Meanwhile Keith Bearman tells Cat that Momentum Pictures have accepted *Dark Moon* for their slate, subject to seeing film footage. So someone, somewhere, must believe this film is going to happen. Meanwhile I limp on from day to day, ever deeper in debt, with nary a glimpse of any payment or pre-payment coming my way even after all this time as the banks prepare to dispose of my financial corpse.

Friday 9th
Had a long troubled conversation with Peter Jaques. He says any screen credit is usually better than no screen credit at all, but in this case he isn't so sure. If I'm hoping to generate more writing work on the basis of this one, having my name attached to something so degraded by others could work against me.

JULY

Saturday 1st
Already it's July, a perfect summer day, but I still don't know if we have

245

a film. It's the 90th anniversary of the Battle of the Somme, when thousands of our lads walked, under the bawled orders of their sergeants and a shrilling whistle of the kind used by football referees, in extended line into a hail of machine-gun fire on just such a morning. Thinking of this, my supposed woes shrank away in shame.

Then Cat rang. The conversation fair made my day, hearing that Palm Finance's $900,000 investment is on again.

Monday 3rd

The heatwave continues, in the 90°s. Took time out to meet Kerry Melanie and enjoy the heat by the river near Kew, have a cooling beer and a catch-up natter. A blissful balmy evening like yestergone and yet to be, like southern France and being young, summers in Bordeaux sailing to and fro... er...

There are swans on the Thames here and, despite the vicissitudes of fortune, life is worth living when dusk shrouds the river and light stays in the sky to northward and Jerome Klapka himself might come sculling past with two friends and a dog, grins illuminate faces and I'm with Kerry whose Pan-like shadow showed mad, glowed dusky... and no doubt still does, though the lass moves rather more sedately these days.

Tuesday 4th

Jeffrey Simmons rang, 'hopping mad', as he put it – the day for payment of my 'first tranche' money was yesterday, and not a word from anyone. Things look dire, and Jenny Knight doesn't return his calls. America being on holiday today there's no chance of hearing from Palm Finance till at least tomorrow. It's incredible how it goes on and on.

Wednesday 5th

Cat phoned first thing: "Today's the day," she announced. Yes, it's crunch time, because if Palm don't complete their offered loan with a Term Sheet, and Keith Bearman's Hedge Fund doesn't come through, *Dark Moon* will collapse and our producers will walk, leaving Cat in one inglorious mess.

An awful email cataloguing debts accrued was sent yesterday by Jenny Knight to interested personnel. Apparently, when Gordon Truscott left

Ireland last week he had to do a moonlight flit from the hotel and borrow cash to get to the airport. So they're wallowing in debt over there, and ICM will 'pull' Andrea Corr this Friday if her £50,000 fee isn't paid into escrow.

No chance to do any work today – nor felt like it. Escaped to a Jewish lunch club in Edgware where Lynda performed. Dodging food trolleys I shook maracas, sang 'Together Wherever We Are' with her, then got drenched in a downpour putting sound equipment back in the car. It's stuff like this keeps me from going insane (?)

From: Richard Broxbourne (Cat's lawyer)
To: Sheila Cheeseman (Lorraine's lawyer)
Date: 5 July 2006
Subject: Dark Moon

Dear Sheila
I now understand that my client has been asked to find a further sum of £8,000 to keep pre-production going. Please appreciate that my client's confidence is being seriously eroded regarding the financing of this film for reasons already known. My client already has a substantial amount invested in pre-production, yet continues to be asked for further monies. I am writing to indicate that my client cannot consider any further investment until a Term Sheet is made available.

Thursday 6th

As far as Cat's concerned, it's all over: keeping her home is more important than risking the money to get *Dark Moon* away. Likewise her sister, who now needs her money freed up for business purposes. Also, Lorraine Ross's contract expired last month. Is that really it then, after all this time?

I told Jeffrey Simmons the bitter news, he rang Cat himself and has also sent a message to Jenny Knight about the non-appearance of my sliver of the financial cake. Lawyer Broxbourne says that bills run up in Ireland in the name of Dark Moon Films are the liability of Lorraine Ross's company, not Cat.

Friday 7th
Jeffrey has written to Jenny Knight saying the July 3rd deadline has passed, and still no money. Her reply makes jolly reading.

From: Jennifer Knight
To: Jeffrey Simmons
Date: 7 July 2006
Subject: Dark Moon

Dear Jeffrey
Robin has not been paid, nor anyone else, because the film is not now going ahead. Finances have failed to close and we have shut down pre-production. Apologies for not returning your call but I have been extremely busy attempting to resolve this situation.
If and when things start to progress I will of course let you know.
Regards
Jenny

Meanwhile Andrea Corr has told her agent she wants to stay on till finances are sorted, and has gone off for a week's holiday. I feel she is warmth amid cold and calculation. Not having been 'locked down' with a pre-payment, the French actor whose name escapes me has gone (why French?) – so a new 'Bryce' is required.

Rang Jeffrey to say the landscape doesn't look quite as bleak as Jenny Knight's email suggests. But he's angry now. On asking Cat yesterday to provide my first tranche payment and claim it back later, she says she has no money. When he said I might have to withdraw my rights in the script, she said dismissively "I don't think you'll find much of it is his any more." "She's devaluing you," says Jeffrey. I said don't worry, I'm used to it – I've been devalued on this project for so long it's become a way of life, but I've always been called back in when things went too badly wrong.

A sombre day – a year ago suicide bombers hit London, today the murdered and maimed were movingly remembered and celebrated.

Wednesday 12th

Weather sweltery hot. A call from Cat gave little heart – just more delays with Keith Bearman. Essentially they're now awaiting the term sheet of another U.S. investor called Grenville Peters. Once terms are okayed, a company called Blue Rider can be approached for pre-production money and we'll be away. So it's not quite belly-up time yet, apparently.

This afternoon drove to Rotherhithe in south-east London with Lynda, where she performed to the local Stroke Club. Her audience had all recovered from strokes, and a more feisty, positive, perceptive, cheerful gathering would be hard to find. Drove there through the old Victorian tunnel under the Thames and performed at a place called The Old Mortuary, and the venue room was where the bodies used to be laid out. The earliest ancestor traced on my mother's side was one Joyce Floyd, who had property at Rotherhithe in the 17th Century. I found myself wondering if Joyce had lain here in this very room when the Grim Reaper caught up with her, the place looked old enough. Hi Joyce, from down the years. We are kin. It felt rather odd to be singing 'Happy Days Are Here Again' in this one-time place of death.

Thursday 13th

Cat a bit brighter this morning – Keith Bearman has now agreed to U.S. film investment banker Grenville Peters's term sheet. Seems he was asking for a share of gross profits, but they reduced him to net.

Gigged with Lynda at a care home in Oxhey this afternoon. Warbled 'Two Sleepy People' and 'Together Wherever We Are' with her to a full room. The carer says that one of the elderly male dementia residents gropes the female staff here (or tries to), but they're very nice about it. The sex urge is the last thing to go, we were told with a laugh.

'In America only the successful writer is important, in France all writers are important, in England no writer is important, in Australia you have to explain what a writer is.' Geoffrey Cotterell on today's diary page.

Saturday 15th

Heatwave weather. With Lynda to Farnham Castle this evening for an open-air performance of Shakespeare's *The Two Gentlemen of Verona* under a gradually-darkening cobalt sky. The play came well to life in that environment, and of course Shakespeare was written for the open-air. The actor who played 'dog' was great, cocking his leg at people in the audience and jumping in their laps. Afterwards, the beautiful young actress who played 'Silvia' was spied having vigorous sex with one of the actors on a car bonnet in the pitch-dark field where the vehicles are parked. The Bard himself would have approved.

Tuesday 18th
94°F on my car's exterior thermometer. Don't think I've ever known it so hot in England.

Wednesday 19th
Cat rang with sad news: there isn't any. Seems Keith Bearman gave verbal abuse to Lorraine Ross when she stressed to him the extreme urgency of getting the $900,000 in from Grenville Peters – who 3 days ago was waiting for documents showing pre-sales and distribution. But Bearman now talks of getting Blue Rider to put up $1.75 million to cover everything, including pre-production funds – so what's going on?

So we thought yesterday was hot. Met Kerry at her place of work and drove to our favourite pub by the river, the Bull's Head at Strand-on-the-Green. On the way to pick the lass up my car's thermo showed 99°F (*37°C*), the so-called air conditioning jetting hot air – it needs recharging with refrigerant gas and I can't afford it – so instead wrapped a chilled wet towel round my neck, stuffed a freezer block inside my shirt and travelled like that, all windows down, and arrived looking like a boiled beetroot with circulation problems.

But what an evening we had, sat out on the towpath, feet dangling, a faint breeze blowing up the Thames. Swans and Canada geese, with a fleet of tiny goslings zooming about the water. When dark came and I drove Kerry back it was still 81°F (*28°C*). It's been the hottest day recorded here since 1911 at Epsom in Surrey.

What hasn't been so hot is the news on *Dark Moon*, of which none was waiting when I got home – just '0' glaring at me from the answering machine's message counter.

Thursday 20th

Dark Moon just refuses to rise, no matter what. Maybe the project is indeed cursed. A bleak feeling walking out in the heat to shore up my heavily overdrawn bank account with cash taken from a credit card to stop them bouncing the latest credit card repayment cheques.

Got back to a call from Cat, who said "Things are looking better." Grenville Peters has emailed our producer to say he's now ready to sign. Can we dare to hope he might do so reasonably sharpish, given that Lorraine is off to China to join her family on holiday. Not on a slow boat, let's pray.

Friday 21st

Escaped to Goring-by-Sea where Lynda's parents have a wedding anniversary. Sitting in the heat beside the sun-sparkled sea got a call from Cat to say the term sheet has now been SIGNED by Grenville Peters, but not to get too excited as we're still £100,000 short. She said Lorraine reckons she can raise this from the bank with pre-sales as security. Whatever, it felt like some kind of reprieve, as if being told I'm not to be executed tomorrow but might be the day after with a different firing squad.

Tuesday 25th

Another terrific day weatherwise, but I dread the post. A message from Cat that we're awaiting confirmation from Blue Rider for the rest of the money – should know today (L.A. time).

Sad call from Lynda. That marvellously talented, beautiful girl doesn't deserve this. A corporate agent put her up for a £200 job in Marlow for a 90th birthday party – the kind of thing she does supremely well. But the woman organising it claims to have seen Lynda performing in a care home for £60 – and says the agent is therefore 'grossly overcharging' for her. End of job. Lynda was nearly in tears at such ill-fortune. I said that woman will burn in hell for not only devaluing her talents but discrediting her in front of an agent who hadn't used her before, and will now possibly never do so again*.

The agent took Lynda off his books.

251

Wednesday 26th

Another long hot one. Still nothing from Keith Bearman via Cat. It's incredible. Mid-morning I texted to her: 'Can't believe this silence! Surely SOMETHING must be happening?? Do we have a film or not??? Has EVERYONE gone on holiday at this critical time?'

To Lynda's for noon in the high heat, which climbed to 92°F as we drove to the care home beyond Twickenham. She was wearing the red and white patterned dress, looking elegant and cool despite the temperature. Thank God for her to take my mind off terminal poverty if the film fails. We duetted 'Together Wherever We Are', then 'Everybody Loves Somebody Sometime', and our cares evaporated a bit. Strange how my teenage dream of being a crooner is creeping into a warped form of reality.

After, to Newens at Kew for tea, a stroll by the river. Magical things with Lynda, sultry herself in this weather.

11.15 p.m. the phone rang and it's Cat from Spain. Lorraine hasn't gone to China yet. The last £100,000 of the money is being signed for with Blue Rider today. With this document signed, pre-production can start in 2 weeks for a September shoot.

The Israelis continue their incursion into Lebanon, trying to knock out the Hezbollah rocket-launchers and regain the unquiet peace. There is so much hatred in the world it's as if insanity is the norm.

Saturday 29th

Set up our sound system on a heat-drenched lawn at a garden fête in Elstree. Lynda was great, we duetted to people prowling about the stalls, then she set in amongst them playing ukulele.

After tea in a café bypassed by time at the prettyesque village of Aldbury in Hertfordshire with pond and stocks, we lay in the grass near Ivinghoe Beacon and talked about all manner of things, including the sitcom pilot I'd like to write for her. She came out with some improvised lines, a natural comedienne. In an otherwise negative world this gave us a positive zing we enjoyed at the time. Such moments of daring-to-believe are to be treasured.

Monday 31st

I remind myself that all my other film scripts I've been polishing till I can see my face in them stand little chance of even getting read unless *Dark*

Moon happens. Left a 'what's happening?' message on Cat's mobile – hope she doesn't think I'm getting neurotic. Minutes later she rang, back from her Spanish holiday and has just heard that U.S. funding company Blue Rider have approved the $500,000 loan for *Dark Moon*! An account is being set up with Barclays in Soho Square to receive the money, so by the end of next week, with all contracts signed, crewing can begin and principal actors can be locked down.

Cat made no mention of 'locking down' the writer too with a nice cheque to ease his financial wretchedness. I expect those in control of the finance will do all in their power not to pay me till principal photography starts in September, so it's good to know that Jeffrey Simmons is there.

AUGUST

Tuesday 8ᵗʰ

Being at the very end of the information chain like this feels a bit like the Free French Brigade at the end of the Gazala Line in the Libyan Desert in 1942, except I don't have Colonel-General Erwin Rommel and his Afrika Korps trying to wipe me out, only the banks. Such a pity about *La Miss*, which I still believe is eminently makeable now that Susan Travers's ghost-written book has come and gone, so to speak. I'd have got at least £100,000 as my writer's fee for that, plus generous profit percentage, with John Glen or John Irvin directing. What a piece of cinema that could still be! – and all clear legally (as it always was).

Cat also says Keith Bearman has secured Momentum's full financial involvement, while Blue Rider are 'slow but getting there'. Slow, did you say?

Slow?

Thursday 10ᵗʰ

Towards lunchtime Cat surprised me by being in Barbados. She tells me she had dinner last night with Laura Heath, daughter of Duncan who owns the ICM agency*, while his ex-wife Hilary is there too, in a chalet up the beach from theirs. It's a tough life for some people.

I told Cat about the Al Qaeda plot in today's news, foiled by our police, to blow up planes in mid-air over the Atlantic using liquid explosives brought on board in drinking bottles by suicide bombers. It's horrifying that this generation is spawning such blind hatred, chilling to know it could go on for years.

Now Independent Talent Group.

Thursday 24th
Gigged with Lynda at a home in Twickenham. It started at 2.30, the same time Jeffrey is seeing Lorraine Ross at her office. It bucked me to know that my literary agent is meeting the *Dark Moon* producer at last.

Had just parked at Kew after the gig when Jeffrey rang my mobile. Lynda saw the dismay in my face. The realities are, he said, the film should have happened in June but $900,000 via Keith Bearman fell away, hence our being still underfunded. The Blue Rider money due in this week will barely cover what's needed to lock down actors and get pre-production going again – not a penny (or cent) of it will find its way to me. Lorraine said shooting is more likely to start October 16th. I went cold. I've gone cold so often these past months I'm deep-frozen.

SEPTEMBER

Friday 1st

From: Lorraine Ross
To: Jeffrey Simmons
Date: 1 September 2006
Subject: Dark Moon payments

Dear Jeffrey
Robin Squire will be paid an initial £9000, due either on first day of shooting or on the closing of finance, whichever comes first. I would guess around mid October. Andrea Corr, who is to play our heroine, is also releasing her first solo album this autumn so we need to dovetail dates. It is good that she, and so many other members of the team, have retained their excitement for the film through what

has been an unusually difficult financing process even by the standards of this industry!

Robin is then due further sums to make up his fee to £75,000. I am not yet able to provide a full schedule of when these payments will become due, as Catherine Frome, his fellow writer* and producer of the film with us, has been out of the country this week.

With best regards

Lorraine Ross

*Once there was an emperor who desired a new set of clothes dripping with opulence and glowing with the colours of the rainbow and a thousand sunsets. And there came unto the palace a person who announced herself a dressmaker, though no cloths did she appear to carry, merely a pair of scissors and a magic thread that none at first made claim to see...

Below the pasted-in email on my diary page the above lines had been scrawled. I will keep them in if only because they indicate something of my stressed state of mind at the time.

Sunday 3rd

Leafing through the local free newspaper today, got to the birthday announcements with photos of cute kids with captions like Gayle Lane, Happy 18th; and a little girl in Wonderwoman costume saying: 'Wonder Woman is 30'; then a monochrome moppet with unfashionable hairstyle saying 'Look who's 50'.

Then I got to one:

MARTIN DONALD
'THE DUCK'
In 14 years we were together,
We had special moments.
You made us happy,
You made us laugh,
And now you have made us cry.
Love always, Mandy x
Keshia x and Tyren x

It hit me in the throat. It was an obituary. The simplicity of the words was so powerful I couldn't speak for some time, and I note it here for that reason.

Monday 4th
Cat says Keith Bearman is demanding that big expenses incurred by his company on *Dark Moon* be paid back from the budget on first day's filming. This includes yacht hire at Cannes, Andrea Corr's travel/hotel, poster design and so on, so to cover this the filming must be cut from 5 weeks to 4.

Now Lorraine is returning none of Cat's phone calls. Has she pulled out? Has Keith Bearman? Are we STILL moon-gazing with *Dark Moon*? I love these morning conversations with Cat, they make me toy with the thought of buying – for the first and possibly last time in my life – a large bottle of sleeping tablets.

Monday 11th
Remembrance ceremonies in America, notably at Ground Zero where the Twin Towers fell five years ago. It was deeply moving. The horror of that day, and how it must have been to be there, invades dreams and turns them to nightmares.

Wednesday 13th
Still summer warm. Cat has signed documents to open a bank account to lodge Blue Rider's half million dollars. The completion bond is to be signed on the 23rd of this month – and 3 weeks thereafter filming can start! Yipppeeeeeee.

Lynda did a late-night solo cabaret spot with her ukulele at Volupté Lounge off Chancery Lane this evening. She went on at 9.20 for 20 minutes and was well received. The sultry, glittery ambience is such a change from the care homes, and inspires her. The female manager liked her, and perked up even more on seeing a photo with Andy Eastwood and Janet Beale in her ex-publicity. "Maybe your group could perform here?" she said. *Group*? Dear Lynda. Drove my Cinderella home for midnight. Rain had drenched the streets. Once there was a dream that could have come true. Is *Dark Moon* merely another?

Saturday 23rd

The final document was signed by Cat yesterday. So at last Blue Rider – and the film of *Dark Moon* – are go! When the half million bucks are in, principal actors can be secured. Pre-production is expected to resume on Thursday the 28th in Dublin for a start-filming date of October 16th. When all is up and running Cat suggests we meet in London for a glass of champagne. She also says she has a storyline ready for her next film, so let's her and me "get together and write the screenplay." At this I turned to the relatively undamaged part of my wall and gave it a meaningful look. Then I felt a bit moved, because despite my having being consigned to no man's land on this film by everyone else, Cat still seems to have enough regard for me to invite me to do this.

Put down the phone.

Didn't jump up and down like once I would have done.

Just let the news seep quietly in and will do my best to believe it.

Thursday 28th

Cat phoned at 8 a.m. Although Blue Rider had all the required documents last Friday and promised to pay (into *Dark Moon*'s UK account) immediately, the money still isn't there and they've stopped returning Lorraine Ross's calls. Have Blue Rider fallen off their horse?

Saturday 30th

Went with Lynda and Nicola to the Imperial War Museum where their parents Peter and Joan talked publicly about being children during the war, evacuation, rations and so on. During the Blitz, Joan's mother told them "If we're going to die we'll all die together." Both came over confidently, with a V2 buzzbomb hanging overhead and the awesome V1 rocket soaring roofwards beside the desk they sat at. To give some inkling of what it was really like, the organiser said the London Blitz was like 9/11 in New York happening for forty nights in succession. Behind them stood an old London bus that ferried troops to the front in the First World War. 'Old Bill' it was called. You thought of the lads who climbed on it, whistling and cheery, not realising that all too many of them were being driven in the Springtime of their lives to pointless death.

OCTOBER

Wednesday 4th
They've managed to track the Blue Rider half million dollars to India. *India?* So it goes on a world tour first before heading for London? It should be here today, they hope, or tomorrow – but even then we're not out of the wood – there's an Inter-Party Agreement to sign yet, and I wonder if even now Denise Cotton might come diving in out of the sun with all guns blazing, bearing some mystifying legal injunction that will stop this film in its tracks forever. Then, too, the ghost of Fons Verhoeven or Saul Wilson might materialise from the shadows claiming authorship of the entire piece.

Friday 6th
With the Blue Rider money having arrived in London at last, blinking shyly around as if surprised to find itself here, all looks like go. 'Shy' the money might well be, though 'positively scared' would be more appropriate seeing as it's about to be hit harder and more often than George Foreman was hit by Mohammed Ali in the rumble in the jungle.

Monday 9th
It's all starting to move forward again like a dancer with a broken foot gingerly trying out a few steps. Lorraine is trying to hire the same crew as before (?), but at a lower rate. Cat warns me about approaching Gordon Truscott yet about the gambling bar sequence to feature Lynda singing. I asked when filming was to start. "November 23rd" she said. I laughed heartily. If these delays go on, Gordon will be directing in a Santa Claus outfit with little elves as runners.

Wednesday 11th
Interesting story from the day centre where Lynda performed this morning: a handsome lady called Kay, in her 80s, tells how she was once a 'bathing belle'. At the Palais de Danse in Nottingham she met a handsome fellow who took a shine to her. He asked if he could take her out. She was attracted, but during their date something about him made her uneasy, so she slipped away when he wasn't looking. It wasn't till later that Kay realised her date had been Neville Heath, the sadistic murderer of women.

Thursday 12th

Okay. Latest delay is, Keith Bearman must secure two more signed pre-sales to act as collateral before Grenville Peters will release the $840,000 he is loaning at interest to *Dark Moon*. So suddenly it's heart-in-mouth time again. Also, Momentum, who agreed to invest, are looking shaky. Irish co-producer James Flynn sent Bearman an email yesterday requesting news on the said pre-sales, without which nothing can move.

Anything good at all, Cat, before I go hang myself? Well, Andrea Corr is still keen. Hubbard Casting have been paid and all outstanding debts in Ireland cleared. Now all are standing by in wait for Keith Bearman's two pre-sales. But will he get them?

If he doesn't it leaves Cat with massive personal debts via loans from friends and family. Which is why she's so worried, and why her lawyer's bill for £30,000, arriving on top of everything else, was about as welcome as a jar of pickled gherkins at an indigestion-sufferers' reunion.

Friday 13th

Keith Bearman is flying into London next week to lock down Momentum, who are good for £750,000. All this potential money flying about, and on this Friday the 13th I find I've overdrawn my newly negotiated £2500 overdraw limit at the Halifax, so again had to take cash from my ever-closer-to-the-limit Barclaycard to shore it up. It's like taking part in a nightmare, and however hard you try and wake, you can't.

Monday 16th

Yes, here they come, like rottweilers sprung from a cage: not one but FOUR letters from Halifax Bank. Gee guys, have a heart. I know what these are about, threatening death by starvation accelerated by a thousand cuts to the flesh, swingeing additional charges and jolly things like that. So I didn't open any of them, life's better that way. They sit there like hand grenades waiting to have the pins removed, fizzing venomously. My financial situation is rapidly becoming untenable and I'm casting about in increasing desperation for a lifeboat.

From: Jeffrey Simmons
To: Lorraine Ross
Date: 16 October 2006
Subject: Update please

Dear Jenny and/or Lorraine
Today was the day predicated for payment of £9,000 to my
client Robin Squire when I spoke to Lorraine.
I know there is some delay but would appreciate an update
please.
Best wishes
Jeffrey
JEFFREY SIMMONS LITERARY AGENCY

★   ★   ★

From: Jennifer Knight
To: Jeffrey Simmons
Date: 16 October 2006
Subject: Re: Update please

Dear Jeffrey
Unfortunately the filming has not restarted today. We
continue to work at bringing Dark Moon to the screen and
are hopeful we might commence production this year but
cannot give a firm date as the financing is not under our
full control.
We will keep you up to date as things progress.
Best Jenny

'The only thing that makes life possible is permanent, intolerable uncertainty;
not knowing what comes next.' – Ursula K. le Guin on today's page of my diary.

Thursday 19th
Good to get out for a gig with Lynda at St Albans this evening. A packed
room and nice atmosphere. We duetted 'Nice Work If You Can Get It'.

Afterwards, an elderly gentleman with ramrod bearing told me how he lost his best friend when a landmine blew him up on landing at Anzio in 1944. He'd been walking just behind him through the hell and fury. They were known as Ted and Ned (Edward and Edwin) and always getting up to escapades like raiding the cookhouse for sandwiches. Clearly he (Ted) had never got over this loss, to tell it to me over 60 years later with fond chuckles and misty distant looks. I said "I'm sorry about your friend," and added "wherever Ned is, he's still young." "Yes, he was 20," came the reply, "and I was 21."

Dined Lynda frugally at the Little Chef nearby. Sitting opposite her she looked enormously pretty, her heart-shaped face and rich russet hair clustered around it, and I suddenly felt blessed and optimistic. There'll be good news tomorrow about the film, surely – and surely she'll get some better-paid corporate gigs soon.

On the way back I thought about Ted Barley losing his friend at Anzio, and how immediate it still is to him. On getting home, I looked it up. It was Operation Shingle. The father of Roger Waters of Pink Floyd also died at Anzio, it's a recurring theme in the band's work. They recorded a song about the battle: 'When The Tigers Broke Free'. It breaks the heart.

Friday 20th

Cat phoned at last. Are we in imminent collapse? It seems not quite. Shooting is intended for November 26th – but this apparently depends on Keith Bearman having his two pre-sales confirmed so that U.S. investment banker Grenville Peters will release his loan money. Bearman is currently in Europe reconfirming the Telepool pre-sale from Germany and hoping to lock down an Italian and French one. He's in London on Monday to lock down Momentum (£750,000), and will meet Lorraine Ross and Gordon Truscott to get them up to date with everything.

So Monday/Tuesday we should have a start date confirmed.

Cat tells me £150,000 of the $500,000 from Blue Rider in the UK account has already been used to settle debts in Ireland and do other 'good works' – but actors can't be secured until filming dates are certain. And the writer is right at the back of the queue and not allowed to make any demands, so shut up.

Saturday 21st

Weather started lousy, but drove Lynda to Hastings to escape the intensifying worry and look up old friends. But they all had gone since our last visit three years ago, including Ruth at Katie's Pantry, now living in South Africa. Lynda was so shaken to be sitting in that same teashop, same furniture and décor but now run by strangers, she had to rush off to the loo, re-emerging red-eyed and sniffling.

We walked on the beach, past the old jetty at dusk and down where the fishing boats park, and a thunderstorm hit us, sheet lightning all over the sky and thundery rumbles. Then rain came down so hard we were soaked in moments. We peeled off our sodden top-clothes and drove home like that, heater at full blast. Had to stop for petrol so dragged my wet trousers back on, filled the tank up and limped soggily to the paypoint. The man watched curiously as I returned to the car and struggled out of my trousers and shirt again, while this curvy redhead, also in underwear, sat painting her nails. We imagined him muttering "London folk..."

Tuesday 24th

A glimpse of the other life – went into London to meet writer pal Alan Wightman. Found him at Hurst House, actor Neil Morrissey's low-lit nightspot behind the Cambridge Theatre in Covent Garden. There too was Michael Vine – Alan's agent, manager to magician Derren Brown and once keen to manage Lynda's 'Red Hot & Blonde'.

Funny how we Brits don't call our Alans 'Al'. He's in town hoping for the job of writing a book of Anita Harris's life. I mentioned how Anita had spontaneously duetted 'Dream a Little Dream' with Lynda at Dave Lee Travis's birthday party.

A crazy evening, Michael in great form. He took us all to Groucho's, excellent meal with laughs and chats. This man pays in cash – for everyone – and if I were a woman I would want to eat him. Couldn't help thinking of how Denise Cotton had once dined Fons Verhoeven in this same restaurant, and later Saul Wilson, under that same ornate ceiling, the same walls listening to their whispers about *Dark Moon* and perhaps me ("Cat has to rewrite him, you know; I'd have done so myself but I was doing a spot of brain surgery at the time..."). Yet now it's they who have been cast into outer darkness on this film and I'm the one still standing within its flickering penumbra hoping the lights don't go out completely.

Thursday 26th

Left on Cat's phone my now routine anxious message as the wolves at my door have begun pushing inside and baring their fangs. The silence ate in. By mid-morning all the stuffing came out of me and the great scribe lay in a daze wondering if he'll ever be able to move his pencil again.

The phone roused me from my stupor. It was Cat! "Sorry not to have been in touch," she said, "had such a day yesterday." Lorraine is now going for January 15th, but is also saying there might be a window to go earlier, on November 26th.

Meanwhile U.S. investor Grenville Peters still awaits written confirmation of two of Keith Bearman's pre-sales. Bearman urges Lorraine: "Get the film started NOW, the money will catch up with you." But our ladies won't, not till all is in place.

Friday 27th

Drove to Epsom with Lynda for a luncheon club gig at a Social Centre. The place was unusually packed – and the organiser said it was because they'd all come to see *her*. She did a marvellous show, holding them for over an hour. During this we duetted 'Together Wherever We Are', and 'Ev'rybody Loves Somebody Sometime' (me doing my much-derided in-the-family Dean Martin take-off).

Now this is weird. While I was packing up the equipment and she was chatting to people as she does, Lynda said "They're raving about you – come over." So I did. At one table they were saying things like "We saw the 'Ratpack' show – you ought to join them." One woman compared my so-called 'voice' to Dean Martin, another *Bing Crosby* (!) (I merely record what was said to show how strange people's perceptions can be). Then a man named Roy, once a *professional singer*, said I have a "rich baritone, reminds me of Matt Monro."

Ha ha. More a poor baritone, methought, with holes in its socks. And the manager at the end, thanking my ukulele-playing songstress, added "and it was a special bonus having Rob to sing too."

Shades of Walter Mitty? Of course. I was quite unable to understand it, but wondered if it has anything to do with Lynda giving out her story of me being an ex-professional singer who has lost his nerve in public and she's trying to coax me back – for these are kindly, decent, encouraging people. Which sure makes a welcome change from the line-up on *Dark Moon*.

Saturday 28th
Tentatively opened a letter from Halifax Bank, expecting it to tell me helpfully the precise state of my account – but it was dishonouring a cheque for £150 and charging me £30 for telling me so. I was so appalled to have already (again) exceeded my new OD limit, checked all my credit card balances. Rarely have I felt such despair, finding I've almost reached the limit with two of them, and exceeded it with the others. Being also at the very limit of my OD facility with the NatWest too, I realised I've actually reached 'the wall' beyond which human life cannot exist. A small voice whispered "There's no future in this." It was right. I am gutted, filleted, eviscerated and left out in the sun to shrivel. My pips are squeaking so loudly I can hardly hear myself scream. Will you hurry up and happen, film – *pleeeeaaaase*!

NOVEMBER

Friday 3rd
Cat was told last night by some smartie that getting an independent film away is a virtual impossibility. So are we all attempting the impossible, which takes a little longer? Keith Bearman, at the American Film Market, is telling Lorraine Ross that until main actors are locked down he is unable to obtain the required pre-sales which will bring Grenville Peters's money in.

Saturday 4th
Lynda performed in a cabaret at St Peter Port, Guernsey, on behalf of the Lady Taverners charity. We flew there from Gatwick, lorded and ladied it in the best hotel on the island, quite a culture shock. She had 20 minutes, and was transcendent, the hall full of well-heeled folk roaring for more: from the wistfully haunting 'My Funny Valentine' to Formby's raucously

rhythmic 'Leaning On A Lamp Post'. Not only that, she looked terrific. Corporate agent Laura Collins (once a dancer with *Pan's People* of sighsome memory) booked her. Such great people, and – being a tax haven – a millionaire at every turn ('there goes one!'). It reminded me of England in some forgotten time of security, greenness and peace.

Monday 6th
My central heating's packed up and the weather's getting cold enough to give a brass monkey reproductive problems. The pump has conked out. Would call in the Corgi man but can't afford to.

Wednesday 8th
Lorraine Ross spoke to Keith Bearman last night, said Cat. YES? WELL? "Keith was very positive, he says everything's in good order and a new collateral schedule is being made out." I imagined telling the Halifax Bank "don't worry, everything's in good order and a new collateral schedule's being made out."

Thursday 9th
Determined now to insist on £5000 advance or close the film, rang Cat's number – she wasn't there. What to do? A thought came to me, something I never wanted to do however bad things got. Well right now they could hardly be badder. Phoned Kerry at work and put the situation to her. "How much do you want, Dad?" she asked cheerily. "Five? Till January? No problem. I'll post you a cheque today."

Mothers and fathers, there is treasure in your lives, and when it gleams with sudden brightness through the murk it warms the soul.

Saturday 11th
Now Lynda, this is when we went to Hampstead Heath carpark after tea at Polly's café down near the station. It was dark by now, the area unlit and at first I stroked your feet because it calms you, and we talked of many things, and I couldn't believe how beautiful you are, your face pallid in the dark car. Sometimes we yell and grumble, nothing's easy, not in your career either, there are too many who are blind. But this was so wispy silky throbbingly fantabulously eruptively magnificent it blew out the skies and dissolved the night.

Tuesday 14th

Troubled calls from Cat – things really aren't looking good on *Dark Moon*, despite all the hype. Here's the latest:

a)   Lorraine Ross refuses to lock down main actors till Keith Bearman's required pre-sales have been signed.

b)   Keith Bearman's required pre-sales can't be signed until main actors are locked down.

c)   Grenville Peters's money won't be released to complete the funding unless/until those pre-sales are signed and the actors locked down.

It seems that Lorraine is thinking of her reputation – she doesn't want to pay out to secure actors, find Bearman's pre-sales don't come good and come a cropper again (as well as losing that money to the actors if the film fails to happen, because they get to keep it).

Friday 17th

Met Peter Jaques at the Queen's Head in Pinner. He says I'm looking stressed. Stressed? I feel more stressed than the elastic on the dancing elephant's tutu. As a producer himself Peter can empathise with the problems Lorraine's encountering, reckons she sees it as a right royal botch-up she'll be glad to be clear of but will expect to see some money after all her work.

Monday 20th

Lynda did the Jewish day centre in Hendon where one of the elderly male diners not in sound mental health once flashed his penis through the glass doors at us when we arrived, before being bundled away by carers (him, not us). In addition to such unexpected excitements, there's a sedate-looking woman called Sophie who likes to get up and dance. Sophie hoists my tired bones from the chair and trundles me around while the nurses clap time, other diners hiss at her to sit down (which she ignores) and Lynda's voice swoops and glides. Then Lynda says "I'm going to call Rob out to the front again to sing a terrific song with me." So I shamble up and grab the condenser mike and say: "Well, it *used to be* a terrific song…" – and off we go with 'Who Wants To Be A Millionaire?'– halfway through which, instead of responding "*I* don't" I mutter "I wouldn't mind, actually" – imagining how *that* would strip the feathers off the doomy prey-birds at the

NatWest and Halifax banks who, thanks to my dear daughter, didn't quite get to pick my bones clean after all. Yet.

Wednesday 22nd

This morning I told Cat (when she asked how Lynda was doing) that she'll be performing this afternoon at a posh private party at the smart riverside town of Thames Ditton in Surrey, with canapés and wine and plush surroundings. The reality was a dementia care home there, bare floor, hard chairs, her audience not entirely focused, yet clip-clapping to the rhythm, and Lynda calls them each by name, and warms them with her smiles and embracing voice – so a party atmosphere is generated, and a lady called Elsie in woollen knitted hat gets up and does a little dancing walk on her wheeled frame, without expression, kicking one foot and then the other delicately to the rhythm as she stares into an unknowable distance, lost to our world.

Thursday 23rd

During a conference call last night with Lorraine Ross and Cat, Keith Bearman said he is seeing Grenville Peters on Monday with those vital SIGNED French and Spanish pre-sales. Come Tuesday Cat sees her lawyer Richard Broxbourne to decide whether it's safe to sign the document making Dark Moon Films liable (with Bluebird Pictures) for the Blue Rider half million – because by then, if Bearman comes good, the full amount of Grenville Peters's money will be released. Cat didn't ask Ms Ross whether she has locked down the main actors yet – but we must assume so or those pre-sales wouldn't have been signed (?)

But now Cat is worried about the current state of the script again – Jenny Knight has been chipping away at it even more, to pare the budget even further to save money.

'Remember, a statue has never been set up in honour of a critic!' Says the composer Sibelius on today's diary page.

Thursday 30th

To my genuine surprise, but according to Cat, the money-people are basing their decisions on the last script I had anything to do with (the same one Keith Bearman's been using, apparently) – so whether any of the financiers would wish to put their money into the spindly thing wobbling wanly out of Lorraine and Jenny's office with much of its lifeblood siphoned off (as if enough hadn't already been drained over the years anyway) is open to conjecture. However, I try to reassure Cat that our UK producers are thoroughgoing professionals who wouldn't take the hatchet unnecessarily to a film that will carry their names – it wouldn't make sense otherwise.

DECEMBER

Friday 1st
Meanwhile Lorraine has seven more days before the €200,000 offer from the Irish Film Board is withdrawn if finance isn't closed. So the question is, will Gordon Truscott be shooting the current script or the one shorn of £400,000 of action, SFX, sex, trains, drugs, ravens, rock 'n' roll and whatever else is deemed too pricey by our gurus of feature film drama? Meanwhile I languish in the rainy outfield up to my knees in mud and wait to see what will be offered up in my name (which is still on that script somewhere).

Tuesday 5th
This latest slosh in the chops actually did take me by surprise. Idly taking a look at the project on the Internet Movie Database website, the entry for *Dark Moon* (designated 'in production') shows as 'Writers': CATHERINE FROME, GORDON TRUSCOTT... then runs out of space so you have to click on (*more*) and wait till a separate page finally comes up, on which is – like a starveling brought in from the cold and sat in an outer room so no one will see it – ROBIN SQUIRE. To cover herself, Lorraine (or was it Jennifer?) has put 'in alphabetical order' (which it isn't quite, unless going by first names). Even so, if my name was Robin Adair I can't help feeling I would still have been on that separate page – kept well away from the main action, as in life.

At first I laughed, then it began to eat into my soul. Then came the next jolt – Cat rang to tell me that filming has been put back to March 1st 2007 on a budget that is now £2.2 million.

Friday 8th

Although streets and shops are lurid with Christmas, my little place remains about as cheery as a crematorium waiting room. Not till I queried the current state of pre-sales did Cat mention that Mexico and Benelux have now signed deals, as has Germany's Telepool. She made it sound like bad news so I wondered whether there was something suitably dire she's decided not to tell me as it's so close to the festive activities.

Monday 18th

Cat sounded glum. The news is we've lost the €200,000 from Ireland because of all the delays. Grenville Peters is more stable now. Blue Rider's lawyer has verbally agreed to half of their $500,000 being used as investment rather than a loan. "Their charges are high," said Cat yet more gloomily, "so more may have to come off the script." I giggled nervously, no longer having any idea what the script looks like. Dry bones, with a few scraps of flesh adhering? I don't want to see it – just pay me something – ANYTHING! – and let me run, run, run...

Maybe tomorrow?
and tomorrow and tomorrow
is another day
never jam today
never comes
to be brave
we die
Suddenly I feel so very... very... tired.

Thursday 21st

From: Lorraine Ross
To: Jeffrey Simmons
Date: 21 December 2006
Subject: Dark Moon

Dear Jeffrey
I'm glad to report that after a tough end of year we feel positive about completing financing in early 07 and the

shoot (based on artists' availability) is now anticipated in March. Will update you in the new year and meanwhile all best for Christmas
Best
Lorraine

Sunday 31st

In a glittery pub at Arundel with poppers, squeakers and yells. Lynda's growing conviction that a malign fate has decided that despite our talents and efforts nothing significant is destined to happen for either of us in the coming year poured water into the wine and diluted the bonhomie.

So I look into the brand new year without the idiotic optimism that has previously marked such occasions. Lynda and I gave each other no celebratory kiss and barely touched when midnight blanged away and shrieks were cracking the ceiling and people roaring "I'm sure this will be your year!" – as if our persistent ill-luck were a mutually contaminating disease best not made worse by personal contact.

Will *Dark Moon* happen in the coming year – the twelfth one since I became involved? If so, will it be in time to save having to sell my little house? Or will everything fall away yet again, this time terminally, and beckon destitution in with its gnarled hands and ragged cloak, leaving Cat overwhelmed with massive debts that will swallow up her palatial residence and condemn my other screenplays and manuscripts, raised with such loving care down the years, to a state of being forever unread?

Happy New Year!

2007

Sunday 7th

Was trying to convince myself that things have gone too far on *Dark Moon* to fall away now when Cat angsted up my day afresh with a call saying Keith Bearman is annoyed that the main actors STILL haven't been locked down, including Andrea Corr. My face is so stretched by silent screams it could model for Munch.

Wednesday 10th

Cat says she's 'concerned' that over £300,000 appears to have been spent with nothing to show for it except a spindly script with sunken cheeks and collapsed abdomen. I like that word 'concerned'. It's so British. How about 'screamingly and gut-wrenchingly appalled, horrified and aghast'? Sound better? And here am I with nerve-ends screeching, flinching when anyone pushes anything whatsoever through my letterbox so I'm even phobic now about pizza leaflets.

What's more, have just read that Paul Andrew Williams's recent award-winning feature debut *London to Brighton* was made for the same amount that would appear to have been expended by others in their valiant efforts to get *Dark Moon* to the screen. So simpletons like me can't help wondering how this could have happened, nor why – although funding of over two million pounds has been organised on paper – we are still left wondering if and when the finance will ever be closed, actors secured, crew hired and filming dates given.

Saturday 13th

Woke in the night and walked bleakly sleepless about my little haven, then sat on the moon-blanched settee and imagined Keith Bearman and Gordon Truscott in a Los Angeles restaurant making urgent plans to keep this film alive in the wake of losing our latest 'Bryce' because the actor hadn't been locked down with the money provided for that purpose.

Just before 9 a.m. Cat rang. Messrs Bearman and Truscott *did* dine together last night and make plans. Andrea Corr has still not been secured. If by Monday evening the situation is the same, Keith Bearman will fly to London on Tuesday and do the things not yet done, such as settle the completion bond, secure actors and whatever else is necessary to maintain the filming date of March 1st – no doubt in order to give a screening at Cannes this year.

Wednesday 17th
Gordon Truscott arrived back in the UK yesterday, Keith Bearman today. When Cat spoke to Gordon he declared bullishly "I've come here to make a movie!"

Friday 19th
Andrea Corr has confirmed that she still wants to play 'Laura'. Such good news after all the uncertainty. No doubt Keith Bearman will ensure she gets locked down financially now. He has a meeting with Lorraine and Jenny at their Soho office at noon today, with the ubiquitous Cat – who tells me that he (Bearman) saw the completion bond man. No doubt our UK producer will handle this new situation with her customary charm, tact, sensitivity, respectful humility, honesty, politesse and élan.

Tuesday 23rd
Pre-production on *Dark Moon* is to start on Feb 26th, filming March 26th. I groaned at this extra delay, it was like a blind quietly closing: I know for certain now that I will have to sell my home. Scripts have gone to various actors for the male lead, but it's hoped U.S. actor Danny Huston will say yes to 'Bryce'. Danny is the son of John Huston, born in Rome in 1962 while his father was filming there. Such a dynastic name would be good for us.

This evening went with Lynda to see *Miss Potter*, the Renée Zellweger film that was being made on the Isle of Man and the reason for them not being able to accommodate us there last year (or was it the year before?). Had things gone differently it could have been *Dark Moon* we were seeing instead of Beatrix Potter and Peter Rabbit, my home would be safe and I would have long since been in the clear with the banks and credit card companies instead of chewing my fingers to the elbow over every bill and drop of petrol.

Saturday 27th

Have been wondering how it could be that those in charge are seemingly content to preside over a script they seem happy to reduce so drastically in quality in order to save money – with no thought of involving the writer in this ruinous procedure. So a piece by Phil Parker in the excellent *ScriptWriter** magazine edited by Julian Friedmann came as enlightenment. Phil writes that the quality of the screenplay is no longer a consideration in the decision-making process – and that the main reason producers want to start filming is not to make something memorable, moving or marvellous, but to cover their overheads and make some money back after their expenditure of time, cost and effort.

The key elements of any package, Phil writes, are: i) the producer; ii) the director; iii) the actors/stars; iv) the budget/financial risk; v) the genre; vi) the subject; vii) the screenplay. In that order. So our producers sit crowing at the top of the list with the humble script grovelling wretchedly at the bottom. Small wonder those in control seem not to care what their version of *Dark Moon* looks like, and why they appear not to give a pig's knacker if the writer is thrown out with the garbage. Phil Parker further argues that until this attitude changes, truly interesting films of depth, power, passion and integrity can never again be made in the United Kingdom.

*Now TwelvePoint, edited by Caroline Ferguson.

FEBRUARY

Saturday 3rd

Was woken by Cat soon after seven. Numb-faced and dribbling I tried to talk, sounding spaced out and mumbly. "Sorry, did I wake you?" she asked. No, no, I always talk like this. Apparently things aren't as bad as I'd dreaded. Finance is expected to be closed some time next week.

Oh my God! – it's like a dream – a miracle – how the crumpled spirits rose and roared as I sprang up shouting like a fool, watching on TV this afternoon the return of Jonny Wilkinson to the England rugby squad against Scotland after years of injury. His last appearance was in 2003 when his drop-goal won us the World Cup against Australia. Now here he is as fantastic as ever, scoring 27 points on his own in goal-kicks, drop-goals and tries, everywhere on the field at once and seemingly involved in nearly every bone-crunching tackle. It made my lone tea and crumpet go down all the better. The score was 42-20. Jonny's back! – from now on everything's gonna be all right!!!

Isn't it?

Wednesday 7th
Apparently Danny Huston praised the *Dark Moon* script to Gordon Truscott. But Cat claims it's the last version I worked on that's still being read (referred to as 'the good script'), that none of the talent is seeing the withered document to which it's been reduced because of budget considerations. How true this is I don't know, but it's what I'm told.

Thursday 8th
Woke in the early hours in despair. Need to get money somehow to keep going, especially as the finance is STILL not closed. But I absolutely can't wait any longer. Thick snow overnight surprised us with a whirling white world.
At 8.30 Cat phoned to say Danny Huston is talking to Gordon Truscott later today: if it's a 'yes', filming won't start till April 11th, with Charles Dance as 'Grimstone'. If 'no', filming is still on March 26th. Whatever, Keith Bearman returns to the UK next Tuesday to take *Dark Moon* by the scruff of its debilitated neck and shake some action and dates out of it.
Two estate agents called round with snow on their boots to value my little house. I'll be sad to see it go.

'The two most beautiful words in the English language are "cheque enclosed".'
Dorothy Parker on today's page of this diary.

Monday 12th
Danny Huston can't do it after all! Never mind, I now know what 'DCMS' is: the Department for Culture, Media and Sport – which up until April 1st this year administrates British film certification, then hands over to the UK Film Council.

Wednesday 14th

On this day of Valentine cards and heart-shaped prezzies, Lynda had 2 gigs at care home parties – in Borehamwood (morning) and Rickmansworth (afternoon). Among her numbers was 'My Funny Valentine', sung with all her heart. I like it when her eyes briefly catch mine when she sings:

"Is your figure less than Greek?
Is your mouth a little weak?
When you open it to speak
Are you sma-a-a-a-art...?"

Not so smart really. And why isn't this girl FAMOUS?

Saturday 23rd

Read this in *MovieScope* Magazine today:

European Screenwriters' Manifesto.

One hundred and twenty five writers from all over Europe gathered in Thessaloniki, Greece, on the 21st and 22nd November and committed to campaign for the implementation of a manifesto which defines the role of the screenwriter in the twenty-first century. Issues related to stories, rights and money.

Speaking at the opening, Wim Wenders, Chairman of the European Film Academy, said that it was important to finally give screenwriters the acknowledgement they deserve.

The conference Chairperson and FSE President, writer Christina Kallas said: "It is writers who face the blank sheet and conjure out of nothing the stories that captivate the world. Everything else – producers, directors and distributors – come later. The writer is a primary creator of the audiovisual work."

Among the speakers was David Kipen, Director of Literature at the National Endowment for the Arts in the United States. He summed up the history of American cinema by saying that the first fifty years belonged to the producers, the second to the directors and the next will be for the writers. "We are historically at a kind of a crossroads," he concluded, referring to the conference, "and this is only the warning shot."

The European Screenwriters' Manifesto was launched at the

recent Berlin International Film Festival with the backing of 21 national writers' guilds, including the Writers' Guild of Great Britain. Collectively this represents approximately 9,000 writers across Europe.

Mogens Rukov, the writer of *Festen* said "We make the story. We should be proud."

Try telling any of that to certain personnel on *Dark Moon*, who – as seen by recent experience – don't consider a fair screenwriting credit of any importance and are happy enough to cut a writer's work to ribbons without consultation if it appears to suit their purposes.

MARCH

Monday 5th

Today I put my little house on the market. It means I'll be able to pay off all the debts that developed while waiting for *Dark Moon* and other stuff to kick in. Kick in? Judging by a silence as deep as any I've known on this project, I reckon it's lost its kicking boots and developed corns, with arthritis in each toe.

Tuesday 6th

Cat phoned, first time in ages. We now have a 'Bryce' again, a Turkish actor has agreed to the part. Filming is set to start April 23rd, pre-production March 26th – though Gordon Truscott wants it a week earlier. Rang and told Jeffrey Simmons all this. He was cheered, because at least it shows that someone somewhere still intends making this film, even if the dates have so far been as fictitious as the plot.

Thursday 15th

Have sold my house! – it 'flew out the window', as the buccaneering young estate agents said it would. At a good price. Not that I'm rejoicing, but these latest delays on *Dark Moon* combined with nothing else happening in time made it vital to start clawing up the slippery slope out of my pit of debt.

It's those Ides of March again, and I'm feeling shell-shocked and numb, having had strangers tramping through my home and not a word from Cat since a week last Tuesday, despite Keith Bearman having been in London since Monday.

Tuesday 20th
Have to keep pushing on somehow. Am unable to pay credit cards this month – merely a token amount – so I anticipate venomous letters and must be prepared for whatever nastiness they serve to people in this kind of trouble. Must keep doing something positive meanwhile till the money for the house sale comes through.

Thursday 22nd
Desperate times, and still the film drags on. No money to keep car on road, pay basic bills or buy food. If I wasn't selling my house I'd be jumping off its roof.

Lynda stayed, raised my spirits. She phoned Halifax Bank on my behalf and arranged to see someone this afternoon. I was shivering, totally gone – it was as if she was talking to a child. "You've sold your *home* for goodness sake! – *surely* these people can tide you over till the cheque comes in? You've only got a tiny mortgage, you'll have thousand and thousands of pounds! Haven't you told them? Who's the mortgage company?"

"They are."

"Well then! They can see your situation at a glance. Are they stupid or something?"

"I think their word is 'careful'."

So after today's gig we went into town – pretty wonderful to have someone rooting for me like this. Into the bank Lynda stormed, my house-sale documents blazing from both hips. But they still couldn't help – "not until contracts are exchanged on the property."

"I can't *believe* they're so impossible," said Lynda, shaken by their inflexibility. "I'd like to take a gun to their stupid heads!"

"Or rip their shirts?" But it wasn't funny.

We got back to what will soon not be my home any more and I rang Cat, ready to kill. Surprisingly she sounded unusually bullish, had just had a 'very positive' meeting with our producers. And a filming date is set for

May 8th, pre-production straight after Easter on April 10th. But it's all too late to save my home.

"Dinner's on me tonight." Lynda handed me a tenner. "Go and buy a chicken – organic, mind – and some potatoes and mushrooms or beans. I'm not having you going hungry any more because of these absolute fools in the bank. And get some wine – bugger them all!"

APRIL

Friday 6th

Can still hardly believe it. Am reeling. At a residential home on Fortis Green in north London Lynda was being brilliant as ever with those blazing Cole Porter, Gershwin, Gus Kahn and Hoagy Carmichael songs (our 'Two Sleepy People' continues to numb most into submission) when I noticed a spry lady of about eighty at the back of the audience mouthing the words to *all* the songs. Afterwards she came up to chat in a quiet, firm voice I was surprised to realise was American. Californian, to be precise. The activities organiser said "This is Anna, she was Shirley Temple's double in her early films." It was one of those moments when reality bent out of shape. This woman stood before me, petite and trim, grey hair going white, wide eyes. I looked at her as if she was some magical being conjured up from the misty distant past, yet alive and whole before me. "I have blue eyes like Shirley," she said "and was blonde like her as a child, with ringlets of course. We looked so alike, sometimes they couldn't tell us apart during the filming. We were friends and playmates, had fun together, rode scooters…" Titles from the 1930s floated into my mind, monochrome and tinnily far, like *Little Miss Marker, Curly Top, The Little Colonel, Rebecca of Sunnybrook Farm,* the song 'On The Good Ship Lollipop' warbled in piping weeny voice… Anna was Shirley's double in them all – and here she was, right here before me. Bizarrely, she flexed her left arm and said "Feel my muscle." I felt her bicep through the woolly cardy, the same arm Shirley Temple no doubt tugged or punched in play in the long ago. It felt as toned and hard as a fit male's. "Exercise," she said. Sort of breathless, I asked: "Did you know Bill Robinson?" "Bojangles?" she answered at once. "Oh my, a lovely man. When Shirley danced with him in those movies I was there watching, just a tot myself." I asked was it true that Fred Astaire was influenced by Bojangles as a tap-dancer. "Absolutely," said Anna. "Mr Astaire came on set quite a few times, I remember, always talked so kindly to us."

I drift. I dream. I see her face now – dimpled, cute, young. Wide bright eyes and tossing ringlets. Innocence. Monochrome flickerings in a world before I existed, yet here-and-now in memory to Anna. Nothing bad has ever happened and never will. Never will…

Goodnight.

Tuesday 10th

Easter over. Lynda's sister Nicola got wed. With my house sale now challenging *Dark Moon* for slowness of movement with a prolonged 'contaminated land' search into its sixth week as banks and credit card companies circle for the kill, I rang Cat. Got her in the hairdresser.

"We've got a film!" she said startlingly.

"What?"

"No, really, we have. Everyone's very excited."

"They are? Why didn't somebody tell m---?"

"It's all been sorted via Grenville Peters. The shooting schedule is five six-day weeks."

"Dates?" I asked hoarsely.

"We're sort of in pre-production from today – unofficially…" (code for 'don't ask for money').

"Still filming May 8th?"

"Er, no. Deal memos have gone to the principal actors. Charles Dance is certain, as is that name I can't pronounce for 'Bryce', and Andrea Corr for 'Laura'. Pre-production looks good to start on April 21st, filming May 21st."

Tonight I dined alone on a tin of stewed steak. Are we greenlit?

Thursday 12th

> **From: Jennifer Knight**
> **To: Jeffrey Simmons**
> **Date: 12 April 2007**
> **Subject: Dark Moon screenplay**
>
> **Dear Jeffrey,**
> **Although the finance is now closing much paperwork still need doing before the film can be called 'certain'. We are looking to a 25/5 closing and a 28/5 start of principal photography. Not until the finance is closed will we have access to funds to pay any fees, which includes Robin's initial £9k. Part of the closing of the film's paperwork is having the completion bond sign off, without which none of the financiers will release their funds, and part of this process is having a script which matches a schedule which they approve, hence I trust this answers your 'concerned' query about the latest changes we have made to the script.**
> **Best, Jenny**

ME: But Jeffrey, the script they've sent for the completion bond looks thrown together by a bad amateur with dyslexia. And my name's on it – and it's at the front now!

JEFFREY: I'm sure it can't be as bad as that.

ME: Trust me, I'm a script doctor.

Monday 16th

Shooting is delayed yet again – to May 28th. Lorraine and Jenny have generously reduced their own first tranche fees, and Cat's fee is entirely withdrawn. Gordon Truscott gets no immediate director's fee, but Keith Bearman has agreed to give him 'something'.

Tuesday 17th

Disaster! We've lost Andrea Corr! A promo DVD for her solo album is being shot in June, so because of the delays on *Dark Moon* (and the fact that she *still* hadn't been financially locked down with the Blue Rider money provided for the purpose) she can no longer play 'Laura'. Hope drained when Cat told me this. Already the Hubbards are on the case to find an alternative, but what hope for *Dark Moon* now? Cat mentioned Anna Friel as a possible. Ah, if only. Hope never really dies until you enter the execution chamber, the bolts slide to and they raise their mobile phones*...

Saddam Hussein had been hanged a few weeks before this, surreptitiously filmed on a mobile phone by one of the jailers.

Wednesday 25th
We've lost Charles Dance! Grim news. He says his "heart's not in it" any more. Maybe *Bleak House* put him off playing dodgy lawyers, or has he caught sight of the latest shrivelled script and decided to get out quick.

Meanwhile Alice Eve (actor Trevor's daughter) and another actress are reading for the part of 'Laura', as is Anna Friel from whom there's still no word.

Around lunchtime Cat rang again – Alice Eve has said yes! However, she's currently doing a film with Harrison Ford so may not be able to do our dates*.

Sadly, this lovely charismatic actress couldn't – a further bitter blow for Dark Moon *in the light of what subsequently happened.*

Friday 27th
It's the sunniest, warmest April since records began 200 years ago. Haven't felt much sunshine on me though, more like gloom and cobwebs. I long for a resolution of this house sale and freedom from the Bank of Scotland credit card ghouls ringing at all hours as they now do. Yet the wherewithal to settle all debts keeps retreating before my advance, grinning mockingly.

Sunday 29th
BoS credit card debt department rang again at 9.30 this Sunday morning. Tired now of saying the same things, always to a different voice, about awaiting completion of my house sale, I pretended to be my own son

and indignantly told the caller that my father has retired in a collapsed state to his bed, so please leave him alone and he'll pay as soon as he can (it made no difference).

Still fantastic weather, and with strength and health and a beautiful woman I'm well aware I shouldn't complain. As dear Grandma Squire used to say, "there's plenty worse orf than yerself unless you're in a boat in a gale holed under the waterline with a reef of rocks twixt you and the shore." Quite right, Flo. So I ventured smiling out into the sunny glare with Lynda to a smart Jewish care home in Golders Green. A terrific show, best I've ever seen her do, including the new Judy Garland ('Get Happy') and Marilyn Monroe ('Heart Belongs To Daddy') tributes. Henry, a resident there and once head of Rank Film Distribution (amazing but true), watched her enthralled and praised her lavishly afterwards: "When I closed my eyes it could have been Judy herself," he enthused. Turns out he knew Judy Garland well. While I quietly packed up in the background, elegant ladies came up to me with congratulations on our duets, bless 'em. Triumphant, we went to Golders Hill Park and sat in the flower garden drowning in its perfume. Life could be worse. I know it could. Listen, I know, okay? But why doesn't that **&@$©**film happen?

MAY

Tuesday 1st

Another perfect day – weatherwise, at least. This afternoon, at a (different) care home on Bishop's Avenue in Hampstead, I sang solo in public for the first time. It was 'A Foggy Day', which Fred Astaire did in *Damsel In Distress* in 1937. Dementia is serious here and feedback was zero as my last note croaked into silence – only Lynda clapped loyally. The 'had me low and had me down' and 'I viewed the morning with alarm' lyrics were delivered with feeling. Great to be away from telephones for a while, though my mobile was penetrated (raped?) by a woman from Barclaycard debt department asking nicely when I intended getting up to date with my account. So much more civilised than the crass scumsters at BoS.

It's May Day. *Mayday, Mayday...* will someone *please* either finish selling my house or cause this film to happen?

'If you know somebody is going to be awfully annoyed by something you write, that's obviously very satisfying, and if they howl with rage or cry, that's honey.' So says author A.N.Wilson on today's diary page.

Wednesday 2nd

At 9 a.m. Cat phones. "Do you want the good news or the bad?"

"Try the bad," I said. "Don't reckon I could take any good news right now."

"The Irish Film Board turned us down. So we're filming in England."

When I finished laughing hollowly I said "So *Dark Moon* is postponed till Christmas?"

"Oh no, it'll only delay it by a week or so. And Lorraine's signing up the new line producer."

"So they'll be paying him something to secure him?"

"I expect so."

I bit my tongue and tasted blood, still fielding calls from credit card debt departments and waiting with accelerating desperation for contracts to exchange on my house. "Like they paid a team of decorators to paint the outside of that huge house in Dublin especially for the film, and now they're not using it?"

"Er, yes."

"But not a penny to pay the writer to create a definitive shooting draft?"

"Gordon's doing it."

I put down the phone. So now, after all this time, *Dark Moon* is back in England, having done a grand tour of the United Kingdom, the Isle of Man, the Irish Free State and (briefly) Hungary, during which (according to Cat) something like £380,000 has somehow been got through and filming hasn't even begun.

I rang and told Jeffrey Simmons they're filming in England not Ireland now. Jeffrey has a calm, deep, authoritative, impeccably modulated voice, but this was the nearest to a wail I've ever heard issue from his throat.

A full moon tonight, big and clear to the south. Felt like howling at it.

Thursday 3rd

Was half awake at 6.30 a.m. when the phone rang. Not, I was blearily glad to find, the Bank of Scotland credit card department putting in a wake-up call like the Nazis' midnight knock, but Cat.

"Sorry, did I wake you?" I felt for her. She's been up since 4.30 a.m. pacing floors. Lawyer Broxbourne has just presented her with a personal bill for £49,000. "Gordon's looking at a big house in Kent today, for Bankside Lodge in *Dark Moon*. It's beautiful."

I said that if we stay with the story, the house shouldn't be 'beautiful' at all, but partly derelict, not having been lived in for years, etc., so the question would be why on earth would 'Bryce' want to overbid for such a decrepit place? Cat saw the point, said she'll talk to Gordon about it. Great, and I'll have a chat with my wall.

Who was it, I continue to wonder, spelt mantelpiece 'mantlepiece' – and kept it there?

Saturday 5th

Weary of the harassment calls from Bank of Scotland, have given up explaining my situation to callers who I now realise are probably school-leaving underachievers or thugs hired solely to badger payment defaulters into madness. Today I switched lines so my previous main number gets the fax machine, which rings six times and goes dead (unless someone's sending a fax). Plugged my phone into the old fax line, sent this number to all who were likely to call me, and had an easier day. That li'l old fax machine kept on a-ringin' and a-ringin', and no answer did it get except six bells and silence. This is what I'm reduced to – and *still* no completion on this house sale because of the crazy 'contaminated ground' survey. Nor is there yet a start date on the film.

Monday 7th

Bank Holiday Monday, but it didn't stop the orcs from the BoS putting in call after call to my fax machine, which shut them off after six rings every time. Then, a couple of minutes later, they ring again. And then again. And so it goes on through the morning, and then the afternoon. I felt sort of sorry for them, wasting their holiday phoning people like me to ask the same question over and over again until everyone is blue in the face with exasperation and despair.

Wednesday 9th

Had an interesting thought this morning. If it's true, I'm more staggered than a binge-drinker with a wonky knee. It recalls the plot of *The Producers* – to deliberately set out to make a show so bad that it will close and make a loss. Then there's the song: 'Angels come from everywhere with lots of jack, and when you lose it there's no attack, where else can you get money that you don't give back...?'

The dark thought that came to me was 'has *Dark Moon* been set up *not* to be made?' Could this be the reason for the unending postponements and delays, so there's no come-back on all that money that would appear, according to Cat, to have been got through? No! Can't be! Are you mad? Impossible! Yeah, sorry – maybe I *am* going nuts – but it's what it's starting to feel like...

Thursday 10th
Tony Blair announces his resignation as Prime Minister/Labour Party leader today. Caught some of his speech on the car radio en route to collect Lynda for a gig. He officially finishes on July 27th. It's been ten years, and bitter to think that when his party came to power on May 2nd 1997 *Dark Moon* was still trying to get made and even now is *still* being mucked about and we weren't at unending war with insurgents in Iraq.

Friday 18th
Cat phoned. *Dark Moon* is still on – pre-production to start 23rd May. Gordon Truscott is at the Cannes Film Festival, which started 2 days ago. Why do I feel so lacklustre and pummelled by blunt instruments? There goes my fax machine again... and again... and again... and again... and again... and again... Ah, it's stopped. Again. Thank you, Bank of Scotland credit card department.

Friday 25th
Put £20 petrol in the car at Tesco's – only to hit my financial wall when NatWest refused my card in full public gaze at the paypoint. Managed to scrape enough cash together under the accusing eyes of the queue then slunk away feeling like a criminal, puzzled as to why a production office for the feature film I wrote is now set up, with people being paid to run it, and I'm being paraded naked and starving through the streets with a placard shouting *Pauper*. Scarcely able to speak through rage and exasperation I got

Cat on the phone and told her a hot lawyer is heading Lorraine Ross's way – yes, I have a rottweiler standing by, called Monica Bond. To avoid the instrument exploding, Cat got on to Lorraine at once, who came back to say (rather astonishingly) that she'll pay £500 into my account this afternoon, and the same again next week, from the £9000 payable on financial closure, which is now imminent so please don't do anything 'rash'. Rash? I'll give them more rash than nappies, plague, measles, smallpox, scarlet fever and black death combined if they don't stop treating the writer on this film as if he DOESN'T EXIST!

Saturday 26th
£500 did go in yesterday, but I can't touch it till the cheque clears. With Monday another Bank Holiday, this means an additional day to drag through. Yet I had a strange feeling that the tide is starting to come back in after ebbing so far out I could walk to France on dry land.

Sunday 27th
Something amazing happened today. Lynda did a gig at a Jewish care home in Finchley this afternoon. Mrs Annie Cohen is 100 years old and having a party. Raining hard. In we went and set up the mikes and sound equipment. Balloons and bunting everywhere, the place packed with folk and family young and old. A uniformed equerry arrived from Buckingham Palace and presented Mrs Cohen with the Royal Telegram on behalf of Her Majesty. In his speech he mentioned, among events that happened in the year of Annie's birth, 1907, that the legendary actress Katharine Hepburn was also born. A cake with 100 candles was brought in, 'Happy Birthday' was sung, and her son Lionel sang 'My Yiddishe Mama' in a surprisingly appealing voice.

When I came on the mike to introduce Lynda's act I added in a smartarse sort of way that Laurence Olivier too was born in 1907, as was John Wayne. Nice to get one over on the Queen's messenger. Then I saw the singer Rod Stewart watching me from across the room…

… wait a minute, can't be… it's someone who looks like him… amazing likeness, though… standing there in the little crowd behind the old lady's table.

But Lynda had seen him too. As astonished as I was, after her vervish opening number on ukulele she kept her head and switched tracks from singalong to swing – the Sinatra cabaret stuff, Judy Garland and Marilyn Monroe and Peggy Lee – and it was as if we were suddenly taking part in a dream in which she was entertaining Rod Stewart. *Rod Stewart?* It really was him, with his fiancée Penny Lancaster vying with my songbird for glamdaz, and they were clocking Lynda's act full on.

We later learned that Rod was a friend of Lionel's, son of the centenarian party girl. When Lynda sang 'I've Got You Under My Skin' in that skin-tingling way, a space was cleared for Rod and Penny to dance to her voice. Next, in this crazy afternoon of unexpected magic, Rod was sitting next to me with Penny on his lap, singing huskily along to Lynda's 'I Can't Give You Anything But Love'. "Well done," he exclaimed when her final note expired. Rod Stewart was clapping Lynda! Tea and cakes were consumed, group photos were taken with their famous guest, kids ran about. Lynda sang 'Baby Face' to baby-faced babies, her ukulele rocking, ending with a bravura Gracie Fields 'Wish Me Luck As You Wave Me Goodbye'. We packed up the sound equipment surrounded by smiles, more photos were taken and Annie Cohen was having a whale of it with prezzies and great-great-grandkids.

And Rod Stewart and Penny Lancaster had gone.

And Lynda and me were out in the pouring rain and reality again. She was paid £55 for making that party go with such a swing, and had to cough up for our tea on account of my extreme poverty when we hit Dominique's near Hampstead Heath station, passing the deserted Bank Holiday funfair where no one was today because of the horrible weather.

Dear Lynda, how hard you try and how brilliant you are. As your song about the nightingale goes, 'was that a dream or was it true?' For you, Cinderella, the ball is over; but there's always tomorrow, and tomorrow, and tomorrow…

In a daft moment I suggested to Lynda that Rod Stewart might be persuaded to re-form her group, which would then be Red, Rod & Blonde. *She couldn't resist texting her old 'Hot', Andy Eastwood, to tell him what had happened, and Andy came back with* 'What's this then, Red & Rod?' *Great minds…*

Tuesday 29th

Pre-production on *Dark Moon* is rumoured to be starting today, but I heard nary a word.

Wednesday 30th

Nor today, which was entirely sausageless information-wise.

Thursday 31st

Phoned Cat and asked has pre-production started on *Dark Moon*? "Yes," she said in a whisper as if it was a secret – an instinctual reaction, no doubt, when saying anything that might trigger a request for money on my part. "But they're still £17,500 short," she added hastily, in case I thought to ask.

Hang on – did you say pre-production has STARTED???

JUNE

Friday 1st

"My name is Mary Stuart, and my head was cut orf." The lady's orotund 1930s' tones rang out as Lynda and I staggered with the sound equipment into the lounge of a new care home in Weybridge down Surrey way. Weather perfect. Lynda's act gets continually better, as if inspired by some watching entrepreneur rather than rows of wheelchair-bound venerables, and we duetted 'Two Sleepy People' to clamorous acclaim. Life could be worse – despite being so badly strapped for cash the welts are screaming.

While Lynda chatted to her audience afterwards I talked to Mary Stuart – handsome, groomed and conditioned, her shingled hair a memory of bygone times. "I was a debutante, presented at court," she said proudly, retaining that old-style warmth-with-breeding. I could see she'd once been a graceful, gracious beauty. 'When was that?' I asked. "1930. I was born in 1911, June the 22nd, the day of the King and Queen's coronation." She gave me a smile that had melted male hearts way back before when was invented. "So I was named after the new Queen – not *that* one, who lorst her head."

Time, thou thief, there you go again. Mary of Teck, the most regal and aloofly remote of all regals – wife of the bearded sailor king, George V, mother of George VI and the dashing but dodgy Duke of Windsor who gave up the throne to wed Wallis Simpson. And this Mary, talking to me right now, was born in their comparative youth, three years before the Great War began and a year before Marie Lloyd recorded on crackly wax cylinder 'When I Take My Morning Promenade' in 1912 ("I don't mind *that* boy staring hard...").

Afterwards, as Lynda and I sat looking across the sun-sheened river to white-water rapids where canoeists practised slalom, I told her my John Lennon story connected with Weybridge. An uncle of mine sold electronic locking devices in the 1960s, and John Lennon's security adviser ordered one for his gate. Lennon had a smart house here and the local police escorted my uncle to it. The Beatle wasn't there, though his little son Julian was. Uncle was shown into the lounge where he was surprised to see, balanced on the back of the settee, a concrete slab the size of a paving stone into which was carved: *Guitar-playing is all very well as a hobby, John, but you'll never make a living out of it.* These were the pearls of wisdom given to John Lennon by his careers master at his Liverpool school when he left.

Full moon again tonight. *Howooooo-ooooo-oooooooo...*

Saturday 2nd

Sunny hot. A sinister postcard arrived from the Bank of Scotland credit card debt department: *IMPORTANT NOTICE. OUR REPRESENTATIVE WILL BE CALLING YOUR HOME ON 13 JUNE 2007. PLEASE TELEPHONE IF THIS IS NOT CONVENIENT.* Considering the fact they've been 'calling my home' several times a day for several weeks now (and getting my fax machine for their pains), and before that had obviously not listened to a word I said any more than have the producers on *Dark Moon*, I wondered if they meant calling *at* my home, as the message didn't otherwise make sense. So I wrote back to say that if they did mean the latter then, given the unceasing harassment to which I am still being subjected by them, I 'would sooner invite a rat into my home, or a traffic warden'. I then explained for the umpteenth time that I'm waiting for completion on my house sale, at which time I will be able to clear my debt, so please bear with me in a civilised manner for a short while longer*.

*It made no difference. That fax line just kept on a-ringing and a-ringing. I *still wonder if it's legal for a company like the Bank of Scotland to harass a private citizen in this way and force him to change his phone number, especially after he has so clearly explained his circumstances. Maybe I could claim compensation from them for unreasonable behaviour?*

Tuesday 12th

I asked Cat are we still filming on June 25th – she said no, June 21st. So for the first time ever the date on *Dark Moon* has *advanced* instead of retreated. And for the first time ever I began to seriously feel that this film will actually happen now.

Friday 15th

Moving day – left the house I've been forced to sell, bought when times were sweeter. After six weeks of waiting, the 'contaminated ground' search came out 'clear'. Sad to go, though the place was too small to ask Lynda to live there. Will regroup in a cheap rented flat for now and hope to start pulling money in at last, then buy somewhere bigger and make dreams come true with my flame-haired soprano.

Will having a film in production make a difference to me as a writer in the marketplace? Will some producer ask to see more of my scripts, or invite me to work on a forthcoming project? Are doors about to swing open for me at last as a writer?

Because NatWest and Halifax had been so unhelpful, even hostile, when I was down, I opened an account with a new bank (Lloyds) to receive the proceeds of the house sale. Closed my NatWest account and will hate them forever. With Lloyds I have a Premier Account, with a wealth creation officer standing by. Smiling, welcoming, hand extended – in stark contrast to the frowns, shaken heads and slammed doors I've had till now from the other two banks – who I vowed would see none of my money when it starts to roll, so ill did they behave towards me when times were tough.

Suddenly I'm awash with dosh, a strange feeling. No more creditors phoning day and night, no more public humiliations via refused bank cards. On the other hand, I no longer own property. Whatever, am determined to call it progress. The very first cheque I wrote in my brand new chequebook was for £5000 payable to Kerry – plus some interest with which to buy herself something nice – she who smilingly saved me when all the banks

290

could do was spit in my face, trample me underfoot, cut my lifelines, eviscerate, emasculate, consign to the incinerator or whatever other lurid analogies might tease the imagination.

Sunday 17th
Went to a care home near Watford with Lynda this afternoon. Plenty dementia here, yet spirit and cheeriness. Weather muggy warm. A trim, dignified lady who carries herself in a stately way was part of the audience enjoying Lynda's act and clearly appreciating her voice – the lady's own voice ringing out now and then in extraordinary bursts of ultra-loud soprano. A resident here, she claims to have founded the Welsh National Opera Company, and we couldn't help thinking 'oh yeah?' Lynda tried a duet with this lady and gave her the second mike – but she doesn't need one, so powerful is her voice. "I'm ninety years old," she said with a Welsh lilt and smile, and sportingly applauded our 'Two Sleepy People' duet. Even Lynda's acute ears hear her name as 'Lilian', but it doesn't sound right to me. Welsh girls are called Caenwen, Rhiannon, Eirian, Nerys, Cerigwen, Angharad – not Lilian.

Father's Day meal with lovely Kerry this evening. She paid for her old man, it was nice to have a treat. I told her about the woman with the amazing voice who fantasises that she founded the Welsh National Opera. By the time I got back to my little rented place, was so intrigued I looked it up on the Internet.

Lilian? – surely not. When the words appeared on my computer screen I froze, staring.

'The Lyrian Grand Opera Company' was formed on 1 November 1943. At the first general meeting on 2 December 1943 the name was changed to 'The Welsh National Opera Company'. The chorus was to be formed from members of the old Cardiff Grand Opera Company, the BBC Welsh Singers and the Lyrian Singers.

So Lyrian was 26 years old when she formed the Welsh National Opera Company. Now she's a proud lady of 90 in a Hertfordshire care home treasuring her memories and singing with the acts that visit there.

Time, thou thief...

Tuesday 19th

Cat says the completion bond for *Dark Moon* has been signed. So we're away? She asked anxiously if I like what Gordon will be shooting. I said I've no idea *what* he'll be shooting, or how, because he never talks to me and I haven't seen the script for so long I'm unable to form an opinion. Even so, let's all believe in it a hundred percent because it's too late now to do anything more this side of the camera. But it will invite loads of publicity, inspire great word-of-mouth, and fill cinemas throughout the world. Gordon was always on 'our' side, and will do a brilliant job. I asked Cat to push again for Lynda to have a part with her ukulele and voice – just a minute or two onscreen to give some colour and dazzle. I've already asked Gordon this myself more than once, and each time he said yes, but now is the time to be setting it up and Cat has both his ears while I have neither.

A contemplative beer. Lynda in *Dark Moon*? Not only would it be good for her showreel, she will make such a positive difference to any scene she appears in. Allowed myself a Scotch chaser, tripping over unpacked boxes in my (temporary) new abode. Meanwhile, to get this film away is of prime importance to opening doors on fresh writing opportunities.

So it's what comes after *Dark Moon* that's important to me, rather than the film itself.

Wednesday 20th

Downloaded a 'Deed of Variation' from Lorraine Ross's lawyer and printed it out. Jeffrey Simmons has talked to Lorraine at length and is encouraging me to sign it – which I don't want to do. But if the gamble works and the monies materialise from sales because of the terrific film Gordon Truscott is about to shoot, the revised deed says I get £79,000 (£4000 more than before), and 6% of producers' net profits (instead of 2%). After £9000 now (or, rather, £8000), my payments will be in three tiers: £25,000, £20,000 and £25,000 once the monies start coming in. It doesn't say when these are likely to be paid, though Jeffrey has asked them to try and be more specific.

It could of course be 'never' if Gordon blows it and the film bombs. But he's NOT going to blow it. Why should he? My future rests on this. Even my nerves are nervous, I've chewed holes in the roughly re-laid carpet which is too big for my tiny rented lounge, and my nails are wondering what happened to the fingers they were once attached to.

Spoke to Peter Jaques on the phone, who advises me on no account to

292

sign that document. But if I don't, will I be responsible for having stopped *Dark Moon* forever, screwing it up for everyone else on the production, after all these years and the immense expenditure of other people's money, advanced in good faith, that will then have come to nought?

Jeffrey rang mid-evening, having spoken again with Lorraine Ross, who urges him that if I don't sign that Deed of Variation deferring my screenwriter fee the film will be held up indefinitely, no one will get paid anything and the producers will move on to their next project. So in the end, hating myself, I signed it. Hating herself, but for the greater good (we fervently hope), Lynda witnessed my signature, with instinctive misgivings that echoed my own, aware also that if I continue to refuse to sign it Jeffrey himself could walk and I'll be without an agent all over again and back to Square One.

Thursday 21st

It's the first day of filming on *Dark Moon*. I am not invited on the set. In fact I wouldn't have known it was actually happening if Cat hadn't told me. The exhilaration and relief I've so often imagined these past eleven years are absent. The silence is deep. Without the combination of Lorraine Ross's name as producer, Keith Bearman's co-operation in raising American money, plus the equity from Cat and members of her family, this 'Britflick' could never have reached this point. As far as I know it's still essentially my script they're shooting, though with modifications, deletions and reductions by a variety of others that have withered and shrunk it in quality and scope. A five-week shoot. Gordon Truscott is already planning a wrap party, but I haven't been invited and would have no desire to go anyway. Feel empty, isolated, side-lined, ditched.

So it was a relief to go warbling this muggy afternoon at a dementia care home with Lynda, whose voice improves every time on what I'd thought was perfection. She knows all their names, makes them smile and dance in the prisons of their chairs, and can hand me a leaflet for Snappy Snaps in the street any time she likes. She still hopes for a part in the film, as I promised her in the long ago. Certainly her presence will enhance it, but it's up to the director now and I've done all I can to persuade him to use her.

As Cat's friend, the distinguished barrister and QC, Graham Lawson, might have said – and on several occasions did: "Do you think this film will ever happen, Rob?"

"Of course, Graham," I would traditionally reply, hoping it didn't notice that my nose was growing longer as I spoke. "Whyever not?"

★   ★   ★   ★   ★

Thus grew the tale of Wonderland:
Thus slowly, one by one,
Its quaint events were hammered out –
And now the tale is done,
And home we steer, a merry crew,
Beneath the setting sun.

Lewis Carroll

1832 – 98

★   ★   ★   ★   ★

Over the eleven years (for her, more like fifteen) it has taken to reach this point, it is Cat Frome's unremitting drive that has ultimately brought her 'baby' Dark Moon before the cameras. So it is she who is the real heroine of this picture: she conceived it, gave birth to and nursed it till it was taking solids and walking. Soon, let's hope, it will be answering cheekily back, be good at sports, pass the Oxbridge exam and make a fortune out there in the big wide world.

But now, like gore-drenched warriors after the battle, only two of the original team are still on their feet, swaying with fatigue yet allowing themselves perhaps a smile of weary triumph as they lower their swords and gaze around the field of slaughter. They are the great conceiver, Cat herself, and your humble author who has penned these lines.

AFTERWORD

Despite my hope-filled closure verse by Lewis Carroll, the tale was by no means 'done'. I had intended to end this epistle on the first day of principal photography – my innocent assumption having been that from then on all would proceed smoothly and efficiently through the succeeding stages of direction and post-production till the distributors took the finished film triumphantly into cinemas throughout the world, money flowed in, everyone got paid including me, and our 'merry crew' continued on, laughing gaily, not so much into the setting sun as a new dawn.

But there was still a way to go yet. Once Gordon Truscott had got his director's hat on (of a type used for baseball) he proceeded to do his own thing in his own way. I think it's called 'director's privilege' or 'auteurism', at which point he became a kind of despotic god to those around him and all he surveyed.

Some two weeks into the shooting, despite my many attempts to speak up for Lynda, it was clear that Gordon had no intention of using her and never had. So, despite being a trained actress from the prestigious Guildhall School in London, Lynda wasn't even deemed worthy by him of a walk-on role in the film I'd once written. For that matter nor was I, the veteran walk-on and one-time *DoctorWho* monster (*see BBC DVD* Mannequin Mania *filmed by Chris Chapman*) who had even, on occasion, been given lines to speak and was on good-chum terms with the close-up lens. However, Cat and her friends got into the bar room scene as extras, while others of her family 'walked on' in the party sequence, looking just a little uncomfortable as inexperienced extras do.

I did take my songstress to the location once, but we felt about as welcome there as a wet cow in Arthur Miller's front room, with the director barely acknowledging our presence as he hurried by with his entourage. I was introduced to none of the cast, and after a brief look round, with Cat as our kindly and concerned guide, we were barred from the set when the afternoon's filming began.

So I felt sad for Lynda as we drove away, never to return. At close of filming the 'wrap' party was thrown, but I heard nothing of it. Indeed, I heard nothing more about anything to do with *Dark Moon* until a few weeks later when Cat phoned me, sounding as if she'd been slammed in the stomach by a runaway truck.

"We all saw the roughcut last night," she began. I'd long since given up asking questions like what does 'we all' mean and why hadn't I been invited to the viewing? "Keith Bearman walked out afterwards without saying a word," Cat went on worriedly. "The editor Lorraine chose was a boy of twenty-two cutting his first film. Gordon thinks he's done a great job – he was with him all through the editing. But I'm so worried I could lose everything if nobody picks the film up. Would you have a look, see what *you* think. I've got a copy at home here…"

So round to Cat's I went and watched the first cut of *Dark Moon* on her TV. During this, people wandered in and out, and a BT man was tracing phone wires in the same room – but I was transfixed. No wonder Cat was worried. The finished film was worse than I could have imagined, with vital plot elements deleted or not shot at all, so the story now made no sense. There was little suspense or build-up of tension, blatant plagiaristic shots of scenes from other films had been incorporated along with gratuitous stabbings with blood everywhere and a climbing sequence that continued for an absurdly long time to no dramatic end; while at the heart of the movie, in place of what could have been one of the scariest moments in the history of cinema as I'd written it, the director had inserted instead a sequence of his own invention incorporating images from Hieronymus Bosch, grotesque monsters, surging crimson seas and hideous half-human figures. 'Bosh' it was indeed – unintentionally hilarious, utterly heartbreaking.

I went home seriously troubled, and wrote worried notes detailing what urgently needed to go back into the film or no one would even know what it was about. I wrote fresh dialogue sequences that would need to be recorded and dubbed in when the actors' faces were turned from camera – only this way would the story have any meaning. I wrote insert sequences and a shock close-up or two to try and imbue the movie with at least some of the sinister supernatural moments that would have made it compellingly watchable and audience-engaging.

These notes I anxiously sent to Cat, urging her to pass them off as her own, knowing from past experience that if I presented them as mine they would be ignored. Already I was thinking with dismay that I would never see any of the £70,000 still owed to me, because no distributor would buy the film as it was.

It was also very obvious that if *Dark Moon* was to be saved it needed a comprehensive re-edit by someone who understood what the story was about, wouldn't miss or squander visual and dramatic opportunities, and could weave in the subtleties that had been so grievously ignored.

And then we (or should that be 'they') had some luck. A legendary film editor known to Lorraine Ross was in London for a wedding and agreed to have a look at the rough-cut and my detailed notes (in Cat's name) with the additional dialogue that would need to be recorded and inserted. This accomplished Hollywood editor promised to do what he could. Of course Ms Ross said there was no money to pay for this rescue task, so the sterling Mrs Chivers stepped forward and offered to put up the £42,000 asked for in order to save her daughter's film.

The result was – if not the tour-de-force ground-breaker I had worked so very hard to achieve in the long-ago – at least a film whose story made sense. I was relieved to note that all of my notes, additional recorded dialogue and other suggestions had been tellingly incorporated by this great editor in the belief that they had emanated directly from Cat.

And so, with fingers crossed and some of our hopes restored, we who had been persuaded to sign for deferred payment of our hard-earned fees under the threat that there would be no film if we refused, could only stand back and pray that the American co-producers and sales agent Bluebird Pictures would now be able to generate sufficient income in the marketplace to cover *Dark Moon*'s really-rather-low budget and see us all paid off as the profits from sales began to build.

And so time passed...

And passed....

And passed some more...

Weeks segued into months, months into years...

And with them, almost shyly at first, then with ever-increasing conviction, hope stole away, fading into sepia distances like echoes of a song when the music has ended, till only silence was left.

It's been said that a person is never really old until the moment when the dreams in their life are replaced by regret.

Don't want to be old...

2011

From: **Kate Peebles** (London-based Sales Agent, Bluebird Pictures)
To: **Robin Squire**
Date: **6 January 2011**
Subject: **Dark Moon, request for update**

Dear Robin
Re: Dark Moon
You will have to excuse me but I am still working my way out of Christmas catch-up. To be brief, following your request for latest information, *Dark Moon* is not doing better after all this time. For verification of this I attach our most recent collateral schedule detailing total collections to date, so you will see for yourself the lack of movement over the past few years to the present day.

I am sorry to be the bearer of bad tidings but the hard fact is that the film is a failure and I doubt whether anyone (including ourselves) are ever going to recoup their investment...

My apologies for the bluntness of this message but I really am snowed under with ongoing projects.

Kate Peebles
Chief Operating Officer
BLUEBIRD PICTURES

After this single entry at the top of the year, cut from a print-out and pasted in, the pages in my 2011 diary are blank. Until, towards the end, comes this:

OCTOBER

Saturday 8th

I sit by the gas-fire in this tiny flat I continue to rent. Weather's got colder the last few days after a crazy-hot Indian summer flourish with the highest temperatures ever recorded for October. Don't know what happened to the real summer, it forgot to show up this year. Haven't been able to buy property again and my savings from the house sale are nearly gone.

Like a creature in its lair I've built a website selling vintage musical films on my ageing iMac in the cobwebbed corner, because I've always liked musicals since my mum used to take me to the cinema to see them when I was a kid – for me they're like a patch of deep sand is to an ostrich – and it was great to write every word of the site myself without some talentless philistine standing by with red pencil and scissors, and if I wanted to put *mantelpiece* instead of *mantlepiece* then that was jake too. It was intended to make me an income, but it runs (or, rather, lies) at a loss because I can't afford to advertise it, which must be a joke of some kind though it doesn't make me laugh. I had a ball putting it together, mind you, but really it was just another escapist fantasy to mop up the hours till doomsday.

Few people ever visit this flat, except the occasional enormously tall impossibly young guy to read the meter so they can send me another bill, or the ever-changing-in-appearance postman, wearing shorts whatever the weather, to deliver a sheaf of junk-mail or a scalp-freezing official letter that needs signing for.

It's dark out, and I've lit a couple of lavender-scented candles and put soft music on. Most of these songs, the torch numbers and classics from the shows of the 1920s and '30s and '40s, were sung by Lynda, so in that way she is often with me in my mind like a smiling ghost. She doesn't do the care homes any more – well she still does *some*, I believe, on a voluntary basis, because she always said she would miss those sweet people and their fascinating stories from the past, their gentlenesses and valiant frailties, so she didn't ever want to fully stop entertaining them and talking to the ladies afterwards about shoes and make-up and hairstyles and fashion. She's doing 'bigger' stuff now, using corporate booking agents who get her work at prestigious themed events like Goodwood and in trendy clubs in London and all over the country. Is she still the same? Perhaps not. No one stays the same. Can't think when we last sang 'Two Sleepy People' together in some other lifetime to a roomful of drowsy smiles. Can't think when we said goodbye forever without actually saying it.

But I'm glad she doesn't have to struggle any more to pay her mortgage and bills, or look with despair into my face as things collapse around us despite all our efforts and everything we try to do. She has her own website now – at www.lyndastyan.com – so anyone can see her and hear her lovely voice if such a thought should take their fancy. I do look sometimes, and it's almost as if she's here again. Except she's not – just a vital burst of energy and colour that vanishes when I switch off. She even found another 'Hot' – Anthony Mason, the only player I've ever heard who's as nifty as Andy on the ukulele-banjo. They call themselves 'Red Hot'.

I don't give up though, that would mean a win for those who ignore you or turn you down as months creep into years and dark hair becomes threaded with grey, russet hair with hints of pale. After plentiful effort, wrong moves, contemptuous silences and summary rejections from whichever quarter I ventured to offer what I see as my very best writing now that my literary agent, too, has gone, I've another film on the go, *The Dance Of The Mantis*, and it's my own script and story so there can be no crippling interferences to bring it down till it can hardly stagger to its feet any more, bewildered and blighted beyond hope of restoration. This one is strong, it grins and drapes its arm around your shoulder. No money up front, yet – but we continue to battle on. My writing fee for this one, built into a budget producer Debi Nethersole drew up, including the rights for my story, is £115,000. So when the film happens (I refuse to say "if") I'll be back on track and be able to recover in some way from never having been paid a penny more of my deferred fee after all those years as so-called principal writer on *Dark Moon*.

With the last of my money I built another website at www.robinsquire.com, mainly to promote my unsold scripts, because a writer without a web presence these days is like a shut shop with blinds over its windows. But does anybody ever go there? Everyone's so busy with other stuff that will probably get them nowhere either, you have to stand on your head in their front room and yodel if you want to get their undivided attention even for a few seconds.

This evening, as I sup my meditative beer, I'm remembering again what happened in the wake of that desperate and expensive re-edit of the already-so-gutted-and-badly-compromised *Dark Moon*. Despite our further attempts to breathe life back into it, the damage had really been beyond repair. All the theatrical distributors turned the film down, so it went straight to DVD. Bluebird Pictures failed to sell enough of those to do more than pay off the main U.S. investor, plus his interest – and maybe reduce some of their own losses, who knows?

So, unless a miracle happens and the world starts thirsting to see for itself just how awesomely bad *Dark Moon* actually is and buys up the DVDs in millions to gaze in appalled fascination at its dreadfulness, Cat will have to accept the loss of all that money raised on her house, on which she continues to pay interest; while the well-meant financial input of her family members looks to be a collective gonner too. Hence the ever more evermore desperately needed £70,000 balance of my screenplay fee looks almost paltry in comparison loss-wise and, although the film is still on sale on Amazon and various other websites, this money remains steadfastly unpaid while operators far shrewder than I continue to coin it from a movie I wrote with such high hopes in the long-ago.

If a single final straw can play havoc with a camel's spine, it was that non-payment of my writer's fee, after all that time and waiting and hoping, that finally did for Lynda and me. And it was almost laughable how, so soon after I had to sell my house because the banks were being such absolute inhuman cold-blooded bastards, they themselves went to the wall because of their vast incompetence as recession swept in, and it was the likes of me, the British taxpayer, who helped them float their boats again to the tune of something like forty-five billion quid for the Royal Bank of Scotland alone.

What a joke, eh?

The beer tastes different tonight, tangy-er on the tongue. I'm feeling sighful, the gas-fire murmurs and the candles shimmer, so when I glimpse my reflection in the mirror as I restlessly prowl, my ancienting phizzog looks younger in the flickery dimness. And needs to.

The funny thing is, he was a bank manager to start with, then became a solicitor. He saw Lynda performing and took one of her publicity flyers, saying he might be able to find her work. Of course he didn't, they never do, but her phone number was on it, which is what he was really after. She didn't tell me she'd gone out for a meal with him. Not at first. That lovely girl, she needs security. I understood. Still do, though the hurt doesn't go. It was only natural that she should have accompanied the same man again when he bought tickets for a West End show at a price I couldn't possibly afford while I continued not to be paid. I don't like to think of them together, planning a life, looking for property to share. It's tough to do that so I keep my mind on other things as much as I can.

Yet life has its ways of surprising you with reminders. Yesterday I was on my way to see Debi and her cinematographer hubby Vincent to talk about the next move on our hoped-for film. They were staying at a house on Wyndham Mews, so I got off the tube at Baker Street. As I emerged into the open, a chilly wind was swirling papers in the gutter. Suddenly I stopped. Amidst the noise and honking and scurry I imagined that I saw again a slender female form with glorious russet hair and troubled lovely eyes handing out leaflets in the street. The illusion was gone in a moment, but as I crossed at the lights and proceeded along the Marylebone Road it seemed that she fell in step beside me again, a ghostly hand on my sleeve and a heartlifting sideways smile, footfalls soft as thistledown, her words like gossamer whispers in my enchanted ears.

But when I looked again, she was no longer there.

Time, thou thief...

THE END

STOP PRESS

The book was supposed to end here. The manuscript was in and my excellent copy editor Lizzie had given it the once-over, pointing out very sensibly and skilfully the areas where it wandered too far off into the desert for its own good. Yet life is an on-running train, and doesn't always like such words as 'The End' thrust upon it while it's still chugging along; if life wants to terminate anything it will damn well do so itself without any help from a seemingly eternally impecunious metaphor-mixing writer.

But it happened – it really, really *did…*

NOVEMBER

Sunday 27th

The phone's ringing. I wake in shock, hand flailing blackness to kill the noise. Is it Cat again after all this time with some further terrible disclosure? It continues to ring, I fall from the mattress and knock my head on the bedside locker. Knees on cold carpet I fumble for the light-switch, can't find it, but jolt the alarm clock, whose face lights up and shows 12.23. The ringing drills on till the answering machine puts a stop to it. My recorded tones boom out, misleadingly jovial, hatefully confident. A click. Silence. Then a voice so quiet I can hardly hear.

"It's only me…" Oh, the times I begged her not to say that: you're worth more, worth a million billion! "You're obviously out… or asleep…"

I find the cordless by the door, lurch through.

"Hey, I'm here."

I collapse on the fold-up sofa.

"Sorry… did I wake you?" Her words fail; then the voice, which soared so strongly and pitched with perfection, can barely find a whisper. "It's no good."

"What?"

More silence. "I just want to be with…" The last word dies.

I can hear her breathing. Raggedly. My brains do a somersault. "Lynda? Is that *you*?" One of the dafter questions I've ever asked in my entire life. My head sinks back on the cushion.

"Can we talk? Meet somewhere? It's just no good…"

Strange gulpings, her words have drowned. I imagine picking the sad things out and shaking them dry so they're clear and strong again.

"But… this lawyer? I thought…"

"I know." She sounds wretched. "It's not working out. He…"

She stops.

"What?"

"He wants us to choose a house. It's everything I've ever wanted. But all I think about is… all I think about is…"

A voice is speaking. It's mine, though I hardly recognise it. "Don't do this!"

"… you."

"I could be a half-millionaire inside two years," I bluster into the phone, "or a pauper by Christmas. Most likely the latter. It's all too hideously shaky, you can't risk your life any more!"

"*I don't care.*"

"I can't do this to you all over again. Go with him, take what he offers!"

In the drab rented lounge, streetlights seeping through tattered curtains that could do with a wash, my vision disconcertingly blurs like once it did while watching *Kramer versus Kramer* when Kerry was little. If Lynda had started to sing 'My Funny Valentine' down the phone, howls would be heard throughout the building, with gagging in the aisles.

Fortunately, she doesn't. She just, very softly, says "I'm sorry," as though they're the last words she ever intends to utter. I should leave her now, as I've already done, to build her life elsewhere in security and prosperity with someone who can look after her properly. I should leave her now, let her go forever. But all I hear is a heartbreaking weeping from the other end of the line.

I'm on my feet. Lights blaze. Madness wins, like it always seems to. "Get the kettle on. Better still, open a bottle."

I'm driving through the night, a journey I've made a thousand times. But this time is different. Stubble-jowled as I am, dressed as if having fled a burning building dragging clothes on *en route*, the sky sings, star-twinkly, cloud-oppressed, yet new as a fresh-minted coin. Cold air rushes through the open window as I speed towards my yesterday and tomorrow. Maybe, together, we can *still* lick 'em all! She's there again with her smiling soul, her beauty, her cock-eyed compassions, gentleness and frailty, her patient strengths, her roaring rages at the world's blindnesses, her uncertainties, her passions, and the peace she only finds with me.

And so it was. And is. Hollywood got it right after all. But life is an ever-changing pageant with all kind of tricks up its crafty, cunning, devious sleeve. I watch it guardedly – sidelined, belittled, ignored or written off by it one minute, invited in with a glorious smile the next. *Plus ça change*, so what else is new? and *also sprach Zarathustra*.

STOP STOP PRESS

The learned media lawyer who vetted the original manuscript of this book was intrigued by my reference in it to a screenplay, now titled Grain of Sand, *about the epic desert battle that changed the course of the Second World War in the Allies' favour in 1942 – and asked if he might read it. On doing so he was sufficiently enthused to take out an option on the script "without changing a word" and is currently hunting finance to get it into production at last.*

It's a funny old world.

With grateful thanks to: Kerry Melanie, Natalie Brigitte, Lynda Styan, Peter Jaques, Mark Westaway, Howard Pays, Jeffrey Simmons, David Alexander, Julian Friedmann; also to Fee Combe for her unfailing help, inspiration and support – and, of course, to the splendid Anthony Grey for his wisdom, belief, bravery and kindness.

The Tagman Press and its Authors

The Tagman Press was founded in 1997 to publish books to help us think in new ways at this time of exciting and unprecedented change in world history. *Books to inspire and transform* has been its motto from the start. Its logo is a modification of the symbol of infinity, the oldest symbol on the planet. Its first book **The Final Message**, by former French racing driver Claude Rael, claims that a highly advanced extra-terrestrial civilisation genetically engineered all life on earth.

Tagman's founder is Anthony Grey, awarding-winning journalist, former foreign correspondent, TV and radio broadcaster, celebrated public speaker and author of international bestselling historical novels, *Saigon*, *Peking* and *Tokyo Bay*. Most recently in 2010 he published a new book *The Hostage Handbook* (hardcover edition) which contains verbatim transcripts of the secret shorthand diaries he kept hidden from his guards when he was held in solitary confinement in China for two years during the Cultural Revolution. On 14 February 2011 the paperback edition of that book was launched, along with his first e-book, *A Christmas Kindle*, which contains a dozen or so fictional short stories interleaved with philosophical poems and prose reflections.

The Tagman Press was merged successfully from 2006 to 2010 with CLE Print Ltd., a digital print company then based in St Ives, near Huntingdon in Cambridgeshire. Tagman maintained its own identity within the CLE group of companies and expanded its list to include a wider range of fiction, publishing Scandinavia's top bestselling author **Margit Sandemo** for the first time in English anywhere in the world. The imprint was returned to Anthony Grey's ownership and became a division of his company, Lovemore House Limited, in September 2010. Now it is run day-to-day by a team headed by its founder – as it was before the merger – from Norwich, England. He is assisted by marketing director Paul Dickson, and promotion, administrative and accounts executives Denise Fiennes, Gill Dalton, Pamela Masters and Sonja Haggett. Our creative editor, copy editor and proofreader is Lizzie Brien. *The Making of a Britflick* by novelist and screenwriter Robin Squire, which was edited and supervised by Lizzie, is Tagman's first e-book, published on 27 November 2011.

Another outstanding Tagman book is *Miracle in Kigali*, a description by Illuminée Nganemariya and Paul Dickson of how Illuminée survived the Rwandan genocide with a newborn babe on her back. It is now selling strongly nationally and internationally. Tagman, unusually for a small publisher, already publishes three international bestselling writers. They include first: **Dr Ferydoon Batmanghelidj**, the celebrated non-fiction author of the famous 'Water Cure' series of books. This six-volume series includes *Your Body's Many Cries for Water* which has itself sold over a million copies worldwide and been translated into more than fifteen languages. Secondly, Margit Sandemo has sold more than 40 million copies of her enthralling supernatural novels in the languages of Scandinavia, Russia, Germany and Eastern Europe. Her most famous 47-book series, *The Legend of the Ice People*, is now being published by Tagman. And although it was originally never the founder's intention to publish his own books through the imprint, Tagman also has now begun re-publishing in new editions all the novels of Anthony Grey, which to date have been translated into 17 languages worldwide. Details of our other leading authors and titles, how to contact us and how to order traditional and e-books are set out below. A full list of all books and audio-visual products that are both published and recommended by Tagman along with a full statement of our philosophy will be available soon on our website at: www.tagmanpress.com

All books, videos, DVDs, CDs by Tagman authors may be also ordered direct from: The Tagman Press, Lovemore House, PO BOX 754, Norwich, NR1 4GY. You may also order traditional books by telephone by calling 0845 644 4186, 01603 454636 or by sending an e-mail to: anthonykgrey@btinternet.com or by going online at: www.tagmanpress.com